Gladys T. Stevenson

Professor and Chairman Department of Home Economics
San Fernando Valley State College, Northridge, California

Cora Miller

Professor and Chairman Department of Home Economics
Whittier College, Whittier, California

introduction to FOODS and NUTRITION

NEW YORK LONDON SYDNEY JOHN WILEY & SONS, INC.

Third printing, December, 1965

LIBRARY OF CONGRESS CATALOG CARD NUMBER: 60-6458

Printed in the United States of America

. . . . To Pearl P. Swanson
and
Belle Lowe

This textbook was written for a one-semester introductory course at the college level. The subject matter of nutrition has been combined with that of food preparation and meal management for the purpose of applying nutritional facts realistically. When the book is considered as a whole, approximately equivalent content is assigned to each of these phases. We assume that the students generally will not have had college science courses, and special care has been taken to use common terms, to explain certain technical terms as they appear, and to include a glossary of terms.

We recognize that both nutrition concepts and the techniques of food preparation are in a state of change. Subjects that are in the developmental stages have not been avoided; each one has been considered in the light of existing information, and the information given is based upon generalizations derived from research. Wherever more than one point of view has been accepted, the merits of each have been discussed and the reader allowed to make his own decision.

The material is organized so that at first (in Chapter 1) a very brief basic background is laid in the overall area of nutritional needs so that the nutrients then can be considered as identities in the selection and preparation of foods containing them. Emphasis is placed upon the importance of fulfilling psychological as well as physiological needs in the selection of foods for the daily diet.

Chapter 2 presents a basic background in the "hows and whys" of food preparation techniques. Included are the chemical-physical properties of food constituents and nutrients and their reactions to air, water, heat, acid, and alkali, as encountered in the total period elapsing from food source to food intake.

The ensuing eight chapters—Chapters 3 to 10—are concerned with the specific food categories of Meats, Eggs, Milk, Cereals, Fats, Fruits and Vegetables, Carbohydrates, and Food Adjuncts. With the exception of Eggs, these follow the four food groupings of the Daily Food Guide of the U. S. Department of Agriculture plus the groups termed "other foods." It seemed logical to isolate eggs from the group in which they are given in the Daily Food Guide, the Meat Group, because of the length of the meat chapter, the versatility of eggs in food preparation, and the differences in the selection and storage of meat and eggs.

A given pattern of subject-matter information is followed in each of the chapters dealing with specific food groups. Each chapter contains more details concerning the role of that group of foods as sources of nutrients than was given in the background chapter. The consideration of nutritional significance is followed by information on the purchase and care of that particular type of food and the preparation procedures necessary to attain desired palatability characteristics with a minimum loss of the nutrients for which the food group is especially stressed.

No doubt some instructors will feel that there is insufficient material given in these chapters about the metabolism of nutrients provided by the specific group of foods. This is not an oversight but a result of considerable deliberation. Certainly eggs and milk will be considered as important as meat in protein metabolism. To offset repetition and permit the individual instructors to proceed with the metabolism of specific nutrients at the desired phase and pace, most of the presentation of metabolism of specific nutrients has been concentrated in a reference chapter, Chapter 13, and frequent references specified in the food chapters. This arrangement of subject matter also permits, if so desired, the study of the metabolism of specific nutrients in the reference chapter before the various foods are considered in any order that seems best for the individual situation.

The amount of food preparation technique to be included was recognized as differing widely from chapter to chapter. An attempt has been made to simplify technique as much as possible, to avoid cookbook dogmatism, to encourage variations in recipes in accordance with the scientific principles involved, and yet to provide basic formulas suitable for laboratory work if this is desired. It is our belief that the dogmatism of recipes inhibits the development of applied science and thus limits the student in his ability to transfer knowledge and to develop judgments.

Chapter 12 deals with an aspect of our foods too frequently overlooked, the agencies and individuals behind the scenes who work unobtrusively so that the consumer will have wide choices among safe, palatable food items at reasonable cost and with consistent standards of quality. The title of this chapter is *The Guardians of Our Food*.

We assumed that some instructors might prefer to teach the course in a different order from that given even though they may cover the same material in a given period of time. Those who wish to conduct laboratories on a meal-planning basis are referred to Chapter 11, *Marketing and Meal Management*, early in the course. The subject matter has been arranged so that the chapters may be studied in any desired sequence. The order given is only one that seemed to the authors, through their years of experience in teaching an integrated course, to be well-adapted to the teaching of students who have had no formal subject-matter background. It was anticipated that generally the parts of a meal would be studied by specific food groups before they were worked into the integrated activity of a whole meal. From the nutritional standpoint, the arrangement of subject matter begins with an explanation of the need for food followed by discussions of the preparation of food into menu plans, the serving of meals, and the ultimate physiological functions of the nutrients contained in the foods consumed.

The international aspects of foods and nutrition are interspersed throughout the text. Many cultures are represented in the United States today, and it is emphasized that food choices and preparation within each food group can be individualized to meet the tastes of any group. Because eating patterns that will provide an adequate diet are limitless, the intake of a variety of nutrients in each of the meals in any established routine is urged, rather than a set eating pattern for everyone.

Interspersed throughout most of the chapters is a consideration of the choices available to the consumer in the purchase of services along with the food. The so-called convenience items that are available in all lines of foods are considered in the chapter where the particular food is discussed, and, in most cases, information for the evaluation of these items has been given.

No documentation of subject matter was attempted, but references are given to substantiate factual information and to strengthen the student's self-confidence and widen his food horizons. Therefore we hope that the material given will enable the student to evaluate new developments as they occur and to arrive at sound decisions concerning them.

As many students enter college with some knowledge and skills in food-preparation techniques, it is recommended that pretests be given to determine what procedure would be best suited to the class before the order of subject-matter presentation is planned. If the course is to be a one-year course, additional references and readings can be assigned and laboratory experiences in all phases of foods and nutrition can be enlarged.

November 1959

GLADYS T. STEVENSON
CORA MILLER

CONTENTS

INTRODUCTION

The possibility of travel into outer space has progressed beyond the dreaming stage. One stumbling block yet to be completely overcome is a suitable food supply. Because man is a product of his environment, the constant need for oxygen, water, and food might appear to be an obstacle to space flights. Living in the atmosphere surrounding the earth, one hardly is conscious of the need for oxygen. Also, within easy reach of abundant water, one can hardly believe that an adult requires about 2 pounds of water daily for internal needs and often takes in twice that amount. In comparison with the need for water, one's total need for foodstuffs—proteins, carbohydrates, fats, minerals, and vitamins—is relatively small in weight. Although more than forty food nutrients are known to be required by man, their combined weights to fill one's daily needs is only approximately one-half pound.

If these weights are minimum needs and if, as the National Science Advisory Board states, 10 pounds of equipment are required to launch each pound of material into space, approximately a ton of additional equipment would be required to permit one 150-pound man a ten-day shaveless, bathless trip into space.

This book may seem to have little or no connection with travel in space, yet the study of the requirements for such a venture has brought many new food and nutrition concepts into our everyday life. Because of man's desire to conquer outer space, he has pushed ahead on new methods of food preservation as well as on a more exact study of body nutrient requirements. An understanding of these new food concepts and the science of nutrition must have a beginning; therefore, it is the purpose of this book:

(1) To communicate and interpret some of the vast stores of knowledge that have been accumulated regarding the function of food in the human body.

(2) To translate body needs for nutrients into terms of food available in retail markets of the United States.

(3) To demonstrate that foods are generally priced according to factors other than their nutritive value.

(4) To present some of the developments in food technology that have contributed toward the improvement of the safety of food products, their prolonged storage life, convenience of their use, and their cost.

(5) To simplify the hows and whys of present food preparation techniques in order that individual tastes and preferences may be stimulated and fulfilled.

(6) To acquaint the student with the mores of food presentation in the present-day society in anticipation of contributing toward putting him at ease either as a host or as a guest and member of a family or group.

(7) To create or awaken an awareness of each individual's rights and responsibilities as a citizen of one of the leading countries of the world toward maintaining a safe and reasonably large supply of food for the expanding population of the world.

Toward these ends, the first chapter of this book discusses briefly the nutrients known to be required by man, the functions of these nutrients in the body and their dependence upon one another, the amounts of the various nutrients that are required, and how these amounts may be obtained by combining items chosen from each of several well-defined groups of foods into a daily diet. These chapters are followed by a resumé of scientific facts applicable in various food-preparation procedures. The chapters concerned with specific foods give their roles in the dietary patterns, the factors affecting the choices and cost of the food items, developments in food technology responsible for the wide choices among items, the hows and whys of preparation techniques, and the care and storage of the different foods. The psychological and sociological values of food are dealt with as a whole in the chapters pertaining to the presentation of foods. This subject includes the method of preparation, table-setting and table service acceptable to social practices, and other aspects of meal management. The chapter relating to consumer protection is concerned only with the machinery necessary in an organized complex society to assure a safe and adequate food supply, which makes possible the wide choices among food items which the people of this country enjoy today. Finally a reference chapter is appended to assist in a more complete understanding of the science of nutrition than is possible in the introductory chapters.

CHAPTER **1**

CHAPTER 1 . . . NUTRIENTS ARE PROVIDED BY FOODS

◀ **Fig. 1.** Well-nourished individuals are alert, and have good posture, smooth skin. and lustrous hair. (Courtesy of Sunkist Growers, Los Angeles.)

CONTRARY TO PUBLIC OPINION, MALNOURISHMENT AS IT EXISTS IN THE United States today is not the result of an inferior or low food supply but rather the result of economic status, ignorance, or self-imposed inadequate diets. It is difficult to comprehend that in spite of surplus food supplies, malnutrition exists at all levels of income. The low income group may feel that they do not have enough money to buy the "right foods" and the upper income groups may buy the food their appetites demand. Inadequate diets may result from misinterpretation of current research and misinformation regarding food values. This coupled with a desire to be lean, glamorous, and have a long life makes fashionable sensational diets that may be inadequate and in reality hasten the onset of old age and shorten the life span.

The total of the foods eaten is referred to as the diet, and the fate or path of the food in the body after it is digested and absorbed is termed nutrition. The component parts of the food that are essential to our existence are commonly known as nutrients. If a variety of foods that will furnish all of the nutrients required by the body are eaten, and eaten in amounts necessary for maintenance, growth, and energy needs, it is said that one has an adequate diet. On the other hand if any nutrients are omitted or are in short supply a state of malnutrition will exist in the body.

Only through a variety of foods can one achieve in a practical manner a diet that supplies all the parts of the body with all the nutrients for all the complicated functions that must be carried out throughout life (see Fig. 1).

The dramatic cases of scurvy, pellagra, beriberi, marasmus, kwashiorkor, and other nutritional diseases plaguing peoples of many countries are few or entirely lacking among the peoples of the United States. However, the vague aches and pains, listlessness, and easy fatigue common among the rank and file of our population may be the result of faulty diets. As Dr. Waterlow[1] so aptly states, "malnutrition is not an all-or-nothing effect but a matter of more-or-less."

It should be a challenge to the individuals who are so ready to try new mechanical things evolving from a changing world, to try also the new food products developed by the food technologists and the scientists in the biological fields as well as new food patterns advised by

---

[1] Waterlow, J. C. (Editor), 1955. *Protein Malnutrition*, Univ. Press, Cambridge —for The Food and Agriculture Organization, World Health Organization, Josiah Macy Jr. Foundation.

specialists in nutrition. New foods and new eating patterns may not be as startling as the developments in space science, but they can have far reaching effects on life and happiness.

Man does not live like other animals, eating only to keep alive. In the complexity of his make up, the psychological and sociological values of his food often reach the importance of its physiological values. Fortunately, the plant and animal life used for man's food are so complex in their composition and the varieties so numerous that the choices to fill nutritive requirements allow each person to have his own dietary pattern. The improvements in food technology and our improved transportation system, together with new developments in the realms of food preparation and presentation, make it possible for the people of the United States today to have an adequate diet while fulfilling their desire for and enjoyment of food.

Because the science of nutrition is concerned with the path of the nutrients in the body, and because nutrients are obtained from food, a study of nutrition reasonably includes the selection of foods, their storage, their preparation, and their utilization by the body. Utilization includes all of the changes that occur from the time the foods enter the mouth until their residues or end products are excreted by way of the lungs, perspiration, urine, and feces.

In addition to food the body needs water and oxygen, items not usually included with the nutrients. Oxygen especially is excluded from this list because it is obtained through breathing rather than from foods. Water, however, may be consumed in the pure form or it may be a part of the food.

THE BODY NEED FOR OXYGEN

Man cannot live without oxygen, which enters the body through the lungs rather than the digestive tract. The red blood cells (*erythrocytes*) pick up the oxygen from the air during the time the blood remains in circulation in the lungs. The oxygen leaves the red blood cells and unites with the energy-supplying nutrients. This union results in a change in the chemical character of the nutrient, and it is said to be oxidized. The final end products of total oxidation of the energy foods are carbon dioxide and water. The gaseous carbon dioxide is transported by the blood to the lungs and released to the atmosphere. The water is added to the liquids of the body.

As a result of oxidation energy is released from the foods for heat and body activities. The body activities that require energy include the heartbeat, breathing, eating, digesting, metabolizing, sitting, running, standing, writing, reading, and so on. Inasmuch as the heartbeat, breathing, and other involuntary activities are continuous, the oxidation process must be continuous, thus energy foods and oxygen must always be available. The body has the capacity to store excess energy foods as fat and some as carbohydrate (*glycogen*), but it does not have the capacity to store oxygen.

There seems to be no possibility of depleting the supply of oxygen in the atmosphere, therefore this is not a contributing factor to malnutrition.

THE BODY NEED FOR WATER

Water participates in a great many of the reactions that are constantly taking place in the body, and more than one-half of the total weight of the body is water. It is used as a solvent to hold and carry materials in the intestinal tract, in the blood, in the lymph, in the tissue fluids, and in the cells.

Water is also used as a chemical in the many changes that take place in the food during digestion and after the products of digestion are absorbed from the intestinal tract. When water is the chemical that causes the change in the nutrients the procedure is referred to as hydrolysis. In hydrolysis a complex compound is split into two parts at the same time a water molecule splits. The fragments of the water molecule attach to the parts of the complex nutrient molecule, thus forming two new compounds. The new compounds may be split by hydrolysis and this process may continue until simple compounds are formed.

The body needs for water are filled by foods and beverages as well as by "drinking water." There are no storage facilities for water in the body; however, a person can exist longer without water than he can without oxygen.

THE BODY NEED FOR FOOD

Food is composed of many substances, or nutrients, that are essential for various processes in the body. They provide energy, promote body growth, maintain and repair body tissues, promote reproduction and lactation, and regulate body processes. All of the nutrients can be obtained from food. The requirement for food is therefore directly related to the specific requirement for the various nutrients.

In general the nutritional needs of the human body may be stated as follows:

1. *Energy need:* the body requires energy for the utilization of the food, the physical activities performed by the body, and the heat necessary to maintain body temperature. Carbohydrates, fats, and proteins are the only nutrients that can furnish energy, but the release of energy from these three nutrients requires many of the vitamins, minerals, and other regulatory substances. Energy is usually reported in terms of heat energy, and is given in Calories.

2. *Maintenance and repair need:* muscles, bones, teeth, fatty deposits, blood cells, plasma, and other body parts are constantly being replaced. This is demonstrated by the growth of hair and nails. Large body frames require large supplies of replacement materials, and small body frames require small supplies. The same nutrients required for forming structures are required for replacement of structures.

3. *Growth need:* children can grow only when they have nutrients beyond their maintenance and energy requirements. A gradual increase in the number of cells, amount of body fluids, and size of structures occurs until each person has reached his mature size.

4. *Reproduction and lactation need:* the reproduction and lactation periods might well be considered periods of growth, therefore the need is similar to the growth need.

5. *Regulatory need:* there are a multitude of processes in the human body that must be instigated, coordinated, and regulated constantly and simultaneously. The substances that perform these functions include vitamins, minerals, hormones, and enzymes. Vitamins and minerals are classed as nutrients, but the hormones and enzymes are manufactured by the body from nutrients supplied by the food.

There are forty or more substances known to be needed in human nutrition. Water and oxygen are two of these, and the others are classified into five categories according to closely related composition or the use that the body makes of them. The classes are:

1. *proteins* as in casein of milk, albumin of egg, and gluten of wheat.
2. *fats* like the oils of seeds, lard from pork, and butter from milk.
3. *carbohydrates* such as starch of seeds, and sugars from plants.
4. *minerals* like iron, copper, calcium, phosphorus, iodine, manganese, and sodium.
5. *vitamins* such as vitamin A, vitamin D, thiamine, riboflavin, niacin, and ascorbic acid.

Specific Functions of the Nutrients

Each nutrient has its own specific functions to perform, but many nutrients must be functioning at the same time in order that the links in the nutrition process are formed at the right time. A diet containing a variety of foods contributing different types of nutrients is important to insure that the right nutrient is ready to function when needed.

The functions of the nutrients may be indicated as follows:

1. *Proteins* are needed for growth, repair, and maintenance of body tissue, and precursors of certain regulatory substances such as hormones and enzymes. The proteins not used for these specific functions may be broken down and used as sources of energy or changed to carbohydrates or fats and stored.

2. *Fats* are sources of energy and carriers of fat-soluble vitamins; they also stimulate caloric intake and increase growth rate and physical performance. At least one of the following of these fatty acids, linoleic, linolenic, or arachidonic, is nutritionally essential.

3. *Carbohydrates* are primarily sources of energy, and those not used at once for this purpose are stored as glycogen or converted to fat and stored.

4. *Minerals* function in the body in three ways: (*a*) as constituents of the bones and teeth to give these body portions their strength and relative permanence; (*b*) as structural parts of the soft tissues, and; (*c*) as constituents of certain substances concerned with regulating body processes.

5. *Vitamins* are organic catalysts that must be derived from a source outside the body. Like all catalysts they change the rate of reactions without entering into the reactions. The vitamins are considered necessary for optimum utilization of other nutrients, as for example:

Vitamin A is needed for growth, normal vision, and healthy condition of skin and body linings.

Vitamin D increases the absorption of calcium and phosphorus from the intestinal tract and may function in the actual calcification of bony structures.

Vitamin C, or ascorbic acid, is needed for the development of the intercellular cementing substance that causes tissues to be healthy and blood vessels to be strong.

Thiamine, in combination with phosphorus, is needed for the oxidation of carbohydrates.

Riboflavin, in combination with phosphoric acid and protein, forms tissue respiratory enzymes.

Niacin, like thiamine and riboflavin, functions in the tissue enzyme systems.

All individuals require the same nutrients for the same body functions but individuals vary in size, sex, age, activity, and environment so that one person may require different amounts of the nutrients than does another for maintenance and growth. That is to say, that although every one needs the same kinds of nutrients, one person may need a greater or smaller amount of each nutrient than his neighbor needs.

Recommended Daily Dietary Allowances

All nutrients can be provided by foods, but the amount of food one should eat each day depends not only on the person's body needs for nutrients but also on the combination of nutrients within the foods eaten, the concentration of specific nutrients in the foods, and one's capacity to digest the food and absorb the nutrients that are present in the food.

Much has been learned through research concerning the amount of nutrients required by individuals of different age, sex, and activity. It has been found that not only do individuals vary in their requirements but also that the same individual may have somewhat different requirements at different times. Nutritionists have studied the data obtained from this research and have formulated recommendations in regard to the amounts of specific nutrients that people in general should try to receive from foods each day. These recommendations are made by the Food and Nutrition Board of the National Research Council and are usually termed Recommended Daily Dietary Allowances. These are given in Table 1. It will be noted that considerably fewer than forty nutrients are listed. It is assumed that the nutrients will be obtained from foods and if the recommended amounts of those nutrients specified are obtained, there is only a small chance that a dietary deficiency in any of the unlisted nutrients will occur because they are present in the same foods.

These recommendations are subject to critical review every five years and may be changed if sufficient evidence has been accumulated to warrant the change. The recommended allowances serve as a guide for the people of the United States to follow in obtaining nutritionally adequate diets. They are based on the available supply of food in this country as well as dietary habits. Other countries have set up similar

Table 1. FOOD AND NUTRITION BOARD, NATIONAL RESEARCH COUNCIL RECOMMENDED DAILY DIETARY ALLOWANCES,* REVISED 1958†

DESIGNED FOR THE MAINTENANCE OF GOOD NUTRITION OF HEALTHY PERSONS IN THE U.S.A.

(Allowances are intended for persons normally active in a temperate climate)

	Age, Years	Weight kg. (lb.)	Height cm. (in.)	Calories	Protein, gm.	Calcium, gm.	Iron, mg.	Vitamin A, I.U.	Thiam., mg.	Ribo., mg.	Niacin,‡ mg. equiv.	Asc. Acid, mg.	Vitamin D, I.U.
Men	25	70 (154)	175 (69)	3200§	70	0.8	10	5000	1.6	1.8	21	75	
	45	70 (154)	175 (69)	3000	70	0.8	10	5000	1.5	1.8	20	75	
	65	70 (154)	175 (69)	2550	70	0.8	10	5000	1.3	1.8	18	75	
Women	25	58 (128)	163 (64)	2300	58	0.8	12	5000	1.2	1.5	17	70	
	45	58 (128)	163 (64)	2200	58	0.8	12	5000	1.1	1.5	17	70	
	65	58 (128)	163 (64)	1800	58	0.8	12	5000	1.0	1.5	14	70	
	Pregnant (second half)			+300	+20	1.5	15	6000	1.3	2.0	+3	100	400
	Lactating (850 ml. daily)			+1000	+40	2.0	15	8000	1.7	2.5	+2	150	400
Infants‖	0–1/12‖	6 (13)	60 (24)	kg. x 120	See Footnote 4	0.6	5	1500	0.4	0.5	6	30	400
	2/12–6/12	9 (20)	70 (28)	kg. x 100		0.8	7	1500	0.5	0.8	7	30	400
	7/12–12/12												
Children	1–3	12 (27)	87 (34)	1300	40	1.0	7	2000	0.7	1.0	8	35	400
	4–6	18 (40)	109 (43)	1700	50	1.0	8	2500	0.9	1.3	11	50	400
	7–9	27 (60)	129 (51)	2100	60	1.0	10	3500	1.1	1.5	14	60	400
	10–12	36 (79)	144 (57)	2500	70	1.2	12	4500	1.3	1.8	17	75	400
Boys	13–15	49 (108)	163 (64)	3100	85	1.4	15	5000	1.6	2.1	21	90	400
	16–19	63 (139)	175 (69)	3600	100	1.4	15	5000	1.8	2.5	25	100	400
Girls	13–15	49 (108)	160 (63)	2600	80	1.3	15	5000	1.3	2.0	17	80	400
	16–19	54 (120)	162 (64)	2400	75	1.3	15	5000	1.2	1.9	16	80	400

*The allowance levels are intended to cover individual variations among most normal persons as they live in the United States under usual environmental stresses. The recommended allowances can be attained with a variety of common foods, providing other nutrients for which human requirements have been less well defined.

† National Academy of Science, National Research Council, Pub. 589.

‡ Niacin equivalents include dietary sources of the preformed vitamin and the precursor, tryptophan. 60 milligrams tryptophan equals 1 milligram niacin.

§ Calorie allowances apply to individuals usually engaged in moderate physical activity. For office workers or others in sedentary occupations they are excessive. Adjustments must be made for variations in body size, age, physical activity, and environmental temperature.

‖ The Board recognizes that human milk is the natural food for infants and feels that breast feeding is the best and desired procedure for meeting nutrient requirements in the first months of life. Breast feeding is particularly indicated during the first month when infants show handicaps in homeostasis due to different rates of maturation of digestive, excretory, and endocrine functions. Recommendations as listed pertain to nutrient intake as afforded by cow's milk formulas and supplementary foods given the infant when breast feeding is terminated. Allowances are not given for protein during infancy.

recommendations for their populaces and although the nutrients listed and their recommended figures may differ slightly from those listed in Table 1, it must be remembered that differences in environment, habitual food intake, and economic conditions exist between nations.

Nutritive Values of Foods

The kinds and amounts of nutrients in different foods have been determined by chemical and other analyses, and a great deal of information is available concerning the concentration of nutrients in foods. From these data originate the many tables of food values. When planning normal diets only the values for those nutrients listed in the table of recommended daily allowances are generally used; consequently food value tables report concentrations for energy (Calories), protein, fat, carbohydrate, calcium, phosphorus, iron, vitamin A, thiamine, riboflavin, niacin, and ascorbic acid. In most instances the figures for these nutrients are averages from a number of analyses because there are many factors that can affect the concentration of a nutrient in a given weight of the food. Thus the figures found in such tables should not be considered absolute values. Causative factors for variation in nutrient content of the different types of foods will be discussed in the chapters dealing with specific foods.

Much of the analytical work on foods grown in the United States has been carried on under the auspices of the United States Department of Agriculture by such agencies as State Experiment Stations, Regional Research Laboratories, colleges, and universities. A comprehensive compilation, *Composition of Foods, Agriculture Handbook No. 8*, is available from the Superintendent of Documents at Washington, D. C. International food value tables are available from the Food and Agriculture Organization of the United Nations.

Food Guides

An adequate diet may be selected by using the food value tables in conjunction with the recommended dietary allowances. However, this method is cumbersome and more practical methods have been devised to provide a quick and easy way to make adequate food selections. These are termed Food Guides. Food guides usually recommend that a person eat at least one to four "servings" of food from each of approximately ten to twelve classes of foods. The foods within each class have common characteristics. Examples of such classes include flesh of animals, mature seeds of plants, leaves of plants, and citrus fruits. Each class of foods contains many different nutrients, but one class may contain a greater amount of one or two nutrients than do other classes. Thus, the total day's menu should contain at least one food that is a good source for each of the nutrients listed in the table of recommended dietary allowances. A person choosing beef, oatmeal, spinach, and oranges would obtain essentially the same nutrients as another person eating similar amounts of fish, brown rice, endive, and grapefruit.

Simplicity in presentation of a food guide is essential to its successful use. Toward this end, the various classes of foods have been combined into groups. The numbers of groups have varied from time

Table 2. THREE COMMON FOOD GUIDES SHOWING THE

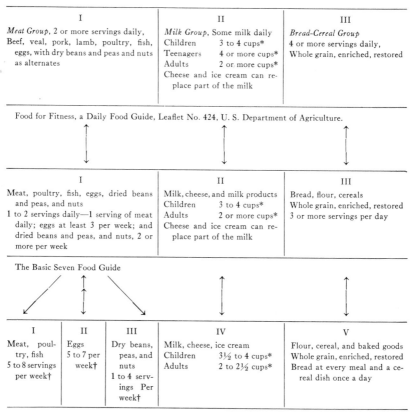

I	II	III
Meat Group, 2 or more servings daily, Beef, veal, pork, lamb, poultry, fish, eggs, with dry beans and peas and nuts as alternates	*Milk Group*, Some milk daily Children 3 to 4 cups* Teenagers 4 or more cups* Adults 2 or more cups* Cheese and ice cream can replace part of the milk	*Bread-Cereal Group* 4 or more servings daily, Whole grain, enriched, restored

Food for Fitness, a Daily Food Guide, Leaflet No. 424, U. S. Department of Agriculture.

I	II	III
Meat, poultry, fish, eggs, dried beans and peas, and nuts 1 to 2 servings daily—1 serving of meat daily; eggs at least 3 per week; and dried beans and peas, and nuts, 2 or more per week	Milk, cheese, and milk products Children 3 to 4 cups* Adults 2 or more cups* Cheese and ice cream can replace part of the milk	Bread, flour, cereals Whole grain, enriched, restored 3 or more servings per day

The Basic Seven Food Guide

I	II	III	IV	V
Meat, poultry, fish 5 to 8 servings per week†	Eggs 5 to 7 per week†	Dry beans, peas, and nuts 1 to 4 servings Per week†	Milk, cheese, ice cream Children 3½ to 4 cups* Adults 2 to 2½ cups*	Flour, cereal, and baked goods Whole grain, enriched, restored Bread at every meal and a cereal dish once a day

Master Food Plan—Sherman, H. C. and C. S. Lanford, 1957, *Essentials of Nutrition*, p. 401, The Macmillan Co., New York.

* Servings in terms of fluid milk.
† No. of servings vary with income level.

to time, for example—ten to twelve, seven, and most recently as four *groups* of foods. These have been termed: the Master Food Plan,[2] the Basic Seven, and a Daily Food Guide.[3] The close relationship between these plans is shown in Table 2.

The use of ten to twelve groups seems cumbersome and indecisive to the lay person because each group need not be included in the diet each day. Such deviations require considerable explanation and direction before this type of grouping can be used as a guide. To overcome this difficulty certain groups were combined and the Basic Seven was devised. However, as research has progressed a better understanding of both food composition and food habits has been acquired, and it

SIMILARITY IN RECOMMENDATION FOR FOOD INTAKE

IV			Other Foods
Vegetable-Fruit Group, 4 or more servings daily, including			Butter, margarine, other fats, oils, sugars, and un-
A citrus fruit or other fruit or vegetable important for vitamin C—daily	A dark-green or deep yellow vegetable important for vitamin A—at least every other day	Other fruits and vegetables including potatoes	enriched refined grain products to round out meals

IV	V	VI	VII
Citrus fruits, tomatoes, raw cabbage, and other vitamin C rich foods, 1 or more servings daily	Leafy, green, and yellow vegetables 1 or more servings daily	Potatoes and other vegetables and fruits 2 or more servings daily	Butter, fortified margarine some daily (served as you like)

VI	VII	VIII	IX	X	XI
Citrus fruit, tomatoes 6 or more servings per week	Leafy, green, and yellow vegetables 7 or more servings per week	Potatoes, sweet-potatoes 7 or more servings per week	Other vegetables and fruit 7 or more servings per week	Fats, oils at every meal	Sugar, syrups, and preserves as desired

[2] H. C. Sherman and C. S. Lanford, 1957, *Essentials of Nutrition*, Ch. 19, Macmillan Co., New York.

[3] Leaflet No. 424, U. S. D. A., 1958.

now seems possible to further simplify the guide. The United States Department of Agriculture now recommends The Daily Food Guide, which includes four groups. These four groups are: (1) meat, eggs, legumes, and nuts; (2) milk and milk products; (3) bread and cereal; and (4) fruits and vegetables (see Fig. 2).

The meat-eggs-legumes and nuts group. The foods of this group are stressed for their protein content, which is needed for growth and maintenance of all the protein materials of the body—hair, nails, skin, muscles, blood, organs, saliva, enzymes, many hormones, and even small amounts in bone and fatty deposits. These foods also consistently supply small amounts of iron, thiamine, riboflavin, and niacin. Liver, eggs, and milk are relatively good sources of pre-formed vitamin A (not carotene, which must be changed to vitamin A in the body) too. With the exception of dry beans and peas the foods of this group contain appreciable amounts of fat. Two or more servings per day from this group are recommended for good nutrition.

1. Meat includes all the lean parts that are eaten of the various animals. Organs such as liver, heart, and kidney, as well as the flesh of the animals, are classed as meat. The Institute of Home Economics[4] defines a serving of meat as 2 or 3 ounces of lean cooked meat without bone. This is equivalent to 3 or 4 ounces of raw lean.

2. Eggs include all types, but chicken eggs are used in the greatest quantity. The Institute of Home Economics[4] defines a serving of eggs as 2 medium eggs, which provide a quantity of protein equal to that obtained from 3 ounces of cooked meat.

3. Legumes include all types of dry beans, dry peas, lentils, garbanzos, peanuts, and peanut butter. Other nuts are valuable for their protein content and may be considered as a part of this group. They are generally used in smaller quantities than peanuts but may be considered as a fraction of a serving. The Institute of Home Economics[5] defines a serving of these foods as 1 cupful of cooked beans or peas or ¼ cupful of peanut butter.

It should be noted that the percentage of protein in eggs and in legumes of specific varieties does not vary appreciably, whereas the percentage of protein in meat decreases with increases in fat content (see Chapter 3).

The milk group. Milk and milk products are included as a separate group in the diet guide because of their high calcium and phosphorus

---

[4] Leaflet No. 424, U. S. Department of Agriculture, March 1958.
[5] *Ibid.*

food for fitness
A DAILY FOOD GUIDE

MILK, CHEESE
2 or more servings
(more for children)

MEAT, FISH, EGGS
2 or more servings

VEGETABLES, FRUITS
4 or more servings

BREAD, CEREALS
4 or more servings

and other foods
as needed for complete
and satisfying meals

UNITED STATES DEPARTMENT OF AGRICULTURE   Neg. DN 1256   AGRICULTURAL RESEARCH SERVICE

Fig. 2. It is not difficult to obtain the nutrients needed if the types of foods listed above are eaten daily and in the amounts suggested. (Courtesy of the U. S. Department of Agriculture, Washington, D. C.)

content. These minerals are needed in large amounts for growth and maintenance of all the bony parts of the body. Milk also provides appreciable amounts of protein, riboflavin, and many other essential nutrients. Only the milks containing natural fat (whole milk) contain vitamin A and vitamin D without fortification.

Children and teenagers need larger amounts of calcium than do adults. It is suggested that 3 to 4 cups (24–32 ounces) of fluid whole milk or equivalent in milk products be provided for children, 4 cups (32 ounces) for teenagers, and at least 2 cups (16 ounces) for adults. There are many forms of milk available and each form may be used in several different ways (see Chapter 4). All the milk need not be consumed as liquid but may be included in prepared foods.

The bread-cereal group. Foods in this group are processed from the seeds of plants termed cereal grains. All seeds of plants are richer in thiamine than are other portions of the plant so that the bread and cereal group is valued for this nutrient as well as for other B-vitamins and iron. Foods in this group also furnish worthwhile amounts of protein and are good sources of energy. Thiamine is necessary in the release of energy from carbohydrates so that this group is especially well-suited for supplying energy needs.

Different grains and different products made from the grains are available on the markets (see Chapter 6), therefore there is a large variety from which to choose. At least four of the cereals selected each day should be either whole grain (only the outer bran coats are removed), enriched, or restored. The enrichment and restoration program requires that specific levels of iron, thiamine, riboflavin, and niacin be attained. These nutrients are added to refined cereal products in suitable amounts so that the level of the specified nutrients compares favorably with that of the whole grain products from which the enriched product was made.

It is recommended that at least four servings be selected from this group each day for good nutrition. The Institute of Home Economics[6] defines one serving as:

1 slice bread (usually 1 slice weighs 1 ounce)
1 ounce ready-to-eat cereal
½ to ¾ cup cooked cereal, rice, cornmeal, grits, macaroni, noodles, and spaghetti.

If griddle cakes, waffles, biscuits, muffins, or other baked products are prepared in the home, the amount of each product that would result if one-fourth cup of whole grain or enriched flour were used may be

[6] *Ibid.*

considered as comparable in nutritive value to one serving of cereal. It should be noted that cake and pastry flours are generally not enriched and when these are used the products should be considered as additional to the recommended four servings from this group of foods.

The fruit and vegetable group. These foods are important sources of vitamins, minerals, and bulk formers. Those plant foods rich in vitamin C (ascorbic acid) and carotene are especially emphasized. At least four servings of fruits and vegetables are recommended daily for good nutrition.[7] These should include at least one serving of a good source of vitamin A (carotene) and one serving of a good source of vitamin C.

1. Dark-green and deep-yellow vegetables and fruits are rich in the carotenes that may be converted to vitamin A by the body. It is advisable to choose one serving each day from these highly colored foods: apricots, broccoli, cantaloupe, carrots, chard, collards, cress, kale, mango, persimmon, pumpkin, spinach, sweet-potato, and turnip greens. Other dark-green leaves and winter squash are good sources of pro-vitamin A. As plants contain no pre-formed vitamin A, some scientists contend that not more than ⅔ of the recommended allowance of this vitamin should be obtained from plant sources.

2. Ascorbic acid-containing fruits and vegetables should be served at least once each day. Grapefruit, orange, cantaloupe, guava, mango, papaya, strawberries, broccoli, green pepper, and sweet red pepper when eaten in full portion servings are better contributors of ascorbic acid than are other fruits and vegetables. Other foods from this group become important as sources of vitamin C especially when consumed frequently and in large quantities—for example, tomatoes, raw cabbage, and potatoes (see Chapter 7). It is recommended that at least one good source of ascorbic acid be served every day because this vitamin is not stored in the body.

3. Other vegetables and fruits such as beets, potatoes, onions, apples, pears, peaches, bananas, and grapes do not contribute appreciable quantities of any specific nutrient, but they are useful in providing small amounts of many nutrients, bulk, water, food-energy, and variety to the menu. Potatoes, corn, lima beans, and similar vegetables are inexpensive, have good keeping qualities, and are readily available throughout the country. Potatoes, especially, contain appreciable quantities of iron and ascorbic acid, as well as small amounts of B-complex vitamins.

---

[7] *Ibid.*

Table 3. COMPARISON OF THE DAILY RECOMMENDED DIETARY ALLOWANCES FOR YOUNG WOMEN WITH THE TOTAL NUTRITIVE VALUE OF 2 MENUS, PLANNED ACCORDING TO THE DAILY FOOD GUIDE*

Food Items	Servings	Energy Value, Cal.	Protein, gm.	Calcium, mg.	Iron, mg.	Vitamin A, I.U.	Thiamine, mg.	Riboflavin, mg.	Niacin, mg.	Ascorbic Acid, mg.
MENU I										
Meat Group										
2 or more servings										
Pork roast	4 oz.	380	25	12	3.6	...	0.96	0.27	5.7	...
Egg, fried	1	77	6	26	1.3	550	0.05	0.14	...	...
Milk Group										
2 C. or more for adults										
Milk, cooking	1 C.	166	8	288	0.2	390	0.09	0.42	0.3	3
Cheese, Cheddar	1½ oz.	170	11	309	0.5	600	0.01	0.18	trace	...
Vegetable Group										
4 or more servings										
Cantaloupe	½	37	1	31	0.7	6,190	0.09	0.07	0.9	59
Broccoli, cooked	½ C.	22	2	100	1.0	2,550	0.05	0.11	0.6	55
Apricots, canned	½ C.	100	1	13	0.4	1,730	0.02	0.03	0.4	5
Potato, baked	1 med.	97	2	13	0.8	20	0.11	0.05	1.4	17
Bread, Cereal Group										
Whole-grain or enriched										
4 or more servings										
Toast	2 slices	126	4	36	0.8	...	0.12	0.08	1.0	...
Oatmeal	2/3 C.	100	4	14	1.2	...	0.14	0.03	0.3	...
Pie, apple	1/6 pie	330	3	9	1.1	200	0.16	0.10	1.3	1
Totals		1605	67	851	11.6	12,230	1.80	1.48	11.9	140
Recommended allowances for adult woman, 25 years		2300	58	800	12.0	5,000	1.20	1.50	17.0	70
Excess or lack		−695	+9	+51	−0.4	+7,230	+0.60	−0.02	−5.1†	+70
Other Foods										
Extras for palatability and energy										
Pear, raw	1	95	1	20	0.5	30	0.03	0.06	0.2	6
Cooky, large	1	100	2	6	0.2	...	0.01	0.01	0.1	...
Sugar	2 Tb.	100	...	...	...	...	...	...	...	...
Butter	2 Tb.	200	...	6	...	920	...	...	...	...
Lettuce, with French dressing	¼ head	190	1	25	0.6	600	0.05	0.10	0.2	9
Totals from extras		685	4	57	1.3	1,550	0.09	0.17	0.5†	15

Food Items	Servings	Energy Value, Cal.	Protein, gm.	Calcium, mg.	Iron, mg.	Vitamin A, I.U.	Thiamine, mg.	Riboflavin, mg.	Niacin, mg.	Ascorbic Acid, mg.
MENU II, Meatless										
Meat Group										
2 or more servings										
Beans, baked with pork and molasses	1 C.	325	15	146	5.5	90	0.13	0.09	1.2	7
Peanut butter	¼ C.	368	17	48	1.2	...	0.08	0.08	10.4	...
Milk Group										
2 C. or more for adults										
Buttermilk	2 C.	172	17	576	0.4	20	0.18	0.86	0.6	6
Vegetable Group										
4 or more servings										
Orange juice, canned	8 oz.	109	2	25	0.7	240	0.17	0.04	0.6	103
Cabbage slaw	1 C.	102	1	46	0.5	80	0.06	0.05	0.3	50
Sweet potato	½ med.	125	2	31	0.7	7,890	0.09	0.05	0.6	20
Okra	8 pods	28	2	70	0.6	630	0.05	0.05	0.7	17
Bread, Cereal Group										
Whole-grain or enriched										
4 or more servings										
Brown rice pilaf	½ C.	174	3	20	1.0	...	0.17	0.25	2.4	...
Bread in sandwich	2 slices	126	4	36	0.8	...	0.12	0.08	1.0	...
Garlic bread	1 slice	65	2	4	0.5	...	0.06	0.04	0.5	...
Totals		1594	65	1002	11.9	8,950	1.11	1.59	18.3	203
Recommended allowances for adult woman, 25 years		2300	58	800	12.0	5,000	1.20	1.50	17.0	70
Excess or lack		−706	+7	+202	−0.1	+3,950	−0.09	+0.09	+1.3	+133
Other Foods										
Extras for palatability and energy										
Banana	1 large	119	2	11	0.8	570	0.06	0.06	1.0	13
Mayonnaise	2 Tb.	184	...	4	0.2	60	...	...	...	...
Margarine	2 Tb.	200	...	6	...	920	...	...	...	...
Sherbet	½ C.	118	1	48	...	...	0.02	0.07	...	...
Sugar	4 Tb.	200	...	...	...	...	...	...	...	...
Totals from extras		821	3	69	1.0	1,550	0.08	0.13	1.0	13

* Nutritive values calculated from U.S.D.A. Handbook No. 8.
† Protein adequate, therefore niacin will be supplemented.

used. Various factors affect the digestive and absorptive processes; these include both physical and emotional factors.

Digestion. The digestive process is a chemical breakdown of complex molecules of the foods resulting in the release of nutrients and the formation of molecules sufficiently small to pass through the membrane of the intestinal wall. Batteries of digestive enzymes aid in the breakdown of the food. The rate of breakdown is in direct proportion to the concentration of enzymes and the surface area of the food available to the enzymes.

An enzyme is known as an organic catalyst[9] because it changes the rate of a reaction. Enzymes must be produced by living cells. Each enzyme usually will act on only one specific chemical combination so that many enzymes are required to hydrolyze a complex nutrient, such as protein, to the simple units needed for absorption.

Digestion is concerned primarily with the breakdown of proteins, fats, and carbohydrates. During the process some of the vitamins and minerals that were bound to these molecules, are released. The products resulting from complete digestion are termed end products and the reactions are as follows:

1. *Protein* hydrolysis is accelerated by proteolytic enzymes—the proteases—and various kinds and proportions of amino acids are produced as end products. Approximately twenty-three different amino acids have been identified.

2. *Fat* hydrolysis is accelerated by lipolytic enzymes—the lipases— and glycerol and fatty acids are the end products formed. The various fats in nature have many different kinds of fatty acids in their makeup. Three fatty acids must form a chemical union with glycerol before a fat molecule is formed.

3. *Carbohydrate* hydrolysis is accelerated by amylytic enzymes— the amylases—and simple sugars, primarily glucose and small amounts of fructose, galactose, and others will be formed. Cellulose is one form of carbohydrate that cannot be broken down in human digestive processes. The other carbohydrates, starch, dextrins, pectin, and double sugars, are digested to simple sugars.

The digestive enzymes are only one class of a larger group that are necessary in regulating the various body processes. Other enzymes occur in the tissues of the body and are necessary for the utilization or metabolism of absorbed foodstuffs.

The digestive process begins with chewing. Some digestive juices

---

[9] A catalyst is a substance that changes the rate of a reaction but does not enter into the reaction.

may begin to flow when one thinks of food or enjoys the odor of food cooking. Chewing is helpful in that it grinds the pieces of food into small particles. It thus increases the surface area and at the same time mixes saliva with the food particles. Saliva moistens the food lubricating it so that swallowing is easy. Saliva also contains a starch-splitting enzyme, and hydrolysis of starch may begin in the mouth.

The stomach serves primarily as a temporary storehouse where some starch hydrolysis continues, some protein hydrolysis begins, milk is clotted by a special enzyme, and acid is added. The partially hydrolyzed mixture is forced in small portions from the stomach into the intestinal tract. As the food enters the duodenum, the first part of the small intestine, the gall bladder is stimulated to release some bile, and at the same time the pancreas secretes enzyme-rich juices. These fluids enter the duodenum through a common duct. The bile serves to emulsify or reduce the size of the fat globules and the pancreatic juices contain enzymes for hydrolyzing proteins, carbohydrates, and fats. The hydrolysis reactions are at a maximum in the duodenum, but in some instances further hydrolysis is necessary and the intestinal juices provide additional enzymes.

The digestive process is also aided by "friendly" bacteria, microorganisms, that live in the intestinal tract. They not only help in hydrolyzing food but also manufacture some of the nutrients required in human nutrition such as vitamin K, folic acid, and certain B-complex vitamins.

Most of the absorption of nutrients must take place in the small intestine because few foods are broken to absorbable units before they are forced into this area of the alimentary canal. Ordinarily a great deal of time is permitted for the absorptive process because the digested material must traverse the entire length of the intestine, which is a distance of about 24 feet. The large intestine is primarily the receptacle for concentrating the residues of foods. These residues might include:

1. Roughage or cellulose materials, which are not digested but are useful in stimulating movement of foods through the alimentary canal, that is, *peristalsis*.

2. Undigested foods that were passed through the canal before they were split into absorbable units.

3. Digested materials that were not absorbed as they were forced through the canal.

4. Some of the microorganisms that live in the digestive tract, as well as those which may accompany the food.

5. Possibly some metabolized materials that have been discarded to the large intestine.

Little or no absorption of nutrients other than water takes place in the large intestine. Any nutrients in the residues cannot be reclaimed, but are excreted in the fecal material.

The digestive process might be likened to the action of a giant hopper into which one puts bread and butter, oranges, fish, cabbage, potatoes, eggs, milk, and other foods and obtains from this mixture glucose, amino acids, fatty acids, minerals, and vitamins.

Absorption. Absorption of food from the digestive tract into the blood and lymph takes place primarily in the small intestine where the digested food has been forced by a special type of muscular contraction, the peristaltic waves. These peristaltic waves also push the food against the absorbing surface of the intestinal wall (see Fig. 3). This wall contains many folds and tiny fingerlike projections, *villi*, which make a tremendous absorptive surface. The intestinal tube which appears to be very narrow is said to have an absorptive surface of 45 square feet. This large area promotes an efficient absorption of all nutrients.

Many factors other than the peculiar configuration of the wall of the intestinal tract seem to affect the absorption of the digested food-

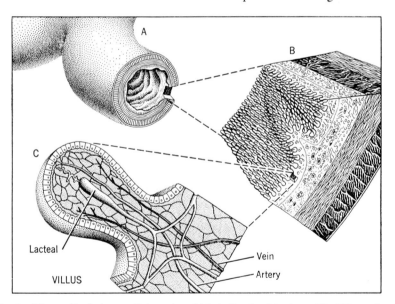

Fig. 3. The wall of the small intestine (A) is lined with tiny villi (B), each of which has the structure shown in C.

stuffs. For example, bile is believed to favor absorption of the fats, calcium cannot be absorbed in the absence of vitamin D, and vitamin B_{12} cannot be absorbed unless a specific substance (the intrinsic factor) is present in the gastric juice. It is believed that some re-forming of nutrients occurs during the passage through the intestinal wall and that possibly some food is broken down in the intestinal wall.

The intestine, which is a semipermeable membrane, is highly selective and will allow for the passage of food substances only under certain special conditions. In addition to selectivity, absorption is influenced by the concentrations of dissolved particles already in the blood. A high concentration in the blood stream may allow less absorption of vitamins and minerals than would be permitted at a time when the blood level of these nutrients is low.

The sugars, amino acids, water-soluble vitamins, mineral salts, and possibly some of the fat products are absorbed directly into the blood stream through the intestinal wall. The remainder of the end products of fat digestion and the fat-soluble vitamins are believed to enter into the lymph system. Some investigators believe that some fat may be re-formed in the lymph before the fatty products are emptied into the blood stream.

Individuals may vary in their capacity to absorb even fully hydrolyzed foodstuffs. The Recommended Daily Dietary Allowances and the Daily Food Guide provide quantities of nutrients generally sufficient to cover the needs of individuals with normal variations in capacities to digest and absorb nutrients.

Interrelationship of nutrients. Although nutrients may be absorbed from the intestinal tract in adequate amounts, it must be recognized that no one nutrient functions alone, and its usefulness to the body may be curtailed by the absence of other nutrients. Therefore, as only a few nutrients are stored in the body, some necessary nutrients may be discarded by the body without being used because other essential nutrients are lacking in the diet. For this reason some foods or combinations of foods are of higher physiological value than others.

The interrelationship of nutrients will be further discussed in succeeding chapters. Throughout the discussions it should be noted that emphasis is put on the desirability of a variety of food for each meal. Mixed salads, stews, casseroles, and certain flour mixtures may have value beyond their individual nutrient content because of the supplemental value of the various combinations of nutrients.

SUMMARY

In addition to oxygen and water, man requires more than forty nutrients to fulfill his physiological needs. Because every human being is composed of the same materials, everyone requires the same nutrients for energy, growth, maintenance, and body functions. The amounts and proportions of the nutrients needed by different individuals vary according to differences in age, sex, activity, and environment.

The nutrients are provided by food. However, the amounts of foods required to meet the specific nutritional needs of an individual depend upon the combination and concentration of nutrients in the food and the ability of the individual to digest the food and to absorb the nutrients.

The Food and Nutrition Board of the National Research Council recommends definite amounts of certain nutrients to be obtained from food each day according to an individual's age, sex, and activity. A food guide to simplify selection and quantities of foods to meet nutritional requirements is recommended.

In any menu plan a variety of foods should be emphasized for each meal in order to maintain a good balance of nutrients and an adequate diet.

Reading List

1. Council on Foods and Nutrition, American Medical Association, 1959. Vitamin preparations as dietary supplements and as therapeutic agents, *J. Am. Med. Assoc.*, **169**:41.

2. Essentials of an Adequate Diet, 1956. Agriculture Research Service, U.S.D.A., *Agr. Info. Bull.* 160.

3. Food and Nutrition Board, National Research Council, Recommended Dietary Allowances, Rev. 1958, Publication No. 589 of the National Research Council, National Academy of Sciences, Washington, D. C.

4. Sherman, H. C., and C. S. Lanford, 1957. *Essentials of Nutrition*, The Macmillan Co., New York.

CHAPTER **2**

Fig. 4. In scientific laboratories means of inhibiting browning of light-colored fruits are determined so that menus may contain attractive, fresh fruit salads—thus illustrating that food preparation is both a science and an art. (Courtesy of Western Growers Association, Los Angeles, U. S. Department of Agriculture, Western Regional Research Laboratory, Albany, California.)

2 . . FOOD PREPARATION IS A SCIENCE AND AN ART

REFERENCE STANDARDS FOR SPECIFIC RECIPES

COMBINING AND AGITATING FOODS

MEASURING AMOUNTS OF INGREDIENTS

Weighing of Ingredients
Volume Measurement of Ingredients

ENVIRONMENTAL FACTORS IN FOOD
PREPARATION

Air and its Relation to Oxidation
  Temperature-Time Factor
  Amount of Surface Area Per Unit Weight of Food
  Acids other than Ascorbic Acid
  General Precautions to Prevent Oxidation
  Aeration of Food
Water in Food Preparation
  The Three States of Water
  Changes in the Properties of Water
Heat in Food Preparation
  Method of Heat Transfer
  Effect of Heat on the Various Constituents in Food
Effect of Acids and Alkalies in Food Preparation
Determination of Doneness in Cooking

SUMMARY

READING LIST

THERE ARE MANY DIFFERENT CHEMICAL ELEMENTS IN EACH INDIVIDUAL food, and these elements are made up into definite chemical compounds. The science of food preparation is concerned with the reactions that these constituents undergo with each other, with the agents used in food preparation, and with agents in the environment. Seldom is it possible to deal with only one compound at a time, even in such highly refined foods as sugar, starch, and fat. Neither is it possible to exclude environmental factors from these reactions.

Desirable appearance, texture, moistness, odor, and flavor must be retained or attained during preparation procedures. At the same time, nutritive losses must not be excessive. To obtain these desired outcomes principles of chemistry, physics, and bacteriology are applied in food preparation, and thus it becomes a very exact science.

The art of food preparation lies in the presentation of an attractive food. China, table settings, and even the room in which the food is served—all are "background" for the food at meal time. The social sciences and humanities also play a role in food acceptance. Congenial companionship and pleasant surroundings make for a relaxed mind and body and favor optimum digestive functions.

Artistry in food presentation need not involve time-consuming furbelows (see Fig. 5), but rather some such simple practices as follow:

1. Prepare food to look attractive and to emit pleasant odors.
2. Vary the colors of foods on a plate so that pleasing color combinations are shown.
3. Vary the shapes of foods so that interesting designs are obtained.
4. Vary the method of preparation so that food does not have a monotonous texture.
5. Keep the food contained within the rim of the plate and use a plate size consistent with the amount of food served.
6. Keep foods separated on the plate unless the combining of them is deliberate.
7. Keep the background of the plate clean and neat.
8. Use touches of garnishes such as parsley or carrot top sprigs with meats; lettuce or cabbage leaves under salads; paprika sprinkled lightly on vegetables or meats; sliced egg or chopped nuts on salads and vegetables; paper frills on bone ends (Frenched lamb chops); cherries, jelly, or colored sugar on puddings; shaved chocolate or whipped cream on desserts; and many others. Generally garnishes should be edible.

Employment of chemical reactions to produce attractive food merges the scientific and artistic aspects of food preparation. For example, the browning of foods results from chemical reactions. Browning of slices of light-colored fruits decreases attractiveness, and scientific principles are employed to inhibit the browning (see Fig. 4). Judicious browning of baked foods, however, enhances attractiveness of these products and again scientific principles are employed to induce the browning.

The appearance of a food influences its acceptance. Successful homemakers and hostesses will employ both science and art principles in food preparation and presentation.

REFERENCE STANDARDS FOR SPECIFIC RECIPES

The description of a product resulting when certain proportions of ingredients have been used with prescribed manipulation is often referred to as a "standard" for the product. Generally it can be assumed that many individuals have found the palatability characteristics of "standard products" desirable, but this is not to be construed as indicating that every person will or even should like them. Unless a result is described, however, there will be no way to judge whether one wishes to duplicate it or to deviate in the formula or procedure. The student should consider the standards given in this book for the different products only as a check to determine whether he has followed the given procedure. If he prefers something different he may use the standard as a reference in making the necessary changes.

If it is desired to reproduce a given result in food preparation, it is necessary to have the type and amount of ingredients, the manipulation, and the cooking conditions identical to those used in the first production. For all practical purposes a recipe may be considered as a complete description of such materials and procedures.

COMBINING AND AGITATING FOODS

The size of the molecules that make up the starches and proteins of foods is relatively large. Molecules of this proportion are said to be of colloidal size, and substances that contain them are termed colloids. Colloids are peculiar in that their reactions are conditioned by their past treatments. It is for this reason that one must know the amount of agitation which is to be used in the preparation of those

Fig. 5. Gourmet dishes require little work if foods are harvested at proper maturity. (Courtesy, Western Growers Association, Los Angeles.)

recipes containing starch or protein. Recipes stipulate the amount of each ingredient and the order and method of combining ingredients but seldom give instruction on the amount of manipulation. No doubt many failures to attain the standard for the recipe or to duplicate a product are caused by too little or too much stirring.

The shape and size of the mixing bowl are important in combining ingredients. These must be consistent with the method of mixing, the amount of the finished product, the amount of agitation which is to be given, and other considerations. For example, if a recipe for muffins is mixed twenty-five strokes by everyone in the class but one student has her ingredients in a bowl that is twice the size of that used by other students, she will give approximately double the amount of mixing in her twenty-five strokes.

Ice cream, egg white, and cream are generally foamed, so they must have room in a bowl or container for two, three or more volumes of expansion. Egg yolk for mayonnaise-making must be confined in a small area so that the beater blades can reach the yolk and agitate it as the oil is added to make the mayonnaise. Flour mixtures cannot be easily stirred or beaten if the bowl is more than half full; egg white to be whipped by a whisk is purposely allowed to spread on a platter to facilitate the whipping movement and maximum contact with air.

Experience is the best teacher in the selection of size and shape of the bowl for the type of product to be prepared, but if the recipe and procedure are carefully studied, one can use common sense and obtain considerable information in this respect. A simple scientific rule can be applied: two objects cannot occupy the same space at the same time. One cup of sugar mixed with one cup of water will not require 2 cups of volume because water can displace the air surrounding sugar granules, but one cup of oil to be mixed with one cup of water does require 2 cups of volume because there is no air in either to displace. One should be able to arrive at a reasonably good estimate of pan or bowl size by totaling the volumes of ingredients in a recipe and allowing for stirring, beating, or foaming space.

MEASURING AMOUNTS OF INGREDIENTS

It is generally most efficient in food preparation procedures to assemble all of the utensils and all of the ingredients for a food product and then to measure each ingredient before any mixing is begun. Either weight or volume measurements may be used. Often a student will say, "My mother doesn't measure anything and she is an excellent cook." This is not an entirely true statement because failures result when the proportions of ingredients are not within a definite range. There is a range for each ingredient in a product within which one obtains an acceptable product, but if one wishes to duplicate exactly, he must measure exactly. Commercial mixes owe part of their popularity to the fact that the ingredients are present in accurate proportions. This favors reproducible products each time a product is made. The experienced cook who does not appear to measure is actually measuring by eye estimate or handfuls, and she may not find it important or even desirable to duplicate exactly a result obtained previously. In fact, consistent duplication might make a monotonous diet. The sameness that is produced with mixes may be the reason some people prefer their own recipes.

The familiar question, "Which weighs more a pound of feathers or a pound of lead?" has similes in food preparation. A pound of flour, for example, occupies 4 cups of volume whereas a pound of oil occupies only 2 cups. The pound of flour, moreover, can be made to occupy different volumes. In order to obtain exactly the amounts designated to prepare a product, all ingredients should be weighed. Many countries utilize weight measurements in recipes and although this seems more efficient than volume, seldom is this practice seen in the average American home. The formulas used in this book are given in both units so that either weight or volume method of measuring may be used. The student is referred to the Handbook of Food Preparation table of weight and volume measurements of common foods for conversion from one method of measuring to the other (pp. 3–6, Ref. 6, in Reading List).

Weighing of Ingredients

This method of measuring requires an accurate balance. Unless the balance is very sensitive it might be more accurate to measure things used in small amounts such as salt, soda, baking powder, and spices even if other ingredients are weighed. Any balance to be used for home food preparation should be calibrated in grams or hundredths of ounces (see Fig. 6).

Volume Measurement of Ingredients

Volume measurements are reasonably accurate if the utensils actually hold the standard amount specified and if care is taken to follow

Accurate amounts of ingredients may be obtained quickly by weighing.

recommended procedures designed to put a definite weight into a given volume (see Fig. 7).

The American Standards Association is set up to test equipment and write specifications, but "standard equipment" is not well marked. It is difficult to test measuring equipment. Some idea of accuracy might be obtained by measuring table salt. Three level teaspoonfuls should exactly fill 1 standard tablespoon or weigh the same as 1 level tablespoonful; 16 level tablespoonfuls should exactly fill 1 standard cup or weigh the same as 1 level cupful. In the laboratory the cup measures might be tested with water. Each cup should hold 236 grams (or 236 milliliters) of water.

Fig. 7. Volume measurements are reasonably accurate if the utensils actually hold the standard amount specified.

Common usage of measuring equipment assumes that the following procedures will be used.

1. Sets of cups of ¼, ⅓, ½, and 1 cup capacity without headspace will be used for dry ingredients when these amounts are specified.

2. Dry ingredients will be fluffed (aerated) before measuring:
   a. by sifting once all white flours, powdered sugar, and cocoa;
   b. by stirring lightly other flours and meals, sugar, dry milk, and baking powder (sift if lumpy).

3. Aerated dry ingredients will be either sifted directly into the measure or gently lifted into it until it is heaped and then leveled by scraping off the excess with the straight edge of a spatula.

4. Moist foods (brown sugar, soft bread crumbs, grated cocoanut, grated cheese, raisins, etc.) will be gently packed so that the shape of the cup is retained when the ingredients are turned out.

5. Plastic fats will be pressed without air pockets into a dry measure and leveled.

6. Liquid ingredients will be measured in clear glass or plastic measures with headspace and clearly marked fractions so that one can sight the surface of the liquid at eye level and adjust the measurement to have the bottom of the meniscus (dip in the surface of liquids) at the desired mark. The headspace permits one to move a cupful of liquid without spilling.

ENVIRONMENTAL FACTORS IN FOOD PREPARATION

Air, water, and heat are factors of first importance in food preparation, but they are not independent of each other, and more than one constituent of a food may be affected by them. Acids and alkalies must also be considered in the preparation of foods.

Air, and its Relation to Oxidation

Oxygen in food preparation is often overlooked because it is the one gas of the air which is so vital to life. Oxygen is a very reactive gas and forms chemical unions with many substances. The oxidized food products may be undesirable either from a nutritional or a palatability standpoint—often both.

Changes in the nutritional value of foods due to oxidation, especially in ascorbic acid, vitamin A, fat, and vitamin E, are perhaps the most important considerations of air in food preparation. Ascorbic acid is particularly susceptible to oxidation, and much of this essential nutrient may be oxidized to substances with lowered or no nutritional value if care is not taken to exclude oxygen from the food. The proportion of ascorbic acid that undergoes oxidation depends primarily upon the temperature and time of holding the food, the amount of surface area exposed per unit weight of food, and the presence of other acids in the food.

Temperature-time factor. The rate of any chemical reaction usually increases with increases in temperature. The amount of oxidation taking place in a given food will be greater at room temperature within a given period of time than it will at refrigerator temperatures. Thus, refrigeration or freezing temperatures should be used to store most ascorbic acid-rich foods. Also, the shorter the time that the foods are held, the less change that will occur at a given temperature.

Amount of surface area per unit weight of food. Chemicals must be in contact with each other in order to react. Round surfaced areas have the least possible exposure of any shape. Oranges, in addition to having this shape, also have a thick protective skin so that oxidative changes of ascorbic acid during the holding of the fruit is not appreciable, even at room temperature. A comparable weight of broccoli will have a large surface area in proportion to the orange, and there is no natural protective skin on broccoli. Leaves of plants used for food also have much exposed surface for their weight. Inasmuch as broccoli and leaves of plants are also excellent sources of ascorbic acid when harvested, they should be treated carefully to prevent oxidation of this nutrient. Either storage in hydrator pans or plastic bags in the refrigerator for only short periods of time, or immediate processing into frozen foods is imperative if large proportions of the ascorbic acid are to be retained.

Acids other than ascorbic acid. Ascorbic acid in the presence of other acids is less susceptible to oxidation changes than it is when alone. Citrus fruits, strawberries, and tomatoes contain other acids and resist oxidation of ascorbic acid to a greater extent than do the less acidic cabbage, greens, broccoli, and cauliflower.

General precautions to prevent oxidation. Any practice that serves to exclude oxygen from food assists in the prevention of oxidation changes of ascorbic acid in the food. A covering of sugar or syrup over prepared fruits, tight covers on juice containers, and other similar practices limit the amount of oxygen coming in contact with the food. Packages of preshredded cabbage or other leafy vegetables on the market may be a convenience but cannot be expected to retain the ascorbic acid value as fully as do the whole leaves kept under the same conditions.

Ascorbic acid is so easily oxidized that it is sometimes used to protect against other oxidative changes in food. When used in this manner it is termed an antioxidant although in its protective action it still becomes oxidized. The ascorbic acid-citric acid combination in lemon, orange, and other citrus fruits serves as the antioxidant against browning when slices of banana, apple, peaches, or other light-colored fruits are dipped in or sprinkled with the acid juices. Powders of these acids are produced commercially and are extensively used in the freezing preservation of light-colored fruits.

The presence of small amounts of copper also increases the rate of oxidation of ascorbic acid. Modern technology has developed non-reactive materials for coating the inside of copper utensils, but many metallic utensils contain traces of copper which may act as catalysts. One should therefore avoid the use of copper sieves for straining fruit juices or puréeing fruits and vegetables rich in ascorbic acid.

Vitamin A and fat also may be changed by oxidative reactions so that they are of decreased value in human nutrition. Oxidized fat develops an unpleasant odor and taste and is said to be rancid. One cannot determine the extent of oxidative changes in vitamin A by subjective means but often deteriorative changes in the palatability characteristics of the food can be used as a gauge. The oxidation of both fat and vitamin A proceed relatively slowly.

Vitamin E is the term applied to a group of fat-soluble compounds essential to the diet of some animals but not yet proved to be essential to humans. These compounds are also very susceptible to oxidation, and their reactiveness makes them useful in inhibiting the oxidative rancidity of solid fats. Vitamin E then acts as an antioxidant for the fat and also prevents oxidation of vitamin A.

Aeration of food. Air is purposely whipped into some foods like egg white, whipped cream, and other foams. Except for whipping cream the foods that are foamed do not contain substances that are easily oxidized. Whipping cream contains both vitamin A and fat, but the oxidative changes that occur during the time the whipped cream is held are not appreciable. Also, cream must be kept chilled to have the fat firm enough to retain the foam, and low temperatures slow rates of chemical reactions.

Air in liquids affects their flavors—as can be observed by comparing the taste of boiled cooled water with water freshly drawn from the tap. Some of the flavor changes are desirable, and others are undesirable. De-aerated milk retains freshness qualities longer than untreated milk. Nutritive values of fruit juices might be decreased if the juices were aerated and held for a long period of time. Carbonated beverages should not be confused with aerated beverages because carbon dioxide is an inert gas and does not react with the food.

Water in Food Preparation

Water is used freely in food preparation. Many foods are washed in water, put into water to cook, or water is added to moisten food. Water is called the universal solvent because so many substances dissolve in it. Colors, flavors, acids, sugar, some proteins, minerals, and certain vitamins (B-complex and ascorbic acid) may be dissolved into the waters that come in contact with cut or bruised surfaces. There are no water-soluble substances lost when intact oranges, pears, apples, potatoes, and similar foods are washed because these foods have protective skins. When the skins are pared away, some of the cells are ruptured and cellular materials may be dissolved if the food is washed or covered with water.

Increasing the area of the cut surface, as in slicing an apple, increases the number of ruptured cells and permits losses consistent with the number of cells disrupted and the amount of soluble substances therein. Thus, the greater the surface area exposed to the water, the greater the solubility losses will be. If the water is to be used, the substances are not lost, merely displaced.

It is not always desirable or practical to keep food whole for cooking or serving, but surface area can be controlled to a large extent. Spheres have least surface area per given weight, but it is not possible to cut food into balls without waste. Cubes will have less surface area than slices or irregular shaped pieces of the same volume. Long thin slices, like leaves, have a large surface area for their weight.

Logical procedure in the washing of foods indicates that the food be left whole whenever possible in order to retain water-soluble substances. Procedures for cooking should be chosen according to whether the water is to be used or discarded. If the cooking water is to be used, solubility losses to the water are not in themselves important.

The larger the amount of water used per given weight of foods, the greater the possibility of solubility losses. When one does not wish to use the cooking water, it is recommended that small portions of water be used for pared or cut foods and, if possible, evaporated during the cooking period.

The amount of substances that go into solution increases in direct proportion to increases in time and temperature of cooking. Therefore, it is desirable to maintain time and temperature conditions that will allow for a good product but at the same time result in minimum solution losses.

Substances that soften foods also permit greater losses of water-soluble materials from that food than would otherwise occur. For example, the tough walls of peas cooked in water to which soda has been added, will break easily and allow the soluble materials to pass out into the cooking water.

The three states of water. Water has three forms: liquid (water); solid (ice); and gas (steam). The changes in its state are of considerable importance in food preparation. The temperature at which water solidifies (freezes) is termed its freezing temperature or melting temperature (some ice can be melting while water is freezing).

Steam is formed rapidly at the boiling temperature of water. Water boils when it becomes turbulent as the vapor pressure within the water becomes equal to the atmospheric pressure on the surface. Atmospheric pressure varies slightly with weather conditions, but it will always decrease with increases in altitude. The temperature of boiling water in Iowa may be 210 to 212° F but only 198° F, or less, in mountainous sections of the country like northern Arizona and Colorado. The temperature of boiling will remain constant whether the boiling is rapid or slow. Rapid boiling, however, increases the rate of evaporation (loss of water through steam). Sometimes rapid evaporation may be desirable (jelly-making), but in other instances the food may either boil dry or the excessive agitation may cause undue damage to the shape of the food.

The expansion in volume when water is changed to steam is tremendous—1600 volumes. A great deal of the expansion of baked products results from some of the water in the flour mixture changing to steam. Gas pockets must be present to entrap the steam or it will be lost to the atmosphere or will form one large hole, as in cream puffs and popovers.

If a cover is placed over a boiling liquid, some of the steam condenses on the cool lid and then returns as liquid to the cooking vessel. Tight-fitting covers prevent evaporation to a large extent. Liquids to be evaporated rapidly must be boiled uncovered.

Tight-fitting lids that can be clamped down to prevent any loss of steam assist in increasing temperatures by building up steam pressure on the surface of the liquid. This is the function of such special equipment as pressure saucepans and pressure canners (see Fig. 8). Increased temperature by means of the pressure saucepan is sometimes used to decrease cooking time of certain foods.

Fig. 8. Specially constructed pressure saucepans must be used to obtain temperatures above the boiling point of water.

Changes in the properties of water. Certain changes in the property of water, caused by the presence of dissolved substances, are of great importance in food preparation procedures. These changes occur in the freezing temperature, the boiling temperature, and the osmotic pressure of the water.

The *freezing temperature* of water is decreased in direct proportion to the number of particles dissolved in it. Salt (NaCl), because each molecule can form two particles (*ions*), is often added to substances, especially water, to obtain low freezing temperatures. If it is desired to freeze another water solution, as in desserts frozen in a hand freezer, ice is used with the salt-water solution. The freezing point of the water is lowered by the addition of the salt. As the salt-water and ice mixture reaches a temperature equilibrium with the mixture to be frozen heat is absorbed from the dessert mixture. Generally there is enough water with ice to dissolve the salt, but the salt cannot be effective until it is in solution.

The *boiling temperature* of water is increased in direct proportion to the number of particles dissolved in it. The usefulness in food preparation of this phenomenon is limited except in sugar cookery—jellies, candies, and frostings. In the preparation of these foods, the increase in boiling temperature of water is used to indicate the concentration of sugar in solution. These products are usually evaporated by boiling in order to keep the sugar in solution. To accurately determine the concentration of dissolved substances by means of the boiling temperature, one should measure the temperature of boiling water without added substances and to this add the requisite degrees increase as given by the recipe or a handbook. For example, if water boils at 198° F, and the desired concentration of pure sugar (sucrose) is attained when the boiling point has been raised 9° F, then a final boiling point of 207° F is indicated. If recipes state only the desired temperature to be attained at sea level, the number of degrees increase may be obtained by subtracting 212° F (100° C) from the stipulated temperature.

It is generally not practical to dissolve substances in the water used for cooking food in order to raise the boiling point and thereby increase the cooking rate. The proteins of meat and eggs are softer when cooked at temperatures below 212° F than when higher temperatures are used, and textures of fruits and vegetables become undesirably hardened when cooked with salt or sugar. Furthermore, if a sufficient amount of salt is used to cause an appreciable increase in boiling temperature, the food becomes too salty for eating. The small amount of salt used for flavor in vegetables will not noticeably affect the boiling temperature. Sugar is added to cooking water for fruits only if it is desired to retain the shape of the fruit and also to sweeten it.

Glycerine is an edible substance that has received some attention for use in increasing boiling temperatures. There would seem to be no valid reason for using it, and its slightly sweet taste and energy value might well be considered disadvantages.

Osmotic pressure of fluids is the result of the pressure exerted by the particles in solution and the pressure increases in direct proportion to increases in the number of particles. This pressure causes the phenomenon known as osmosis, which is the passage of substances across a semipermeable membrane. Osmosis occurs only in situations where the membrane separates two solutions of unequal concentrations. The fluid passes through the wall until the pressures are equalized. If conditions are right and if particles are of molecular size or smaller, some of the particles can pass through the wall.

Osmosis can be demonstrated by putting salt (NaCl) on the surface of cut meat or sugar on sliced peaches. The salt or sugar dissolves in the surface fluids and causes the cellular fluids to exude from the intact cells of the foods. When foods are cooked in water, some of the water-soluble vitamins and minerals can move with water from the cells to the cooking water because of differences in osmotic pressures. In some instances, the osmotic reaction may proceed in the other direction. When cooking waters contain greater concentrations of minerals such as calcium or iron than do the plant cells, the cooked vegetable may contain greater quantities of these nutrients than it contained when raw.

The tissue-hardening that occurs when fruits and vegetables are cooked in solutions of salts or sugars is due partly to the loss of cellular fluids, caused by osmotic pressures of the dissolved particles in the solution. The food is literally dehydrated.

The principles of osmosis are particularly important in the control of microorganisms in foods. Like the higher plants, microbes in solutions of high osmotic pressures lose their cellular fluids, and some types of microorganisms cannot survive this dehydration. Some microorganisms are able to tolerate higher osmotic pressures than are others. A 3 to 5 per cent salt (NaCl) concentration with shredded cabbage prevents growth of undesirable types of bacteria while "friendly bacteria" grow and produce the familiar sauerkraut (fermented cabbage). Other vegetables can be similarly fermented. Different flavors in cheese are obtained by controlling salt concentrations to permit growth of a desired microorganism while inhibiting undesirable strains.

Salt-rising bread owes its name to the fact that the bacterium used in making the bread is more tolerant of salt than are other microorganisms. The specific bacteria were first isolated from cornmeal to which a relatively high salt solution had been added. This mixture was kept warm until it fermented, and the solution from the fermented cornmeal was then used in making a wheat bread in which the organism continued to grow and develop the distinctive flavors characteristic of salt-rising bread.

The yeast plants used for fermenting special flour mixtures for bread, rolls, and other products, are also sensitive to osmotic pressures. Care must be taken to control amounts of sugar and salt in these products so that the yeast can grow and produce the desired changes in the dough.

Colloids like starch and protein molecules do not affect osmotic pressures and are not able to pass through semipermeable membranes (cell walls).

Heat in Food Preparation

Heat in food preparation is generally thought of in conjunction with the actual cooking of food, but the absence or removal of heat is as important as application or addition of heat.

"Refrigerator temperature" and "room temperature" are terms used frequently in food preparation terminology. Approximately 45° F is to be understood when "refrigerator temperature" is used and 72 to 75° F when "room temperature" is stated. Changing the temperature of food even at these low temperatures can affect both the nutritional value and palatability.

The higher the temperature the more rapidly chemical reactions proceed. However, the maximum rate of a reaction is not always the most desirable. For example, bread doughs fermenting rapidly at the upper limits of heat tolerance for yeast (140° F) become very sticky and are difficult to handle.

Ingredients for most prepared products are generally used at room temperature because they blend readily. Temperatures of mixing higher than room temperatures, although occasionally used, may be either impractical, or ingredients may become too intimately mixed for desired results.

The practice of either cooling or warming of food materials is useful in attaining certain results. Some liquids are viscous at low temperatures. If a more fluid product is desired, warming increases the fluidity. Egg whites for foaming are preferred at room temperature rather than refrigerator temperature because they foam more readily and attain a larger volume than when cold. Cream for whipping, however, is kept cold to keep the fat firm. Eggs for poaching or frying may purposely be kept cold to decrease their spreading when broken out, but eggs for cake-making are warmed to room temperature before they are used.

The growth of microorganisms in foods may be controlled by controlling the temperature. Foods are frozen or refrigerated if bacteria, yeast, or mold growth is to be inhibited, but they are warmed if this growth is to be encouraged (yeast in bread).

Method of heat transfer. There are relatively few mediums used for transferring heat in food preparation—air, liquids, metals, glass, paper, or plastics. Air, liquid, metals, glass, and paper are used for cooking, and, in addition to these, plastic containers are used for cooling. These mediums vary in the rate of heat transmission and give different appearances or flavors in foods.

Air transmits heat less rapidly than do other mediums. A muffin baked at 400° F will require the same cooking time as dough steamed (dumplings) at 212° F. The muffin, which requires 20 minutes in an oven at 400° F, will require only 3 minutes in hot fat at 400° F. A hard-cooked egg will chill thoroughly in 5 minutes in ice water at 32° F but will still be warm to the touch after 20 minutes at 32° F in the freezing cabinet of the refrigerator.

Methods of heating in which air surrounds the food and evaporation is permitted, are termed dry methods of cooking. These include:

1. Roasting or baking in a ventilated oven in which heated air is circulated around the food.

2. Broiling, barbecueing, and similar methods of cooking in which one side of the food is placed close to the source of heat. On barbecue spits and rotisseries the food may be turned constantly so that all sides cook uniformly.

3. Immersing in hot fat. Moisture from the food escapes into the atmosphere through the fat.

When the heat is transmitted to the food by water the method of cooking is referred to as moist heat. Moist methods of heating are those in which the food is immersed in water or enveloped in steam. If meats or other foods are wrapped in foil or placed in a covered pan and heated in an oven there will be a sufficient amount of liquid from the food itself to make this a method of moist heat cooking.

Methods of heat transfer may combine or use two media. Baked products are in contact with metal or glass which transmits the heat from the air to the food. If the transfer of heat through the pan is too rapid, the food may burn on the bottom before the top is browned sufficiently. Paper liners may be used to decrease the rate of browning because paper transmits heat slowly. In a similar manner paper covers may be used to prevent overbrowning of the tops. Metal skewers are sometimes used to conduct heat more rapidly to the center of roasts and potatoes than is possible by only baking in heated air.

It must also be remembered that the food itself, in the conventional methods of heating or cooling, transmits heat. The heat must penetrate to the center of the food if the entire piece is to be cooked and heat must be transmitted from the center to the surface if food is to be cooled. Obviously, the shorter the distance to the center, the more quickly the food will cook or cool. Large products are often baked a longer time at a lower temperature than similar substances made into smaller pieces. The lower temperature is necessary if the surface of the large piece is not to become overbrown before the center is cooked. Likewise, large pieces of food cool more slowly than small or thin pieces.

The amount of surface area per given weight of food influences a great many reactions, and heat transfer is no exception. In heat penetration and cooking, the greater the surface area exposed to the heating medium the shorter will be the time required for cooking. Cake batter cooks more quickly as cup cakes than as loaf cake; rolls bake more quickly than loaves of bread.

Effect of heat on the various constituents in food. Most of the weight of a food is in water, protein, carbohydrate, and fat. However, small amounts of other constituents are present, and many times their presence influences the cooking procedures. These constituents, found in small amounts, include minerals, vitamins, enzymes, pigments, flavors, gums, tannins, and organic acids. The substances, for example carbohydrates, are also comprised of a number of different members—cellulose, starch, and sugar—and different members of a class react differently to the same stimulus. The generalizations that might be made concerning the effect of heat on food include:

1. Water evaporates from any food unless it is covered. This accounts for the fact that fresh vegetables wilt when exposed to air, baked products weigh less than their batters, surfaces of baked products brown, a heavy skin forms on uncovered sauces and puddings, and meat shrinks in cooking.

2. Most proteins coagulate (become set) when sufficiently heated; custards gel, meats become firm, flour mixtures hold their shape. The temperature of coagulation varies among different proteins, and interfering substances (sugar in custards and flour mixtures) may change the coagulation temperature.

3. The carbohydrates in the starch category all imbibe water and swell (gelatinize) resulting in the thickening of products such as sauces and puddings. The temperature of maximum gelatinization varies among starches, and added ingredients such as sugar may change the gelatinization temperature.

4. The carbohydrates in the cellulose category soften on cooking unless some hardening agents are present such as the minerals in hard water, table salt, sugar, or acid.

5. Heat inactivates enzymes so that they lose their catalytic power. Different foods require different heating times to completely inactivate enzymes. This reaction is only incidental in home food preparation, but it is of considerable importance in commercial processing of many foods.

6. Cooking may cause color changes in food. Green vegetables may show browning of the chlorophyll pigment—this is especially rapid if acid is present.

7. The acid content of foods may decrease on cooking; volatile types can escape in steam, and some of the nonvolatile acids may be lost in the cooking water. Generally food acids are given consideration only when one food is to be used with another, for example, tomatoes with green beans or orange juice in cake.

8. Flavors change in cooking. Some flavors are lost in the steam and others may decompose. Some of the changes such as the browning

of meat are highly prized, others such as the bitterness that develops in cabbage cooked a long time, may be considered unpalatable.

9. Those vitamins sensitive to oxidation are changed more rapidly when food is cooked. When vegetable and fruit textures are softened in cooking, the water-soluble minerals as well as vitamins can be readily dissolved into the cooking water.

10. Cooking destroys microorganisms. This aspect of heat in food preparation is often overlooked, but at times can be the most important reason for cooking food. Organisms causing communicable diseases are relatively easy to destroy. If one cannot obtain pasteurized milk, safe water, or fruits and vegetables known to be produced under sanitary conditions, these foods should be cooked before they are eaten.

Effect of Acids and Alkalies in Food Preparation

Edible acids used in food preparation are usually limited to cream of tartar, vinegar, or those provided by foods themselves, notably lemon juice, sour milk, and molasses. Acids are those constituents, present or added to foods, that give the tart sour quality. Sugar can offset the tartness of food but cannot decrease the acid content. An alkali cannot sweeten the food, but it decreases acidity by neutralizing the acid. Soda (sodium bicarbonate) is the edible alkali used in food preparation. Its chief use is in flour mixtures where it produces a leavening gas, carbon dioxide (see Chapter 6), in its reaction with acid.

Acids may be used in cooking of vegetables for flavor or for producing desirable color changes. This is discussed fully in the chapter pertaining to fruits and vegetables.

Pure water is said to be neutral in reaction because it is neither acid nor alkaline, or it can be said that the acidic and alkaline qualities are equivalent. Most foods are acid in reaction but to varying degrees. Milk and meat contain so little acid they are almost neutral. Vegetables contain larger amounts of acid than meat or milk contain, and fruits are generally acidic. Egg white is one of the few alkaline foods. Tap waters also are usually alkaline in reaction.

Determination of Doneness in Cooking

The determination of doneness in cooking requires some experience, even with the automatic toasters, thermometers, and egg cookers. Also, one person may prefer greater changes during the cooking procedure than another. Changes in appearance, rigidity, thickness of sauces, tenderness, and flavor; the length of the heating period; and the attainment of a definite temperature are the methods commonly employed in determining doneness.

Proteins become opaque when they are coagulated, therefore meat, fish, poultry, and eggs lose their translucent quality. Starch, on the other hand, becomes transparent when it is completely gelatinized.

The surface of baked products changes color and becomes brown when they are done. They may, however, be brown before they are thoroughly cooked on the interior, therefore other methods of determining doneness of these products have been devised. The "toothpick" and "spring" tests are two of the more reliable of such tests. A toothpick, knife, or other small instrument is inserted into the center of the product; if the product is not done, moist particles of batter cling to the testing instrument. When testing for "spring" the depression made by light pressure of the finger should not remain after the pressure is released.

Evaporation of liquid from baked products will cause them to shrink from the sides of the pan, and in like manner thin sauces may be thickened by evaporation of liquids after the starch has become transparent. In either case the degree of evaporation may be indicative of desired degree of doneness.

Cooking softens the tissues of vegetables and in some instances the tissues of meat. The amount of softness may be determined by piercing with a fork or other sharp object. This test requires experience but can become a reliable test for doneness.

Steamed products, roast meats, baked potatoes, muffins, cookies, biscuits, etc., may be cooked a definite length of time as suggested in a recipe, however, differences in piece sizes and shapes may make this a very unsatisfactory method.

The attainment of a definite temperature is particularly recommended for jelly, certain candies, and meats (see Fig. 9). The temperature of coagulation of various meat proteins has been determined and may be used as a guide to doneness. The sensitized part of the thermometer must be in the center of the thickest portion of lean, and, when the reading is made, the eye level must be at right angles to the thermometer scale.

Fig. 9. The temperature of coagulation of various meat proteins has been determined and may be used as a guide to doneness. (Courtesy of Southern Counties Gas Co., Los Angeles.)

SUMMARY

Foods are complex chemical compounds containing varying proportions of both related and unrelated chemical substances. Air, water, and heat are factors that must be considered in the preparation of foods in order to retain or attain desirable products from the aspects of nutrition and palatability. Inasmuch as the principles of physics, chemistry, bacteriology, and other sciences must be applied in the preparation of food, food preparation is an exact science. Generalizations in the application of these principles are discussed.

The psychological and sociological values of foods are often of as great importance as their physiological values. In preparing food to fulfill sociological values, artistry in food procedures must be practiced. Oftentimes a scientific principle is employed to obtain an artistic effect. Food preparation therefore constitutes both a science and an art.

Reading List

1. Heseltine, M. and U. M. Dow, 1957, *The New Basic Cook Book*, Houghton Mifflin Co., Boston.
2. Hughes, O., 1955, *Introductory Foods*, The Macmillan Co., New York.
3. Justin, M. M., L. O. Rust, and G. E. Vail, 1956, *Foods*, Houghton Mifflin Co., Boston.
4. Niles, K. B., 1955, *Food Preparation Recipes*, John Wiley and Sons, Inc., New York.
5. Sweetman, M. D. and I. MacKellar, 1954, *Food Selection and Preparation*, John Wiley and Sons, Inc., New York.
6. Terminology Committee, Am. Home Econ. Assoc., 1959, *Handbook of Food Preparation*, American Home Economics Association, Washington, D. C.
7. The Editors of Esquire, 1955, *Esquire Cook-book*, McGraw-Hill Book Co., New York.

CHAPTER **3**

Fig. 10. Meats, poultry, fish, legumes, and nuts are all high in protein value and provide many choices for the "first item on the menu." (Courtesy: National Association Margarine Manufacturers, Lincoln, Nebraska; Southern Counties Gas Company, Los Angeles, California; V. B. Scheffer Fish and Wildlife Service, Washington, D. C.; *Better Homes and Gardens,* Des Moines, Iowa.

CHAPTER **3** . . MEAT,
THE FOCAL POINT
IN THE MENU PLAN

Meat, Poultry, Fish, Legumes, Nuts

THE ROLE OF MEAT, POULTRY, AND FISH
IN DAILY MEAL PLANS

Quantity and Quality of Meat Proteins
Mineral Contributions of Meat
Vitamin Content of Meat
Fat Content of Meat

BUYING OF BEEF, PORK, LAMB, AND VEAL

Meat in the Family Budget
Meat Inspection
Meat Grades
    Conformation
    Finish
    Quality
Meat Cuts
Ripening of Meat
Types of Meat Preservation
    Curing
    Freezing
    Canning
    Radiation Sterilization

BUYING OF POULTRY AND FISH

Poultry
Fish

CARE OF MEAT, POULTRY, AND FISH
IN THE HOME

PREPARATION OF MEAT, POULTRY, AND FISH

Factors Affecting Palatability
    Tenderness
    Juiciness
    Flavor
Method of Cooking Meat, Poultry, and Fish

T︎HE UNITED STATES IS A NATION OF GREAT MEAT-EATERS; STATISTICS show that the per capita consumption of meat is higher in this country than in most of the countries in the world. The average per capita consumption of flesh foods in 1955 (World Almanac, 1957) was 191.6 pounds which averages more than ½ pound per day. Meat is universally liked, and it is not due to lack of desire that many other countries have a lower intake than the United States. Rather, it is because meat is more expensive than plant foods to produce, and the United States at present is in a more favorable position than are many other countries to both produce and process meat.

The types of meat, exclusive of poultry and fish, commonly sold in the markets in the United States consist of beef (cattle), pork (swine), veal (calves), and lamb or mutton (sheep). More than 75 per cent of the total sales consists of beef and pork.

Animals are commonly fed on roughage that human beings cannot eat. In 1951 Bull stated that approximately 80 per cent of American beef is raised on such roughage. When plant foods that are suitable for people are fed to animals, however, only 4 per cent as many Calories can be regained from the beef as from the original plant food. Countries with limited amounts of cultivatable land and little or no roughage cannot afford to convert their plants to animal products. A comparison of consumption of cereals and legumes with available meat, fat, and total daily Calories available is shown in Table 4 for ten selected countries including the one with the lowest as well as the one with the highest meat intake. It will be noted that as the available meat supplies decrease the amount of cereal grains increases.

Because meat is expensive to produce, it commands a higher proportion of the family food dollar than is required for other foods of similar nutritive value. No doubt the pleasures of flavor and chewing as well as the feeling of repletion after eating meat account for its popularity, and it has become common practice to budget 20 to 30 per cent of the food money for this item alone.

Taste appeal places meat high on the market list. Generally it is the first item to be chosen when planning a menu or when ordering a meal in a restaurant. It is logical therefore, in a study of foods, that initial attention be directed toward the "first item on the menu."

The selection of the kind, cut, and amount of meat to satisfy tastes without overspending the budget may be one of the most difficult parts of food buying, but the cooking procedures are the simplest.

Table 4. AMOUNT OF TOTAL DAILY CALORIES AND MEAT AND POULTRY, CEREALS, LEGUMES AND NUTS, AND FAT AVAILABLE PER PERSON FOR THE YEAR 1955 IN EACH OF 10 COUNTRIES*

Country	Total Daily Calories	Meat and Poultry, Pounds	Cereals, Pounds	Legumes and Nuts, Pounds	Fats, Pounds
Australia	3190	237.6	200.2	11.0	37.4
Argentina	2840	228.8	217.8	8.8	28.6
United States	3100	202.4	154.0	13.2	44.0
Canada	3190	184.8	167.2	11.0	44.0
Denmark	3310	129.8	202.4	8.8	52.8
Austria	2910	101.2	261.8	8.8	39.6
Greece	2590	35.2	325.6	39.6	33.0
Philippines	1920	19.8	288.2	26.4	8.8
Japan	2220	6.6	332.2	13.2	6.6
India	1850	2.2	279.4	57.2	8.8

* Yearbook for Food and Agriculture Organization 1957, FAO, Rome, Italy.

Selection of meat in present-day markets should include application of knowledge not only of cuts but also of the inspecting, grading, ripening, and preserving processes. In the preparation of meats knowledge is needed not only to obtain a product with the desired palatability characteristics but also to retain the nutrients.

The dry mature seeds of plants known as *legumes* are included with the study of meats because they contain similar amounts of many of the same nutrients that are found in meat. Nuts are also used in the Daily Food Guide (Fig. 10) with the meats because they have a higher concentration of protein than is found in other plant foods.

THE ROLE OF MEAT, POULTRY, AND FISH IN DAILY MEAL PLANS

Meat serves several purposes in the meal plan. It is popular because of flavor and texture qualities that are different from any other item in the menu. It therefore fills psychological needs as well as physiological ones. Meats enhance the flavor of plant foods like bread, rice, spaghetti, and vegetables, which are often served with them. This characteristic is especially important when the budget does not permit purchase of a sufficient amount to satisfy the appetite for meat.

Meat is valued primarily for its protein contribution, but even in so-called lean meat, the water and fat content outweigh the protein. The fat may be 10 to 40 per cent of the cut and contributes to the high satiety value of meat as well as to flavors. The water is important to eating quality.

In addition to protein and fat, certain minerals and water-soluble vitamins are present in appreciable amounts in all meats. Inasmuch as man is one of the species of the animal kingdom, it should be expected that animal composition would more nearly approximate human composition than would plant tissue. Thus, meats should contain many of the essential nutrients in a proportion similar to that found in the human body. It should be noted, however, that humans do not consume the bones of animals so that bone-building materials are missing from much meat as are fat-soluble vitamins and ascorbic acid.

Quantity and Quality of Meat Proteins

The proportions of the various amino acids making up the proteins, as well as the total amount of protein in meat, are factors of prime importance in the diet. A 4-ounce serving of lean meat provides approximately 20 grams of protein. It would take 3 large eggs, 2½ cups of milk, 4 ounces of cottage cheese, 1⅓ cups baked beans, or 10 slices of white bread to give an equivalent *amount* of protein. The amino acid components of meat proteins include all of those known to be essential to man so that meat proteins are classed among the complete proteins of the diet. Therefore they are said to be of good quality for human nutritive requirements. Meats also include the amino acids low or lacking in cereal proteins so that when they are eaten with cereals, as in a meat sandwich, the cereal protein is improved.

One serving of meat per day, or 20 grams of protein, is planned to provide only a portion—approximately one-third—of the day's protein needs and not the entire amount. Other foods, important for essential nutrients that are low or lacking in meat, must not be crowded out of the diet and these foods will also contribute some protein. Nutritionists recommend that at least one-third of the total protein needs be filled from foods of animal sources. If the pint of milk recommended for calcium needs is consumed, this proportion of animal protein is automatically obtained, and one should have no hesitancy about planning meatless meals with plant foods contributing the quantity of protein that meat would provide in other diet plans. Vegetarians who abstain from all meat-eating can remain perfectly healthy, but many vegetarians do consume milk and eggs.

One kind of meat, poultry, or fish serves as efficiently as any other in protein value when an equivalent amount of protein is consumed. The bone, fat, and water content of meats must be taken into consideration in purchasing adequate weights for the family meal plan so that each person receives the amount of *protein* planned for him. Meat always loses moisture and fat during cooking and because the protein is then more concentrated, 3 ounces of cooked lean will contain protein approximately equivalent to the suggested 4-ounce portion of raw.

Ordinary cooking processes do not appreciably change amino acids in meat proteins, so there is little if any change in the potential protein value of meat caused by the method of preparation. Inasmuch as proteins must be subdivided into amino acids by digestive processes before they can be absorbed into the blood stream, cooking methods may indirectly affect the nutritive value of the meat. Deep-fat fried products, for example, may contain too much fat for complete digestion. Hot spices may irritate the digestive tract and prevent efficient absorption of amino acids. Not only the method of preparation but also the other foods in the meal and the likes and dislikes of the family members must be considered in selecting the meat for the menu.

Mineral Contributions of Meat

The minerals contributed in appreciable quantity by a 4-ounce serving of lean meat include phosphorus, iron, and trace elements, but no calcium. The phosphorus content of meat is related to the proportion of lean or protein and does not vary appreciably among different types of meat.

Meat, particularly from the warm-blooded animals, is well-suited for providing the materials for building the hemoglobin of the red blood cells and the myoglobin of the muscles of the body inasmuch as it contains the protein, iron, and copper necessary for their formation. Livers, being storehouses of iron and copper, are unexcelled providers of these elements and menu plans might profitably include liver frequently. Kidney and spleen will also contribute more iron than do muscle meats.

Seafoods and ocean fish contain iodine in addition to the minerals contained in other meats. Since meat has little or is entirely lacking in calcium, adults who are inclined to neglect milk or cheese in their diets in favor of higher intakes of meat should find other sources of calcium, if the body need for this material is to be met. However, some calcium can be obtained from meat dishes if the meat is simmered in calcium-containing water, or if bones are included during the cooking process. The yield of calcium from bones may be increased if tomatoes or other acids are added to the meat while it is simmering. The soft bones of canned fish such as salmon and sardines can also increase calcium intake.

Minerals are not destroyed in the cooking of meats so the method of preparation will affect the mineral value of the meat only if drip losses are excessive or cooking water is discarded. Preparation techniques designed to retain the vitamin values of meat will also serve to retain minerals.

Vitamin Content of Meat

The vitamins present in meat are in general limited to those that compose the B-complex. They are involved in the oxidation processes of metabolism and include thiamine, riboflavin, niacin, folic acid, vitamin B_6, and vitamin B_{12}. Liver is a notable exception. Not only are the vitamins of the B-complex present in liver in higher concentration than they are in muscle meats, but also large amounts of vitamin A and an appreciable quantity of ascorbic acid are present. A 4-ounce serving of liver can contribute as much vitamin A as 3 pounds of butter or margarine, or as much as 30 quarts of whole milk, and at the same time provide ⅔ of the amount of ascorbic acid contained in an equivalent weight of orange juice.

Food value tables show higher vitamin A values for beef and lamb livers than for pork or calves liver. However, pork liver ranks higher than other liver sources in the content of thiamine. It should be remembered that variation in the amounts of the nutrients stored in the liver would depend upon the feed of the animal as well as the kind of animals. All livers are such extraordinarily rich sources of so many nutrients that choice among them can well be determined by palatability preferences and cost rather than nutrient content.

Among muscle meats, it might be well to note that pork is consistently higher in thiamine content than are other meats and that diets containing few or no whole grain or enriched cereal products or legumes may be improved nutritionally by selecting pork often as the meat choice.

The B-complex vitamins present in meats are water-soluble, and a portion of these can be lost from meat if drip or cooking waters are not used. The practice of serving pan-gravy with the broiled meat and roast beef *au jus* (with its juice) has advantages from both the nutritional and the palatability aspects.

Fat Content of Meat

The fat content of so-called lean meat varies considerably. Liver contains only about 5 per cent fat, but muscle meat may contain 10 to 40 per cent, and pork contains higher amounts than other meats. One can estimate the amount of fat interspersed in the muscles of intact cuts, but it is difficult to estimate the amount in ground meat, cold cuts, sausages, and the like. Some states prohibit including more than 30 per cent fat in these items.

The fat content of the meats should not be ignored in the diet plan. In addition to energy value, much of the flavor of the meat is carried in the fat, and essential fatty acids are also obtained from it.

From the nutritional aspect, one 4-ounce serving of meat per day is adequate for normal adults when recommended amounts of the other foods in the Daily Food Guide are consumed. This is not to imply that the appetite will be satisfied with this amount. However, as has been noted, meat is a relatively expensive source of protein and if there is insufficient money to provide enough meat to satisfy appetite, one need not feel inadequately nourished by supplying protein and extra energy from sources other than meat. However, there seem to be no ill effects produced by consuming larger quantities of meat than the recommended 4 ounces unless, as noted, one inadvertently obtained an excess of fat beyond digestive capacity or energy needs. Also, meat should not displace other foods required for a well-balanced diet.

BUYING OF BEEF, PORK, LAMB, AND VEAL

Many questions about food preparation asked by the inexperienced person are concerned with the selection and preparation of meats. No doubt people stand in awe of this cookery more than the cookery of any other food because of the relatively high cost of meat. It is, therefore, understandable that students need much encouragement and assurance in this area.

The selection of meats begins at home when the menus are planned. Cost, type of meat, and method of preparation are inseparable considerations. Meat selection might also be related to the facilities for home storage. The period of time that meat can be kept without developing off-flavors even at freezer or refrigerator temperatures varies among types and treatments. Menu plans therefore should be arranged so that the meats that have limited storage life will be used first, and when weekly or monthly purchases are made, there should not be a preponderance of the items that do not keep well when refrigerated or frozen.

Meat in the Family Budget

The cost of the meat to serve the family is a factor in the choice of kinds and cuts. Comparisons of prices can often be made at home by utilizing the newspaper advertisements. This comparison should be on the cost of edible lean rather than the prices per pound. For example, if a pound of short ribs at 50 cents contributes only one 20-gram portion of protein, the cost of an equivalent amount of protein will be less from tenderloin selling at $1.50 per pound but yielding four times as much protein. Some differences in costs of edible lean from various cuts and types of meat are illustrated in Table 5. The market prices will vary but the percentage of lean can be taken as relatively constant. One can calculate the cost of lean at a different market price by dividing the figure given for the percentage of lean into the new market price per pound.

The comparative cost of the edible lean meat can be expected to vary with the following factors:

1. *Class or grade* of a specific cut within one type of meat. For example in beef, a sirloin steak of Prime grade will cost more than sirloin cut from Commercial grade.

2. *Location of the cut* from animals of one type and grade—for example, loin lamb chops are generally higher in price than shoulder lamb chops.

3. *Cuts from the same location in different species of animals,* as for example, cuts from the loins of beef, pork, veal, and lamb.

4. *Treatments* given certain cuts, such as fresh, marinated, cured, and canned.

Meat Inspection

Considerations in choosing the meat to buy should include the sanitation of the market and the health of the animals offered for sale, that is *Meat Inspection.* Various laws and practices have been set up at

Table 5. COST OF EDIBLE LEAN OF SELECTED CUTS OF MEAT AS CALCULATED
FROM THE PHYSICAL COMPOSITION OF THE CUT

Cut	Bone,* %	Fat,* %	Lean,* %	Assumed Market Price per Pound	Calculated Cost of One Pound of Lean
Beef, Choice grade:					
Brisket	14	36	49	$0.29	$0.58
Club steak	17	27	54	1.00	1.85
Flank	0	62	37	0.99	2.70
Hind shank	56	13	31	0.49	1.60
Neck	19	19	62	0.49	0.78
Porterhouse steak	9	35	56	1.25	2.23
Rib roast (7th)	19	27	55	0.89	1.64
Round steak	4	14	81	0.99	1.23
Sirloin (boneless)	0	25	75	1.80	2.40
Lamb, Choice grade:					
Breast	9	45	45	0.39	0.86
Leg	13	21	66	0.89	1.38
Loin	13	34	53	1.40	2.64
Ribs	16	34	50	0.99	1.98
Shoulder	13	27	59	0.79	1.34
Pork:					
Bacon	. . .	49	45†	0.59	1.31
Ham	10	24	63†	0.65	1.02
Loin	18	15	67	0.89	1.33
Spareribs	41	. . .	59	0.69	1.17
Veal, medium fat:					
Cutlet, boned	0	1	99	1.80	1.82
Shoulder	20	1	79	0.89	1.12
Chicken, ready to cook:					
Broiler	25	5	70	0.79	1.13
Hens, stewing	20	20	60	0.69	1.15

*Adapted from S. Bull, 1951, *Meat for the Table*, McGraw-Hill Book, Co.,
New York; except for chicken.
† Skin accounts for remainder of waste.

local, state, and national levels to protect the consumer (see Chapter 12). One such practice is a Sanitary Code relating to sanitation of premises where food for the public is prepared and sold.

A federal law requires that all meat entering interstate commerce be examined during slaughter, and that the diseased animals be withdrawn from sale. The condemned meat is destroyed or processed for fertilizer. The accepted meat is marked with approval stamps. These are round marks the size of a 50-cent piece that are put in one or more places on each wholesale cut. These stamps record the code number of the packer as well as the approval of the inspector (see Fig. 11). Meat slaughtered within the state, however, may be sold in that state without inspection unless there are state or local laws prohibiting this practice. All meat sold to the military services must be slaughtered under federal inspection services.

An inspection stamp must not be regarded as a substitute for cooking. This is especially true of fresh pork, which is the meat most likely to contain a dormant parasitic roundworm of microscopic size, *Trichinella spiralis*, that cannot always be detected by inspection. If these organisms are eaten, they are freed in digestion from their capsules and can enter the blood stream and embed themselves in muscles causing pain, fever, and stiffness. The disease is known as *trichinosis*. The organism is killed by heat, and pork, therefore, should always be cooked to the well-done state. It has been suggested that 185° F internal temperature be the end-point for doneness for pork; this insures a margin of safety. A simple rule to follow is, "Never eat pink

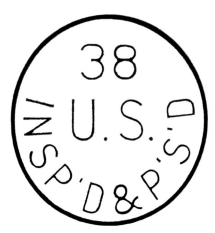

Fig. 11. The meat inspection stamp indicates that the animal was free from disease at the time of slaughter. (U.S.D.A. photograph.)

pork." It follows that any tasting of pork, as in the making of sausage, should be done only after it is cooked. This not only protects against trichinosis but also gives a truer flavor evaluation than testing the raw material.

Trichinae are also destroyed by other means such as:

1. *Freezing and storing* at temperatures no higher than 5° F for no less than 20 days.
2. *Heating* to temperatures of 128–137° F and holding a stipulated length of time.
3. *Curing* by using at least 4.5 per cent salt in a dry cure and holding 20 to 25 days at specified temperatures.
4. *Radiation sterilization.*

These methods or combinations of them are used for products like summer sausage and frankfurters, making them safe to eat without further cooking.

Not all pork is infected with *Trichinae*, but there is no sure way of determining the infection, and precautionary measures should always be taken. Bear, other omnivorous animals, and carnivorous animals should also be suspected of *Trichinae* and cooked to well-done. Herbivorous animals are generally not infected because the organism is passed from one animal to another by either eating the flesh of the infected animal or through the ingestion of feces of animals that have eaten trichinous meat. Under some conditions cattle can pick up the organism.

Meat Grades

True grading of meat is done by meat specialists and is based on definite characteristics which concern only potential palatability differences, and are commonly known as conformation, finish, and quality (Fig. 12).

Conformation is determined by the build of the animal; a block-built animal will have more meat in proportion to bones than will one with a lanky frame. Short stocky legs, broad chests, and broad rumps are desirable.

Finish is evaluated on the basis of the character and amount of fatty layer covering the entire carcass resulting from fatty deposits under the hide of the animal. Generally, the thick layers of white fat are preferred although it means more waste fat in cooking. Animals with good finish are expected to be of better eating quality than animals of

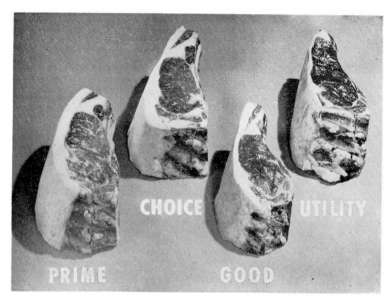

Fig. 12. Higher grades of meat have a thicker layer of finish fat as well as more marbling in the lean than the lower grades. (Courtesy of Swift and Company, Chicago.)

poor finish. However, veal (calves under three months old) will have very little finish.

Quality is determined by the grain of the lean (size of muscle fibers), firmness of lean, and amount of fatty deposits—marbling—in the lean. Best quality implies a well-marbled, fine grained, firm lean, with a color typical of the particular meat being judged.

Grading takes into consideration the age and the sex differences of the animals, and these factors determine the class to which an animal belongs. In the young animal the sex differences are not apparent. However, as the animal ages and the characteristic sex differences develop, the structure and composition of the carcass changes. The female carcass usually has the most desirable eating qualities, therefore, many of the male animals are castrated when very young so that the male characteristics do not develop. The steer is an example of a castrated animal.

The grading of meat for sale to the public is not compulsory by law and may be done by either a certified government grader, the packer, or the retail merchant. Grade designation may be either government or packer terminology. The retail merchant seldom uses any distinguishing grade mark. If the packer wishes the government grading, the United States Department of Agriculture provides accredited graders who work at the packing plant during the slaughtering of the animals. Terms used to designate grades under this service are uniform throughout the country no matter which packer sells the meat. The terminology used under the government grading program is given in Table 6.

Packers who do their own grading use the same criteria as those used for government grades. However, the terms used to designate the grades are different for each packer and are not the same as the government terms. Packers' terms are referred to as "brand names." This system may become too involved for the consumer who settles upon one brand he has found to be satisfactory. Some of the brand names for different grades of beef used by various packers are shown in Table 7.

Table 6. GRADE DESIGNATIONS IN ORDER OF QUALITY FOR BEEF, VEAL, PORK, LAMB, AND MUTTON AS ESTABLISHED BY THE UNITED STATES DEPARTMENT OF AGRICULTURE

Beef	Veal and Calf	Pork	Lamb and Yearling	Mutton
US Prime	US Prime	US Choice†	US Prime	US Choice
US Choice	US Choice	US Medium	US Choice	US Good
US Good	US Good	US Cull	US Good	US Utility
US Standard	US Commercial		US Utility	US Cull
US Commercial			US Cull	
US Utility				
Cutter*				
Canner*				

* Meat of Cutter and Canner grades are commonly used for prepared products.
† US Choice grade of pork has three divisions according to ratio of fat to lean.

Table 7. BRAND DESIGNATIONS OF FOUR GRADES OF BEEF OF SELECTED PACKERS*

Packer	Top Grade	Term Designation 2nd Grade	3rd Grade	4th Grade
Armour	Armour Star Deluxe	Armour Star	Quality	Banquet
Swift	Swift Premium	Swift Select	Swift Arrow	
Wilson	Certified	Special	Ideal	
Cudahy	Puritan	Fancy	Rex	Rival
Rath	Blackhawk Deluxe	Blackhawk	Kornland	Racorn
Morrell	Pride	Famous	Special	Morrell

* According to the National Livestock and Meat Board, Chicago, Ill.

USDA PRIME	USDA CHOICE	USDA GOOD	USDA STNDRD	USDA COMRCL	USDA UTILITY
USDA PRIME	USDA CHOICE	USDA GOOD	USDA STNDRD	USDA COMRCL	USDA UTILITY
USDA PRIME	USDA CHOICE	USDA GOOD	USDA STNDRD	USDA COMRCL	USDA UTILITY
USDA PRIME	USDA CHOICE	USDA GOOD	USDA STNDRD	USDA COMRCL	USDA UTILITY
USDA PRIME	USDA CHOICE	USDA GOOD	USDA STNDRD	USDA COMRCL	USDA UTILITY
USDA PRIME	USDA CHOICE	USDA GOOD	USDA STNDRD	USDA COMRCL	USDA UTILITY
USDA PRIME	USDA CHOICE	USDA GOOD	USDA STNDRD	USDA COMRCL	USDA UTILITY

Fig. 13. Meats are marked with their designated grade in a continuous line the length of the carcass (U.S.D.A. photograph.)

Federal grade or brand designations are printed on the outside of the carcass in a continuous line like a ribbon (see Fig. 13). A harmless purple vegetable dye is used and need not be removed for cooking. Many of the retail cuts on the market may be too small to show any of the grade stamp or the grade stamp may be removed with the trimmings. Some dealers include a printed label with prepackaged meat, that designates the grade or brand.

Grading has become a common practice in the United States, but the larger markets are adopting the practice of carrying only one grade. The overall quality of meat may vary with the climatic conditions—when there is no shortage of feed or water more animals will be marketed well finished and of higher grades than during droughts or feed shortages. When price is a major consideration in food selections, one should bear in mind the fact that there is more fat and therefore less lean in a pound of the high grades of meat than in low grades. Individual variation among animals increases the difficulty of finding consistent eating quality differences between adjacent grades of the same cut of meat, for example in Choice and Good porterhouse steaks.

Finally, Grade of meat is concerned only with expected palatability differences among animals. The higher the grade of meat, the higher the fat content of a specific cut and the higher the expected tenderness. The quality of the protein or the quantity of vitamins and minerals contained in the meat is not dependent upon grade designation; neither is keeping quality of the meat nor cleanliness associated with grade.

Meat Cuts

Modern markets with their array of cuts, types, grades, and processed meats (see Fig. 14) are fascinating places where one can spend considerable time choosing a cut of meat for the family meal. Fortunately, the terminology used for cuts of meat is fairly uniform throughout the country and among packers, therefore, it is not difficult, once having learned cuts, to recognize them in the market display.

The domestic animals furnishing the world's meat supply are all

Fig. 14. The consumer is offered many choices in types and cuts of meat displayed in open-top refrigerated cases. (Courtesy of Swift and Company, Chicago.)

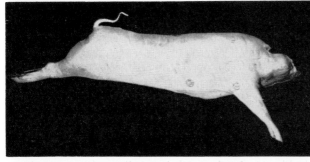

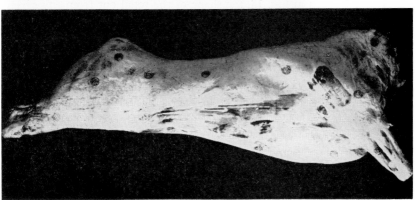

Fig. 15. The carcasses of meat animals are very similar in shape but may vary considerably in size, as illustrated here compared to a 6-foot man (U.S.D.A. photograph.)

very similar in shape (see Fig. 15). When slaughtered, they are hung head down because this is the most convenient position for the removal of entrails. The carcass stiffens, therefore, in the characteristic stretched-out position (see Fig. 15). A carcass too heavy to handle easily for wholesale marketing will be cut into smaller pieces termed "wholesale cuts." Beef is cut into a larger number of such pieces than other carcasses because of its larger size. The wholesale cut will be further subdivided when the retail merchant offers it for sale. Hotels and restaurants may purchase the wholesale cuts, but seldom is the homemaker interested in other than the retail cuts.

A particular style of cutting meats—for example, Chicago, New York, Philadelphia, Boston, or a combination of these four styles—has been adopted in each of the various areas of the country. The major muscles of the retail cuts are the same in any style of cutting. They all make use of the natural joining of muscles at joints or separation of major muscles of the body and as much as possible cut across the muscle fibers. Thus there are only minor differences among the cuts in different cutting styles. Retail cuts may be further trimmed and the consumer need not be concerned about the style used in cutting the carcass.

Not only are techniques of cutting standardized among meat cutters but also the cuts of the different types of animals are similar. Familiarity with bone and muscle structure of animals in general should, therefore, make for easy recognition of the specific cuts of meat from any animal (Figs. 16 and 17). Figure 16 is a skeletal drawing of beef and the heavy lines indicate where divisions would be made in the Chicago style of cutting. The terminology used for both wholesale and retail cuts of beef, veal, lamb, and pork are tabulated in Table 8.

As can be seen in Fig. 18, the shape of the retail cut from any given place in the carcass is the same from animal to animal; only the size of the pieces and the color of the lean will vary. Beef and lamb are dark red; veal and pork are pink.

The retail cuts may be trimmed according to the practice of the particular market. For example, the long ends of rib roast of beef may be cut from the one side and a portion of the feather bone cut from the other (Figs. 16 and 17) so that there is a minimum of the bone left for a rack in roasting. Trimmed roasts will cost more per pound than will untrimmed. Fat, also, may be trimmed from the higher grade cuts, therefore one cannot always judge grades of retail cuts from thickness of outside fat.

A lean roast from any grade may have an extra layer of fat tied

BEEF CHART
LOCATION, STRUCTURE
AND NAMES OF BONES

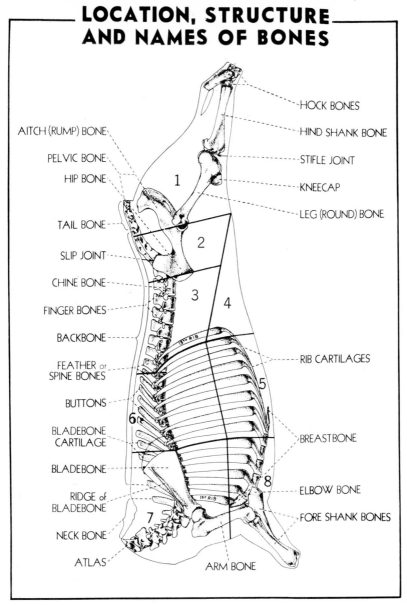

HOCK BONES

HIND SHANK BONE

AITCH (RUMP) BONE

STIFLE JOINT

PELVIC BONE

HIP BONE

KNEECAP

LEG (ROUND) BONE

TAIL BONE

SLIP JOINT

CHINE BONE

FINGER BONES

BACKBONE

FEATHER or
SPINE BONES

RIB CARTILAGES

BUTTONS

BLADEBONE
CARTILAGE

BREASTBONE

BLADEBONE

RIDGE of
BLADEBONE

ELBOW BONE

FORE SHANK BONES

NECK BONE

ATLAS

ARM BONE

Fig. 16. Meat cutting methods take into consideration the bone structure of the animals. *Wholesale cuts:* 1. Round with shank and rump. 2. Loin end used for sirloin steaks. 3. Short loin used for loin steaks. 4. Flank. 5. Plate and rib ends. 6. Rib. 7. Chuck. 8. Brisket and fore shank. (Courtesy of National Livestock and Meat Board, Chicago.)

BEEF CHART

Wholesale Cuts

Retail Cuts

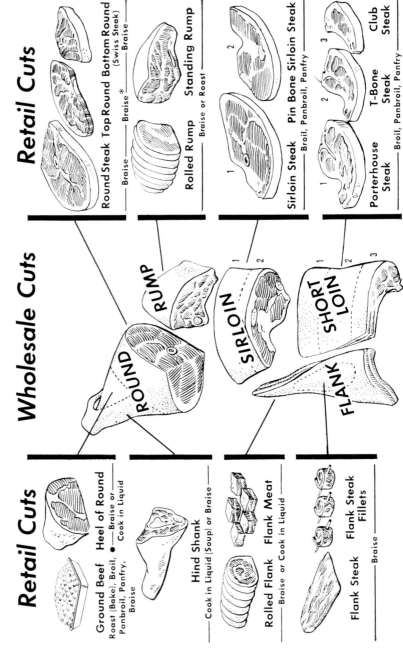

Round Steak Top Round Bottom Round
(Swiss Steak)
—— Braise —— Braise * —— Braise ——

Standing Rump

Rolled Rump
—— Braise or Roast ——

RUMP

ROUND

Sirloin Steak Pin Bone Sirloin Steak
—— Broil, Panbroil, Panfry ——

SIRLOIN

Porterhouse T-Bone Club
Steak Steak Steak
—— Broil, Panbroil, Panfry ——

SHORT LOIN

FLANK

Retail Cuts

Ground Beef Heel of Round
Roast (Bake), Broil, ● Braise or
Panbroil, Panfry, Cook in Liquid
Braise

Hind Shank
—— Cook in Liquid (Soup) or Braise ——

Flank Meat

Rolled Flank
—— Braise or Cook in Liquid ——

Flank Steak Fillets

Flank Steak
—— Braise ——

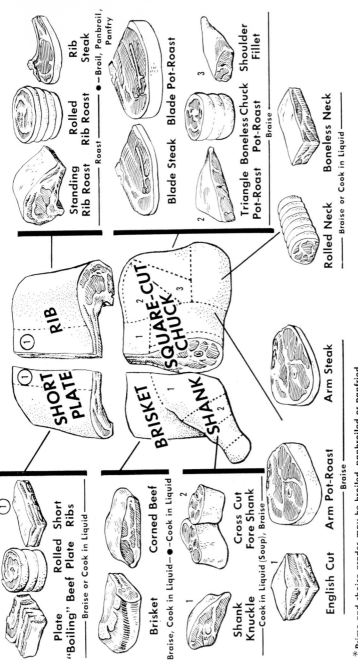

Fig. 17. Meat cuts and how to cook them. Meat cuts are made across the muscle fibers as often as possible and can be recognized by bone shape as well as muscle. (Courtesy of National Livestock and Meat Board, Chicago.)

Rib Steak
—Broil, Panbroil, Panfry

Standing Rib Roast   Rolled Rib Roast   Rib Steak
— Roast —

Blade Steak   Blade Pot-Roast   Shoulder Fillet

Triangle Pot-Roast   Boneless Chuck Pot-Roast   Boneless Neck
— Braise —

Rolled Neck   Boneless Neck
— Braise or Cook in Liquid —

RIB

SHORT PLATE

SQUARE-CUT CHUCK

BRISKET   SHANK

Arm Steak

Arm Pot-Roast
— Braise —

Plate   Rolled Plate   "Boiling" Beef   Short Ribs
— Braise or Cook in Liquid —

Brisket   Corned Beef
Braise, Cook in Liquid— ●—Cook in Liquid

Cross Cut Fore Shank

Shank Knuckle
— Cook in Liquid (Soup), Braise —

English Cut

* Prime and choice grades may be broiled, panbroiled or panfried

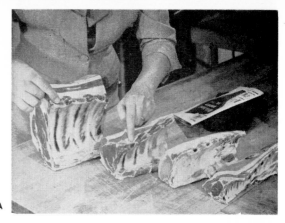

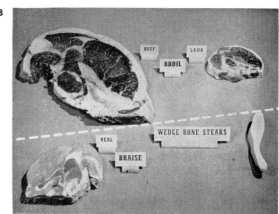

Fig. 18. Cuts from the same position in the different animals have the same shape of muscle and bone; the size of the cut will vary as shown by standing ribs of beef, veal, pork, and lamb (a), cuts from the sirloin (b), and the full leg (c). (Courtesy of Swift and Company, Chicago.)

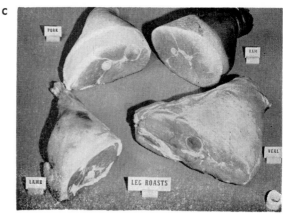

around it. This is natural fat from another location and is termed *cod*. Small chunks of fat (lardoons) may also be drawn into the muscle itself (larding) with a larding needle. Larded cuts are seldom seen today possibly because the animals are more commonly finished before marketing and the process was possibly found to be too tedious and costly for the results attained.

Thick chops may be made into *butterfly chops* by splitting almost through the muscles and then spreading them open; or a pocket may be made in a thick loin pork chop for stuffing. *Minute* or *cubed steaks* are made by pounding or cutting thin pieces of lean meat. This tenderizes and further thins the cut so that it will cook quickly. In western markets *New York cut steak* means a boneless steak generally cut from top sirloin, whereas in eastern markets it may be cut from tenderloin. The *tenderloin* sold as such may be taken from lower grade animals than are used for other retail cuts, since it is normally a tender muscle. The tenderloin is seldom more than three inches in diameter (in beef). It may be cut thick and flattened with a cleaver to provide a larger steak for broiling. This is the method of cutting a real filet mignon. However, the tender rib muscle may also be sold as a filet. It is choice meat but not as tender as the tenderloin muscle. Fancy work may be affected in meat cutting also. For example, one or two inches of rib ends of chops may be scraped to make a *Frenched chop*. A frilled paper ornament is often attached to the bone after the meat is cooked. A whole rib roast may be Frenched and rolled together so that the scraped ends form the prongs of a crown. *Crown roasts* may be made of veal, pork, or lamb. These garnishes in meat are used in place of, or with, parsley or other garnishes to make a more attractive plate.

Organs of animals are known as variety meats and commonly include brains, liver, kidney, heart, tongue, sweetbreads (thymus gland), and tripe (stomach). Chitterlings (intestine), lungs, pig tails and ears, lamb heads, pigs' feet, oxtails, and melts are marketed either as variety meats or as regular cuts.

Many markets cut entire carcasses into the retail cuts, wrap these cuts in transparent material and display them in open self-service refrigerators. This is referred to as prepackaging of meat. From the standpoint of the retailer this is more efficient handling than cutting to order because an entire wholesale piece can be cut before taking up the next piece. There are a number of disadvantages to the consumer, however, including:

1. Buyers can see only one side of the cut. The effect presented by the other side might be considerably different.

Table 8. COMPARISON OF TERMINOLOGY FOR BEEF, VEAL, LAMB, AND PORK WHOLESALE AND RETAIL CUTS ACCORDING TO LOCATION IN THE ANIMAL*

Beef	Veal	Lamb	Pork
Round (whole leg)	*Leg* (long cut includes sirloin short cut without sirloin)	*Leg* (long cut includes sirloin short cut without sirloin)	*Ham* (whole)
Hind shank (much bone)	Hind shank or shank half	Leg of lamb, may be cut into shank half and rump half	Ham hocks
Heel of round (no bone)	Heel of round		Ham, shank half
			Ham shank
Round steak, full cut	Leg roast	Leg steak (chop)	Ham, center cut
Top round steak or pot-roast	Round steak (cutlet)		Ham, center slice
Bottom round steak or pot-roast			Ham, boneless
Tip roast or steak			Ham, butt half
	Scallops		
	Rosettes		
Standing rump	Standing rump		Rump half included in ham cuts
Rolled rump	Rolled rump		
Sirloin	*Sirloin*	*Sirloin*	
Sirloin steak	Sirloin roast	Sirloin roast, boneless	
Pin bone sirloin steak	Sirloin steak	Sirloin chop	
Boneless sirloin steak			
Short Loin	*Loin*	*Loin* (usually 2 loins, unsplit)	*Loin*
Porterhouse steak	Loin roast	Loin roast or rolled loin	Sirloin roast
T-Bone steak	Loin chop	Loin chop	Loin chop
Club steak	Kidney chop	English chop	
Tenderloin roast or steak			Tenderloin
Filet Mignon			Canadian style bacon
Fillets			
Flank			*Flank*
Flank steak	(included in breast)	(included in breast)	Bacon
Flank meat			Salt pork
			Side pork

76

Rib	Rib	Rack	Picnic Shoulder
Standing rib roast (short cut)	Rib roast	Rib roast	Arm steak
Rolled rib roast	Crown roast	Crown roast	
Rib steak	Rolled roast		Boston butt
Short ribs	Rib chop	Rib chop	Blade steak
	Riblets	Riblets	
Chuck	*Shoulder*	*Shoulder*	*Side and Spareribs*
Arm pot-roast	Arm roast	Arm chop	Spareribs
Arm steak	Arm steak (chop)		
Blade pot-roast	Blade roast	Cushion shoulder	
Blade steak	Blade steak (chop)	Blade chop	
Boneless chuck pot-roast	Rolled shoulder roast (boneless)	Mock duck	
Boneless chuck steak	City chicken		
Boneless neck		Neck slice	Bacon (included in picnic shoulder)
Boston (English cut)			
Short Plate	*Breast*	*Breast*	
Plate "boiling" beef	Breast	Breast	
Rolled plate	Rolled breast	Rolled breast	Ham hocks
Short ribs	Riblets	Riblets	
	Stew meat		
Brisket			*Jowl,* Bacon
Brisket (corned beef)	(included in breast)	(included in breast)	*Feet,* Fresh or pickled pig's feet
Fore Shank	*Fore Shank*	*Shank*	
Shank knuckle	Fore shank	Shank	
Shank cross-cuts			

* Adapted from *Ten Lessons on Meat*, National Livestock and Meat Board, Chicago, Ill., 1950.

2. Labels and folds of meat might hide bones that the buyer finds only when he opens the package.

3. Packaging materials may conceal the contents from view so no estimation can be made of the fat content.

4. Cuts may develop off-flavors from microbial growth in the drip when held a long time.

5. Buyers must take the size cut as packaged.

Oftentimes the meats are cut but not prepackaged. Precutting allows faster service and permits closer customer inspection, but surface drying may detract from the appearance of the meat. Other shops cut meat only on order.

Ripening of Meat

Some foods, including meat, improve in flavor on holding. This is called "ripening" or "aging." The meat to be aged or ripened is kept at low temperatures to discourage microbial growth, but the enzymes within the meat slowly continue their normal reactions during a two- to six-week holding period. Enzyme actions go on until the breakdown products accumulate and block the action. In the living organism the end products are carried away and there is no problem of blockage. The formation and retention of these substances are desired conditions in the ripening process. The aged meat becomes more tender, and to the connoisseur, more flavorful. However, evaporation losses are inevitable, as well as trim losses due to mold growth, and since it also means that extra refrigerated space is required for holding, ripening will increase the unit cost of the meat.

At this time only well-finished beef is ripened; it is commonly held fifteen to twenty days at temperatures just above freezing (36° F) at relatively low humidities so that it dries on the surface and thus discourages mold growth. Ultraviolet light may be used to sterilize the surface of the meat in the ripening rooms. The ultraviolet light in conjunction with an elevated humidity and temperature speeds the ripening process because the higher temperatures permit more rapid enzyme action.

Generally only the ribs, loins, and hindquarters of beef are ripened. Sometimes lamb is aged, but pork is preferred not ripened, and veal does not have the necessary finish fat for ripening. The ripening process does not affect either the digestibility or nutritive value of meats.

Types of Meat Preservation

Curing. Considerable pork, a little beef, but practically no veal or lamb is cured commercially. There are several methods of curing meat, each producing a characteristic product. Some meats are treated with only salt, which preserves them against bacterial spoilage. *Sodium nitrate (saltpeter)* and *sodium nitrite* are often added to retain the red color of the meat. Sugar and spices are used to give different flavors, and smoke is used both as a preservative and for flavor. Fat pork sides may be rubbed with dry salt and sold as *salt pork*. *Corned beef* is cured brisket, plate, and rump cuts of beef but it is not usually smoked.

Chipped or dried beef is made from the cured rounds of low grade beef after the muscles have been separated. The muscles are cured in brine, and they may or may not be smoked. *Pastrami* is dried beef with special seasonings added.

Hams are made from legs of pork, "ham" usually refers to the hind leg. The foreleg is termed *picnic shoulder,* and the rump may be made into *cottage ham. Tenderized hams* are made by injecting a sweet pickle cure into the circulatory system so that the cure comes into contact with tissues very rapidly. Under these circumstances there is less hardening of the tissues than when the hams are immersed in the brine, and curing is effected in two weeks. Curing in brine requires six weeks.

Country hams are cured by a slow process either in a dry cure or brine and are heavily smoked. They are not as tender as tenderized hams. *Virginia* or *Smithfield hams* are dry-cured, usually without nitrate. After curing they are rubbed with black pepper, smoked by special process, and aged. They are very dry and hard and should be given an opportunity to hydrate before cooking. *Boiled hams* are cured, smoked, boned, defatted, and cooked in a metal mold. Ham may be partially or completely cooked when bought, but unless the label states "no further cooking is necessary" ham should be thoroughly cooked.

Canadian style bacon or *back bacon* is cured in a way similar to ham but is the boned loin of the pig. This cut has much less fat than true *bacon,* which is the cured and smoked fat pork sides. *Boston Butt* from the shoulder area may also be cured.

Cold cuts not only permit outlets for low grades of meat and cutting trimmings but they also provide a variety in menus. Many of the cold cuts contain mixtures of types of meats and flavorful seasonings.

Freezing. This is a common method of preserving any kind of meat. There is no loss of nutrients as a result of freezing. However, when cooked, frozen meat may seem to be somewhat less juicy than a similar cut which has not been frozen. Pork, especially, has a limited freezer storage life as the fat becomes rancid after three to five months. Salt in fat hastens rancidity development in frozen storage and causes off-flavor in cured meat. Cooked meat may be preserved by freezing, and this is an excellent method of storing left-over meat. Frozen cooked meats are also available in the markets and are sold in many forms—dinners of all types, individual servings, and family size portions.

Canning. Preservation by canning is used for a small portion of the meat supply. The high heat necessary to sterilize the meat changes the flavor and texture. There is little or no loss in food values due to canning if the entire contents of the can are used, however, slight decreases in the nutritive value of the protein have been reported from some laboratories.

Possibly flavor and texture differences account for the fact that canned meats are not as popular as are fresh meats despite convenience and good keeping qualities. When canned meat must form a large part of the meat supply for a long period as in the military for combat forces, it has been shown to be better tolerated if some of the available fresh meat is used with it.

Radiation sterilization. Radiation is a new innovation in meat preservation. It may be used extensively in the near future. By this procedure the food products can easily be sterilized without heating so that afterwards there is no spoilage caused by bacterial growth. Palatability changes have so far discouraged this method of preservation, but much research is being continued in an effort to produce satisfactory products.

BUYING POULTRY AND FISH

Poultry

The federal poultry program consists of optional grading, but inspection is required for all poultry entering interstate commerce. Dressed birds not eviscerated may be graded but not inspected because inspection requires judging of entrails. The official grade mark is a shield with Grade A, B, or C on it and it is put only on the box for dressed poultry. Ready-to-cook poultry may be individually marked with both Grade and Inspection stamps. If only one mark is used it is a shield with a circle, as shown in Fig. 19.

A

B

Fig. 19. Grading stamps (*a*) and inspection stamps (*b*) for poultry are shaped like those for meats but may be combined into one stamp (*c*). (U.S.D.A. photographs.)

C

Optional standards and grades have been established by the United States Department of Agriculture for chickens, turkeys, ducks, geese, guineas, and pigeons. For each of these groups there are classes based on age, sex, and weight. The classes most commonly found are given in Table 9.

Poultry may be sold live, dressed but not drawn, whole, in halves, or in pieces. When fully dressed and drawn a bird may retain only 55 per cent of its live weight. Cutting of poultry, like the cutting of the larger animals, follows natural joints (Fig. 20). Bones are separated at the joints whenever possible so that sharp points are not exposed. Large turkeys may be disjointed and the thighs and breasts cut across the grain into *turkey steaks*. Poultry may also be boned and rolled for roasting. A chinese delicacy is roast pressed boned duck served with a coating of almonds and termed *Almond Duck*.

Young birds are more tender than older birds. One cannot distinguish age by size alone as adult birds vary greatly in size. A young bird's skin is pliable, soft, and tears easily, bones are easily disjointed, and the breastbone is soft as distinguished from the fully calcified breastbone of the mature bird. If the feet are left on for the market, they are soft in young birds but tend to become scaly and horny with age.

Sex differences are not significant in young birds, but in older birds the females are more juicy than the males, less tough and stringy, and

Table 9. THE CLASSES OF POULTRY MOST COMMONLY FOUND IN THE MARKETS*

Kind, Class, and Style of Processing	Ready-to-cook Weight, pounds
Chickens	
Broilers or fryers	1 to 3½
Roasters	2¾ to 5
Capons (castrated males)	4 to 8
Stewing hens or fowl	2¼ to 5
Turkeys	
Fryers or roasters	3 to 7
Young hens	6½ to 12
Young Toms	14 to over 20
Ducks, all classes	3 to 5½
Geese, all classes	6¼ to over 9½
Guineas, all classes	1½ to 2
Pigeons, all classes	6 oz to 14 oz

* Agriculture Marketing Services, U.S.D.A.

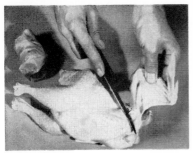

a.
Cut into the wing joint, rolling knife to let the blade follow through at the curve of the joint.

b.
Score skin between leg and breast. Bend leg up until joint pops out. Turn knife down and pull to free the "oyster."

c.
Grasp the back, as shown, and cut downward closely along the back to sever the rib connections.

d.
Repeat cut on the opposite side of the back, pulling the backbone free and cutting the connective skin and tissue.

e.
Nick cartilage as shown, cutting down thru flesh and skin. Breast section can then be pulled apart and keel bone removed.

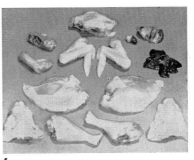

f.
The component parts of a cut-up frying chicken.

Fig. 20. Preparing the chicken for frying. (Courtesy of Poultry and Egg National Board, Chicago.)

have wider fuller breasts for greater yield of white meat. Young males may be desexed by castration or other destruction of the sex glands in order that the male characteristics do not develop. Such birds are referred to as *capons*. Some controversy has arisen over the desirability of injecting hormones into the base of the brains of young male birds to bring about changes in meat characteristics during growth. The Food and Drug Administration has permitted the use of hormones since any that were not absorbed would normally be discarded when the head is removed during slaughter.

Poultry is generally considered to be one of the expensive meats since it has such a large proportion of bone to lean. Smaller birds have less lean than larger birds, however, some breeds within each group tend to have a greater proportion of lean to bone than others, for example, the Cornish chicken and the Beltsville turkey.

Fish

The terms fish and shellfish designate water animals without shell and those with shell respectively. The kinds of fresh fish available differ in various markets. Fish may be purchased *whole*—as they come from the water, *drawn*—only the entrails removed, or *dressed*—all inedible parts removed; or they may be cut into pieces and sold as *fillet*—boned sides of fish, *steaks*—cross-section slices, and *sticks*—small and uniform pieces.

Fish deteriorate rapidly, and the odor of spoiled fish is unmistakable. Fresh fish has little odor; eyes that are bright, full, and moist; flesh that is firm and does not pit when pressed; gills that are blood red in color; scales that are shiny and cling to the skin; and skin that is free of slime (see Fig. 10). Unless fish is frozen, one should remember the old Chinese proverb, "Fish and a visit are both old in three days."

Octopus, squid, and eel are marine foods similar to fish. Although scales are not present all other indications of freshness are the same as for fish.

Shellfish include *crustaceans* with segmented shells—lobster, crab, and shrimp—and *mollusks,* usually with "pocket-book" shells—clams, oysters, abalone, scallops, and mussels. The market forms of shellfish include:

1. live—if purchased in the shell they should be alive (exceptions are cooked crab and lobster).
2. shucked—removed from shells.
3. headless—shrimp are an example.

4. cooked—hard-shell crab, lobster, and shrimp may be cooked in the shell (uncooked shrimp are termed green shrimp).

Shrimp or prawn vary considerably in size from large, less than 15 per one pound, to tiny Alaska shrimp over 60 per pound: they are graded according to the count per pound. The varieties of shrimp include white or the common, brown or grooved, and the pink or coral. There are two varieties of scallops, small bay scallops and large sea scallops. Crab meat found in the markets includes: (1) Blue or hard crab from the East and Gulf coasts; (2) Rock crab of New England—this meat is brownish; and (3) Pacific Coast or Dungeness Crab—this meat is reddish in color.

Certain shellfish are graded according to size as follows:[1]

Type	Size	Number per Unit
Hard-shell clams (in shell)	Chowder, large	100–150 per bushel
	Chowder, medium	150–225 per bushel
	Cherrystone	225–350 per bushel
	Littleneck	350–650 per bushel
Soft-shell clams (in shell)	Large	400–600 per bushel
	Steamers	600–800 per bushel
Eastern oysters (shucked)	Counts or extra large	Not more than 160 per gallon
	Extra selects or large	Not more than 161–210 per gallon
	Selects or medium	Not more than 211–300 per gallon
	Standards or small	Not more than 301–500 per gallon
	Very small	Over 500 per gallon
Pacific oysters (shucked)	Grade A	40–64 per gallon
	Grade B	65–80 per gallon
	Grade C	81–96 per gallon
	Grade D	97–120 per gallon
	Grade E	112–144 per gallon
	Grade F	Over 144 per gallon
Lobster	Chicken	$\frac{3}{4}$–1 pound each
	Quarters	$1\frac{1}{4}$–$1\frac{1}{2}$ pounds each
	Large	$1\frac{1}{2}$–$2\frac{1}{2}$ pounds each
	Jumbo	Over $2\frac{1}{2}$ pounds each

The problem of holding fresh fish from catch to market to consumer is serious because this food is very perishable. Many of the large fishing fleets have mechanical refrigerators with a capacity great

[1] Adapted from Handbook of Food Preparation, American Home Econ. Assoc., Washington, D. C., 1959.

enough to accommodate the entire catch. Some of the older fishing boats have attempted to carry ice, but ice in itself is often inadequate and requires much space. Various preservatives have been tried; the most promising are the antibiotics.

Frozen fish can be of very high quality because many of the shrimp, tuna, and other fishing boats have adequate equipment for freezing their products as soon as they are caught. Fish may be frozen in blocks of ice to prevent dehydration, but cooked shrimps are packaged loose. Fillets of fish are usually brined lightly before freezing so that the meat will remain firm when thawed. Recently, however, fillets have been pressed into uniform blocks, frozen, and marketed in pound packages. The blocks are about one inch thick. This block form cooks uniformly and the cooked fillets can then easily be cut for serving, or, if desired, the portions can be cut before cooking. Many types of fish are packaged and frozen ready for frying. They may be breaded, batter dipped, or coated with corn meal. Various cooked fish are frozen and need only heating before serving.

Fish may also be marketed dried, pickled (marinated herring), salted, or canned. Dried salt cod is the most popular dried fish used in the United States and is an economical source of flesh food. It blends particularly well with potato; cod-potato puff is a popular dish.

Shellfish, especially lobster and crab, are often the most expensive of meats. Some of the gill fish, however, such as rosefish, halibut, and cod are especially economical. Often, canned fish has advantages over fresh fish from the point of view of nutrition, economy, and convenience.

CARE OF MEAT, POULTRY, AND FISH IN THE HOME

Fresh fish spoils more readily than poultry or meat and should be cooked or frozen if it is not to be used immediately. Liver also should receive prompt attention and be used with a minimum of holding. Meats, in general, decrease in keeping quality with decrease in size of pieces. Thus ground meat keeps the least well of any style cut, and off-flavors develop very rapidly.

Microorganisms require moist conditions for growth, therefore it is considered desirable to refrigerate raw meats sufficiently uncovered to let the surface dry. Paper does not transfer heat readily, and meat that is wrapped in paper will not cool rapidly. Most refrigerators provide meat trays with racks to allow circulation of air and to prevent meat from remaining in the drip. Cooked meats may be covered for storage.

Meats that are to be frozen should be wrapped tightly in special moisture-proof vapor-proof freezer paper or foil. Meat inadequately wrapped before freezing dries out very rapidly in the freezer and becomes white and unpalatable. The dried spots are referred to as "freezer burn." Poultry, rabbit, and cuts of other meat with sharp bones may need to be trimmed before packaging to prevent breaking the wrap. Irregularly shaped pieces of meat will not tear the paper during handling if they are tightly wrapped with stockinette before the paper wrap is applied. The leg portion of discarded nylon stockings makes a suitable wrap. Ground meat may be formed into patties and separated with waxed cardboard or two rounds of waxed paper or foil. The two pieces provide an easy means of separation. Chops and steaks may be separated in a similar manner.

If cured meats and cold cuts are refrigerated at the market, it follows that they need refrigeration in the home. Ham is often stored in a careless manner because it is thought that the salt acts as a preservative, but the concentration is generally not high enough to be a complete preservative in itself. One should follow the storage directions on the package.

PREPARATION OF MEAT, POULTRY, AND FISH

Meat is the simplest of meal items to prepare for two reasons: (1) there is little or no preparation—one wipes the meat with a damp cloth to remove bone particles and places it in the oven or broiler or pan; and (2) there are usually no other ingredients to influence manipulation, baking time or texture, as there are in egg, milk, and flour mixtures, or other food mixtures. The four general purposes of cooking meat products are:

1. To destroy microorganisms and make meat safe to eat.
2. To improve flavor.
3. To coagulate plasma proteins.
4. To soften less tender cuts and make them tender.

Factors Affecting Palatability

Desirable eating quality in meat is evaluated on the basis of tenderness, juiciness, and flavor. Cooking methods that emphasize one of these characteristics at the expense of the others are generally undesirable. For example, roasts cooked very slowly (200° F) become exceedingly tender but when cooked to the well done stage are unpalatably dry. The procedures developed for the cooking of meats therefore are designed to obtain "something of each but not everything of all."

Tenderness. Tenderness qualities of meats as purchased are not constant. Connective tissue proteins, primarily *collagen*, are believed to be responsible for toughness in meats. *Collagen*, a white fibrous tissue, generally softens on cooking in the presence of moisture and may be converted to water-soluble gelatin. The other type of connective tissue, *elastin*, is yellow, tough and fibrous, does not change with any type of cooking, and is resistant to organic acids and enzymes. The elastin is easily removed from the meat so that little attention has been given in cooking procedures to the possible elastin content in the muscles. Attempts to isolate collagen and elastin in order to compare the amounts present in cuts of varying tenderness, have shown some inconsistencies with the theory that connective tissues alone are responsible for lack of tenderness. Nevertheless, the softening effects of long moist-heat cooking are real and undeniable.

It should be recognized that tenderness is a quality that is difficult to predict or even to evaluate. The following factors have been found to affect tenderness:

1. The age of the animal. Apparently this is dependent upon development of the muscle and size of the muscle fiber. Older animals are generally less tender than younger ones.

2. The location of the cut in the animal. This also seems to be dependent upon the development or use of the muscles. Those muscles used least are the most tender, thus the loin and rib muscles are more tender than other cuts.

3. The amount of fat interspersed in the lean. As indicated previously (see meat grading), this is predicted by the grade of the animal. Increased amounts of fat in the lean give increased tenderness.

4. The post-mortem stage of the animal. One must allow muscles to relax after rigor has set in or the meat will be tough. Large animals require a longer time for rigor to pass than do small animals. Massaging the muscles, as in cutting chicken into pieces, hastens the passing of rigor. Possibly four hours will be sufficient time for rigor to pass from chicken, but beef will require four days.

5. The length of the muscle fibers. If muscles are cut in short lengths the teeth bite between the muscle fibers rather than across

them and, there seems to be less resistance to mastication. Meat-cutting methods are aimed at having a maximum amount of muscles cut across the fibers.

6. Freezing may tenderize slightly. The tenderizing effect may be due partly to a stretching of fibers and possibly to some enzyme action during frozen storage.

7. The ripening period. This has a tenderizing effect but does not continue indefinitely. Thus, holding of the meat after the enzyme action has reached a maximum does not increase tenderness.

8. Proteolytic enzymes injected into the muscles of the meat. These may help to tenderize the meat if they are given time to act. Several enzyme preparations made from papaya are on the retail market. It should be remembered that (*a*) enzymes must be in contact with the proteins; (*b*) rate of enzyme action is increased with increased concentration of enzymes; and (*c*) heat inactivates enzymes and therefore stops the action.

Natural tenderness in meats can be decreased by cooking more easily than it can be increased. Overcooking, particularly in dry heat, causes decreased tenderness. This often is demonstrated in the cooking of liver, lobster, shrimp, and all fish. These foods are naturally tender and need only to have the soft proteins coagulated. Cooking beyond this point causes them to become hard.

Marinating meat, that is, soaking in an acid-oil mixture, or cooking meat in an acid such as tomato was at one time thought to tenderize the finished product and has been popular as a device for tenderizing meats. Recent studies comparing cuts cooked with and without acid seem to indicate little if any difference in tenderness. The flavors derived from the tomatoes or other acids may be highly desirable, however, and this may account for the good acceptance.

Meat cookery to develop tenderness is concerned primarily with the effect of heat treatments on the proteins present. Short periods of heating, usually with dry heat, are utilized for cuts judged to be "market-tender," and long periods of heating in the presence of moisture are used for less tender cuts.

Juiciness. Juiciness in meats cannot be increased by any method of cooking, but juice losses can be prevented by appropriate means. Fat interspersed in the muscle tissues enhances juiciness, probably by preventing evaporation. A covering of fat on meats decreases drying, and roasts are often wrapped with a layer of fat if a good natural layer is not present. More protection against drying is obtained if the fat layer is uppermost during the cooking process so that the melting fat provides self-basting, than if the fat is on the sides (Fig. 21). A strip of fat, bacon, for example, is often put on meat loaf, around tenderloin, and over lean cuts to prevent drying. Lean meats may be basted with fat or a fat-sauce mix. This is particularly desirable in broiling fish, which are naturally lacking in fat. Breast of poultry has a tendency to become dry in roasting. The backs of turkeys and other fowl are usually fat, therefore, if the bird is roasted breast down, it will be self-basting and minimize the dryness. The bird may be turned breast up during the latter part of the cooking process to crisp the skin. Hand basting should be used at this time to prevent drying.

The longer meat is cooked, particularly in dry heat, the drier it will become. Poultry-roasting presents particular problems in this respect as the legs and wings are small and cook more rapidly than the body of the bird. Overdrying will be minimized if legs and wings are tied closely to the body during the entire roasting period.

Juiciness in any cut decreases with increases in degree of doneness. This is related to the length of the cooking period. Rare meat will be juicier than the same cut cooked to medium, and medium will be juicier than the well-done meat. Pork, veal, seafood, and fish are commonly cooked to the well-done stage. Beef, poultry, and lamb, however, may all be served rare or medium and thus will be juicier than other types.

Although juiciness does decrease with increase in amount of evaporation, total dryness does not seem to be entirely dependent upon volatile losses. It is known that if protein is heated, the heat-coagulative substances become firm. Continued heating beyond the coagulation temperature continues the firming action and, as easily seen in overcooked custards, water is forced out as the water-loving molecule is changed to a water-hating one. Some of the normally free water, however, is trapped and bound to the molecule so tightly that even mastication cannot loosen it, and the protein feels dry in the mouth.

Flavor. Flavors in meats are affected by many factors. These include the following:

1. The type of meat—pork has a different flavor from beef of the same age, and sex.

2. The feed of the animals—meat of turkeys fed large amounts of fishmeal will have a fish flavor.

3. The treatment given the meat—ripening and curing both change flavor.

4. The absorption of flavors during the hold period—fat absorbs odors very readily and meat usually contains large quantities of fats.

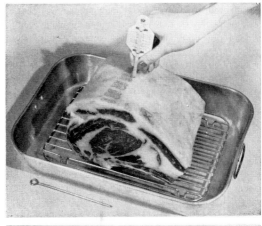

A

B

Fig. 21. Roasts will be more flavorful and juicy if the surfaces are covered with fat; rib roasts (A), leg of lamb (B), and ham (C) have sufficient fat to be self-basting. (Courtesy of National Livestock and Meat Board, Chicago.)

C

5. The development of spoilage—this may be both microbial spoilage and chemical rancidity. As noted previously, fish, ground meats, and liver develop off flavors very quickly during holding. Other meats also need protection.

6. The seasonings added—in days when refrigeration was unknown, meat was highly spiced to cover deterioration flavors.

7. The method of cooking and the degree of doneness—browned meat has a richer flavor than unbrowned meat.

Except for the factor of feed of the animals, the consumer is responsible for the flavors obtained in the meat served. At the market he selects the type and treatment of the meat desired, protects it against absorption of flavors and spoilage until used, and then cooks and seasons it for serving.

Methods of Cooking Meat, Poultry, and Fish

Each family, each region, and each country has its favorite way of preparing meat, as well as its favorite type of meat. Variations in seasonings, length of the cooking period, method of applying heat, together with variations in type of meat make limitless variety in menus. Whatever method of preparation is chosen, it will be based on the coagulation of proteins, and with the exception of *microwave* cooking, coagulation will be due to the application of heat in either of two methods. One is by *dry heat* in which the meat is left uncovered and allowed to cook in an atmosphere of hot air, and the other is by *moist heat* in which the meat is enveloped in a moist atmosphere. Dry-heat methods are used when the raw meat is naturally tender or has been tenderized by mechanical or chemical means, and the cooking is needed only to coagulate plasma proteins. Moist heat is used when cooking must be prolonged to soften less tender cuts. Moist heat cooking is usually done in a covered container. The covering can be a covered roaster, closed foil wrap, parchment paper bag, or liquid. Many terms are used to signify whether dry or moist heat is to be used, how heat is to be applied, or other significant treatments. These are defined in the glossary of terms.

Washing of meat is usually undesirable because some of the juices are lost. Whenever that happens extractives which give both flavor and nutrients are lost. A damp cloth can be used to remove bone particles from the surface if desired. Fowl and fish are washed after viscera are removed.

Steaks and chops may have a portion of the tough outer skin of the animal left on one side. This shrinks more during cooking than does the muscle and draws the muscle into a cup shape. Cutting through this fiber at inch-length intervals before heat is applied will prevent cupping.

Poultry and lamb have a "wax sack" near the tail. This may impart an undesirable flavor to the meat if not removed. The skin of lamb, termed the *fell*, is easily removed. This is usually done before the cooking of chops but after the roasting of a full-sized leg of lamb. No other preparation for cooking is necessary.

Salting of the meat for cooking is a natural reaction in food preparation. However, before salt is added the possibility of increased drip loss due to the increased osmotic pressure on the surface should be considered. The drip contains not only water-soluble nutrients but also flavoring substances. Therefore, it would seem logical to follow the practice of cooking meat without salt when it is desired to have the flavors retained in the meat, and cooking with salt in those few instances when flavor is as desirable in the juices as in the meat. Meat loaves, Salisbury steak, and other mixtures of meat are normally seasoned and salted when mixed. Usually, these mixtures contain crumbs or other absorbing material to retain juices and furnish moist heat within the meat mix. The no salting practice is usually followed with all methods of dry heat cooking. If salt is desirable it can always be added at the table. Often a sauce is served with the meat, and this might be salted.

Meat proteins become coagulated by heat transferred from the outside surface to the interior. Length of the cooking period, therefore, must take this fact into consideration. It may be said that length of cooking time at a given temperature depends upon: (1) the internal temperature when cooking is started; (2) the rate of heat penetration; (3) the thickness of the cut; and (4) the degree of doneness desired. It would be impossible to predict length of cooking time for meat under all of these conditions. It is urged that each person keep records of grade, type of cut, thickness, temperature of cooking, and time of cooking whenever a piece of meat is cooked and thus acquire reliable time tables individualized to his need.

The approximate times that have been reported as satisfactory for cooking of meat with different methods of heating are given in Table 10.

Many factors must be considered when meat is prepared—time is only one of these. Therefore, the following generalizations concerning meat cookery will be helpful in various situations.

Frozen cuts require about one and one-half times as long to cook as do thawed cuts. It is impossible to insert a thermometer into a frozen cut, therefore it might seem to be advantageous to thaw large cuts. However, a meat thermometer can be inserted after the roast is partially cooked if one wishes to cook meat without thawing it.

The rate of heat penetration is faster the higher the temperature at the surface of the meat. Oven temperatures of 275 to 325° F are recommended for roasting because meats cooked rapidly in dry heat have charred, tough, dry exteriors before the interior is coagulated. Also, at high temperatures there is excessive shrinkage and drip loss (Fig. 22), and the fat may spatter over the oven and burn onto the sides. On the other hand, roasts cooked too slowly tend to be dry when done.

Stuffed birds require a longer roasting time than do hollow birds because of the increased distance for the heat to penetrate. Unless frozen stuffed birds are thawed before roasting, the meat may be overcooked before the stuffing is heated.

Meats cooked on spits can be expected to require approximately the same cooking time as roasting or broiling of similar cuts. The metal

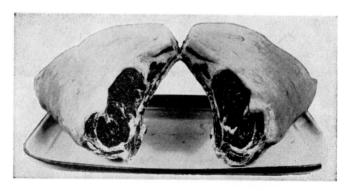

Fig. 22. Paired roasts of the same weight were cooked to the same internal temperature (140° F). The roast on the right was cooked at 300° F, and it had less shrink, less dripping losses, and less charring than the roast on the left, which was cooked at 425° F. (Courtesy of National Livestock and Meat Board, Chicago.)

spit could conceivably help to transfer heat to the interior and thus hasten cooking.

The temperature for broiling is regulated by the distance between surface of the meat and the source of heat. Generally, three inches from the heat source gives satisfactory results for steaks, kabobs, lamb chops, and other cuts of approximately one inch or thicker; less than three inches from the heat source is indicated for thinner cuts except bacon in which case one is actually only frying out the fat of the meat. If the top element of an oven is also the broiler, the meat is broiled with the door open; if a separate unit with adequate air circulation is used, the broiler door is closed.

Fat for deep-fat frying must be hot before the meat is immersed so that the proteins coagulate quickly before an excessive amount of fat can be absorbed. Temperatures of 350 to 375° F seem to give satisfactory results for frying shrimp, scallops, fish sticks, chicken, and other small pieces of meat. Electric fryers may have thermostatic controls, and in other kettles thermometers for deep-fat frying may be used to gauge temperatures, or the thermostatically controlled surface unit may be used. It should be remembered that a large volume of relatively cold food put into the fat at one time will lower the temperature appreciably, whether the fryer has a thermostat or not. Also, hot fats will froth when wet food is added. At least half the depth of the container should be allowed for this. Amounts of meat consistent with the amount of fat not only cook more uniformly but also are less likely to foam over the edge of the pan than are larger amounts.

Microwave (electronic or dielectric) cooking of meat takes place rapidly. Because the waves penetrate only a short distance into roasts and other thick pieces of meat the outer layers are cooked before the center is heated. Unless the meat is removed from the field of the microwaves and the remainder of the meat is allowed to cook by transfer of heat from the outer layer to the center, the outer portion of the meat will be overcooked and dry before the center is heated. One objection to this type of cooking has been the absence of browning, which occurs during slower methods of dry heat cookery. Broiler units for browning are now being built into some electronic ovens.

The softening of less tender cuts of meat by cooking in moist heat is usually more satisfactorily accomplished by simmering (190 to 200° F) than by boiling. Some use is made of pressure saucepans, which makes it possible to obtain temperatures as high as 250° F, and this appreciably shortens the cooking time. The flavor of meat cooked in pressure saucepans is different from that of meat cooked more slowly and is disliked by many.

Fig. 23. Live lobsters are plunged directly into boiling water so that there is no opportunity for post-mortem enzyme activity, which would cause rapid development of off-flavors. This is an unusually large lobster weighing approximately seven pounds. (Courtesy of U. S. Fish and Wildlife Service—Rex Gary Schmidt.)

Fish, a tender meat, is often cooked by moist heat, but will become tough quickly at temperatures above simmering. Small pieces of fish such as scallops, shrimp, and oysters require only 2 to 7 minutes of simmering, and even live lobsters of 1 to 1½ pounds will seldom need longer than 15 minutes (Fig. 23).

Cuts of meat to be cooked in moist heat may be given preliminary browning by dry heat (see Fig. 24). This is usually done by pan-frying in a small amount of fat but could also be accomplished in a broiler if it was desirable to avoid adding fat.

The amount of liquid added for moist heat methods of cooking is determined by personal preference. Meat may be sufficiently cooked without any additional liquid—tightly covered pans and low temperatures allow slow coagulation and softening with the juices from the meat serving as the liquid. Varying amounts of liquids may be added

A

B

Fig. 24. Meats are often browned before steaming and juices are retained if meats are handled in such a way that the lean is not pierced, using either tongs (A) or by hooking a fork into the fat (B). After browning, a small amount of water may be added for steaming (C). (Courtesy, National Livestock and Meat Board, Chicago.)

C

Table 10. APPROXIMATE COOKING TIME FOR VARIOUS TYPES OF CUTS OF MEAT COOKED BY DIFFERENT METHODS*

	Broil				Roast				
	Cut	Thickness, in.	Distance from Heat, in.	Time, min.	Cut	Degree Doneness	Weight, lb.	Oven Temp., °F	Time, min.
Beef	Liver	½	2	10	Standing ribs	Medium—160°F	4	275–300	120
	Steaks	1	2	14			6		150
		1½	2	20			8		180
		2	2	35	Rolled ribs (boneless)	Medium—160°F	4	275–300	150
	Ground beef patty	1	2	14			6		195
					Rolled rump	Medium—160°F	5	275–300	180
					Sirloin tip	Medium—160°F	3	275–300	160
Lamb	Liver	½	2	10	Rolled shoulder	Medium—170°F	3	275–300	120
	Chops	¾	2	12			5		150
			2	14	Leg, half	Medium—170°F	3–4	275–300	150
	Ground lamb patty	¾	2	12	Leg, whole	Medium—170°F	6–7	275–300	180
Pork	Bacon		2	4	Fresh pork Loin	Well—185°F	5	275–300	180
	Ham, slice Uncooked	1	2	20	Shoulder		5		210
	Cooked	1	2	10	Leg		6		240
					Leg		14		360
					Cured pork Ham	Well—160°F	6	275–300	150
					Ham		12		210
					Ham		16		250
Veal	Kidney, split	½	2	10	Roast (bone in)	Well—170°F	5	275–300	150
	Sweetbreads		2	10	(bone out)		5		180
	Liver		2	10					
Poultry Chicken Duck Goose Turkey	Steak	½	3	15	Stuffed birds or portions§	Well	2	275–300	120
	Broiler	1½	3	15			4		180
							6		240
							8		270
Fish	Steaks, Fillet	½	2	10	Cut pieces (½ in.)	Well		275–300	35
	Scallops		2	10	Stuffed	Well		275–300	60

Deep-fat Fry

	Cut	Thickness, in.	Pre-cooked or Raw	Frying Temp., °F	Time, min.
Beef	Ground beef patty	1	raw	375	5
	Croquettes	1	cooked	375	1
Lamb	Croquettes	1	cooked	375	1
Pork	Breaded cutlets and chops	½	raw	375	8
Veal	Breaded cutlets and chops	½	raw	375	8
Poultry Chicken Duck Goose Turkey	Cut pieces or steaks		pre-blanched raw	375 330	3 15
Fish	Fillet			375	5
	Shrimp, clams			375	3
	Mussels			375	3
	Scallops			375	4

Moist Heat (Simmer—200°F)

Cut	Thickness, in.	Weight, lb.	Time, min.
Tripe			90
Stew, short ribs, etc.			150
Swiss steak	1½		150
Tongue, heart			190
Shanks			190
Pot-roast		3–5	200
Oxtails			200
Liver			5
Liver			5
Kidney			15
Shoulder chop	¾		40
Shank and stew			50
Shoulder			120
Shoulder, loin, rib, or tenderloin	½ ¾		30 45
Spareribs			120
Liver			10
Liver			5
Chops, steaks, cutlets	¾		45
Stew	1		90
Pot-roast		3	150
Young birds in pieces			45
Stewing hens			120
Shrimp, clams			5
Scallops			10
Steak, fillet			10
Lobster			15

* Times given by the American Meat Institute.
† Panfry times are approximately the same as for broiling.
‡ If weight and thickness are not given, they are not important factors.
§ Add 30 minutes for each addition 2 pounds of weight.

for other purposes, as for cooking the vegetables in soups or stews, steaming dumplings, or for gravies or sauces (Fig. 24c). Relatively large amounts of liquids are used when making "stock" because the liquid rather than the meat is important. Flavors of stock are more dilute when large proportions of water to meat are used than when small proportions are used. Boullion cubes may be added if extra flavor is desirable.

Degree of doneness in meats is a matter of personal preference. Some people even prefer raw meat; raw fish is a common item of the diet of Hawaiians and other islanders, and many people consider raw oysters or clams as a delicacy. As pointed out previously, untreated pork should never be eaten raw, and it would seem wise to cook other meats as a safety precaution.

Doneness of meat cooked by dry-heat methods is judged on appearance of the interior or the internal temperature. Thermometers cannot be used for very thin cuts because there is insufficient meat to cover the sensitive portion of the thermometer, and change in appearance of the meat must be the sole criterion. Plasma proteins are coagulated when the translucent appearance characteristic of raw meat becomes opaque. One should check the appearance of the center of the meat rather than judging from only the outside. In steaks and lamb chops it is well to make a slit near the bone in the thickest part of the lean. Steaks are rare when the interior color is still quite red, but the translucency is lost. Medium-done meat shows pink, and well-done meat is usually gray throughout. This same test for doneness may be used for chicken broilers and fryers. Chickens may be served rare if desired but most people prefer the flavors developed by longer cooking and many enjoy crisp skin. If the thickest part of the meat is cooked to the desired stage, the rest of the cut will be done. Roast poultry may be tested by moving a thigh to see if it disjoints easily. At this point, however, it may be overcooked. A thermometer inserted into the center of breast or thigh meat, or into the stuffing, is a more dependable gauge. Thoroughly cooked fish tends to flake and pull apart easily as well as to lose its translucency. Most fish contain little fat in the flesh, thus tending to become dry and overcooked easily.

The only sure way of obtaining the degree of doneness desired in a roast is to insert a thermometer and cook to the temperature specified for that degree of doneness. The bulb or sensitive part of the thermometer must be in the center of the lean if it is to record the temperature of the lean (Fig. 21). The indicated temperature of the meat should begin to rise 20 to 30 minutes after cooking begins. If this does not happen, the thermometer may be embedded in a fat pocket and should be moved slightly. If the thermometer is left in the fat, a change in the indicated temperature will take place suddenly when the fat begins to melt—at which time the meat may be overcooked. It is advisable to push the thermometer down slightly when the roast registers "done." If the temperature drops, the meat will require longer cooking. Since the internal temperature of any large roast tends to rise after it is removed from the hot atmosphere, it should be removed from the oven while still three to five degrees below the desired temperature. Meat will not always have the same internal color at the same internal temperature, but it should be remembered that fat content and other factors which influence doneness are not constant.

Doneness in roasts can be estimated without a thermometer, but this is very difficult. The age-old gauge is in minutes per unit of weight, but this does not allow for variations in thickness, fat content, or shape (see Table 10).

Meats cooked by moist heat are generally judged done when tenderness is satisfactory. With this method of judging doneness cuts are always cooked to the well-done stage. Tenderness, however, can have a wide latitude. The plasma proteins are coagulated more quickly in moist heat than in dry heat since water transfers heat more rapidly than air. However, connective tissue softening requires longer cooking than needed for the coagulation of plasma proteins. A pot roast can become dry as a result of overcoagulation just as a roast cooked with dry heat can become dry. Therefore, low temperatures should be the rule for any type of meat cookery. Thermometers are not practical for moist-heat methods because the cut may not be softened sufficiently at a definite internal temperature. Meat that is easily pierced with a fork, will be tender for chewing.

Changes in Nutritive Value Caused by Cooking of Meat

Thiamine, and this not to a great extent, is the only nutrient destroyed during ordinary cooking of muscle meat. The longer the heating time and the thinner the cut, the greater this loss will be. Some minerals and water-soluble vitamins in addition to flavoring constituents are contained in both drippings and broths (cooking water) and the nutritive losses will be great if these are habitually discarded. Pan gravy (water added to the pan to dissolve the browned matter) from sautéed meats and drippings from broiled meats can be saved for "planned-overs" if they are not used when the meat is served. An

English delicacy is a special hot bread—Yorkshire Pudding—designed to catch the drip from roasting meats and be served as a meat accompaniment.

Fat losses in the cooking of meats can be considerable. However, many uses can be made of the fat that melts out during heating. These fats will normally be flavored but selecting uses in which the meat flavor enhances the product or subduing the flavors with stronger ones is a challenge for cooking skills.

Planned-Overs in Meats

Many homemakers lament their inability to take advantage of inexpensive cuts of meat or their curtailment of choice because careers keep them away from home so that they never have time to cook anything but steaks and chops. This problem can be overcome by installing adequate equipment, using tenderizing methods so that less-tender cuts can be cooked more quickly, or by making wiser use of planned-overs.

Planned-overs add variety to menus as well as being time-savers. For example, meat sauce for spaghetti gains in flavor with some holding. Ground meat may be purchased for several meals at one time. After pan-broiling the amount for the immediate meal, the remainder can be browned and slightly cooked without even washing the pan. A portion taken out at this later stage can be refrigerated for quick creaming the following evening. (Children at the University of California, Los Angeles Nursery School have especially liked creamed ground beef.) Onion, tomato sauce, seasonings, and long slow cooking of a portion of the browned meat makes a delectable meat sauce to be used several days later with spaghetti, lasagna, rice, or other cereal food. The sauce can be simmered during the dinner hour or favorite television program.

Freezers make possible long storage of both raw and cooked meat. A large turkey roasted on a weekend can be cut off the bones and frozen in one-meal packages. Salads, casseroles, cold cuts, and many other dishes can then be made in a very short time (Fig. 25).

Fish cook so quickly that they are seldom used for planned-overs. However, the person living alone may feel that the one pound package of frozen fillet is not for him. Chunks can be cut off without thawing and the remainder kept in the frozen state until another serving is desired. Or, the whole package can be cooked at one time. Cooked fish keeps as well as other cooked meat and can be used in the same type of dishes. Why not make up a fish salad with part of the

Fig. 25. Beef-vegetable pie with crisp flaky crust is just one of the many possibilities for planned-over dishes. (Courtesy of Sperry Operations, General Mills, Inc., Minneapolis.)

planned-over and have it ready for next day's lunch? Fish mixed with other meats also make excellent dishes. Tuna, chicken, and veal are similar in color and texture and make very acceptable blends. Fish cakes or croquettes can be made of any planned-over fish just as the familiar canned salmon is used.

All meats for planned-overs should be promptly refrigerated. Food poisoning organisms that cause digestive upsets, thrive on meat at room temperatures and may be present without affecting appearance or flavor. Cleanliness is *not* a sufficient preventative measure, but refrigeration is. Moist dishes such as creamed ham or chicken, or salads are even more favorable for growth of microorganisms than drier meats and therefore should be promptly chilled. If cooked meats are to be kept longer than three or four days, they should be frozen.

LEGUMES AND NUTS

Mature dried beans, peas, and lentils make up the class of foods known as legumes, often called "poor man's meat." Everyone has his favorite kind of beans: large limas, baby limas, marrow, navy, and tiny pea beans; black, red, pink, pinto, and black-eyed peas. The waxy-textured soybeans are less popular but nourishing; the chickpea (Garbanzo) is a favorite in the southwest; the Fava, questionable because of a possible toxic effect, is used in certain Italian dishes; and Mung beans are used commercially for bean sprouts. Lentils are generally brown, but some imports of pink lentils are available. Peas are whole or split and may be yellow or green.

Legumes in the Daily Food Plan

The primary role of legumes in our dishes is to furnish an economical source of protein and to provide variety. When no animal proteins are eaten with the meal, beans should be supplemented with other protein-containing foods. The Mexican meal common in our southwestern states consists of tortillas (corn), rice, and refried beans—a fortunate combination. Similarly, rolls with chili or baked beans should be encouraged, and a slice of cheese melted on the top of a bowl of chili considerably improves the nutritive value of this inexpensive food.

Legumes are good sources of phosphorus, iron, thiamine, and niacin, as well as protein. Unless sprouted they contain no ascorbic acid, but soybeans make excellent sprouts, especially some of the field varieties. The calcium contribution of legumes is sizable (160 milligrams per 100 grams dry—approximately 3 ounces) when they are the mainstay of the meal. Their composition is such that some form of legumes several times a week would be a good routine to establish even when meats are plentiful.

Legumes may be graded for market according to size, uniformity of color, and freedom from insects. They are usually packaged in pound or multiples of pound bags so prices are easy to compare. The seeds keep unusually well even without refrigeration and insect infestation is the major concern.

Peanuts may also be classed as a legume. Generally peanuts are roasted and eaten out-of-hand, ground into peanut butter, or incorporated with other foods. However, some use is made of boiled unroasted peanuts in much the same manner as beans are used.

Almonds, Brazil nuts, chestnuts, cocoanuts, filberts, hickory nuts, pecans, pine nuts, pistachio, and walnuts are among the most popular nuts for general use. Hawaii and California both produce a very delicious nut similar to filbert, the macademia, but they have an extremely hard thick shell and have been most expensive. Butternuts are found in the middlewest but have not been produced commercially to any extent.

Nuts are as high in food value as legumes. However, with the possible exception of peanuts, they can hardly be classed as "poor man's meat." Nuts can be purchased in the shell, shelled blanched (skins removed) or unblanched, sliced, in pieces, or ground into pastes or butter. In addition, many of them are roasted, salted, or seasoned (Chili, garlic, spiced, or smoked nuts), and a few green walnuts are pickled. Nut butters can be made of any of the nuts, but peanut butter is the only one sold in quantity. Usually part of the oil is pressed from the roasted nut before being ground. Butters may then be homogenized or hydrogenated so that oils do not separate from the products.

The high oil content of nuts makes them a more perishable food than beans. Whenever the nut meat is exposed to air, it is susceptible to oxidative rancidity. Sliced and broken pieces are the most perishable because of their large surface area. Vacuum packaging decreases rancidity and a light dusting with an antioxidant is an added protection. Refrigeration of nuts, especially sliced nut meats will prolong storage life. Heating of nuts during roasting increases the tendency to rancidity especially in French-fried nuts, as oils are heated for long enough periods to start a breakdown in the fat structure.

Cooking of Legumes

It is well known that the soaking of dried legumes shortens the cooking period. Swelling can be hastened by bringing the soaking liquid to a boil and then withdrawing the heat and allowing the legumes to stand for a few hours in the warm liquid. However, if they are soaked for a long period of time they may ferment unless they are kept cool.

Cooking is necessary for complete digestion and to soften the unusually hard texture. The hull of seeds is primarily undigestible cellulose and becomes toughened with certain salts, sugar, and acids. If available, distilled water makes more tender products than most tap waters. Both table salt and sugar harden textures. If the beans are salted at the end of the cooking period, therefore, they will be softer than if salted at the beginning. After beans are cooked, they may be seasoned in various ways. One of the most popular dishes is Boston Baked Beans in which seasonings, including sugar, are added and long slow baking allows thorough penetration into the bean. One should expect the sugars to have some firming effect on the whole beans in this instance.

Soybean consumption in the United States has not been extensive despite the generous contribution this bean could make to the nutritive value of the diet. Possibly the firm rather waxy texture and strong flavor differ too much from the better known beans. They could be used to advantage in casseroles where their distinctive characteristics could be highlighted or hidden. Certain field varieties of soybeans make excellent sprouts for chop suey, egg foo yung, and salads; and this bean can be roasted and used as a snack. *Choplets*—pseudo-meat—are primarily soybean. Tofu is a soybean curd used in Japanese dishes.

Split peas and lentils are primarily puréed for soups, but can be used in numerous other ways. Marinated lentils, for example, would be an especially good accompaniment for a vegetable plate, macaroni, rice, or other bland main dishes.

Garbanzos (chickpeas) are popularly used in the southwest states and many Mediterranean countries. They have a mealy texture and enhance tossed salads, stews, soups, and casseroles especially when used with barley or rice. Cooked garbanzos may be sautéed in butter or seasoned with special sauces, such as Creole sauce, and used as a main dish or vegetable in a manner similar to the black-eyed peas popular in the south; they also make an excellent "dip" if mashed with lemon, sesamé seed purée, olive oil, and salt.

The loss of nutrients during the cooking of legumes is primarily due to solution of vitamins and minerals into the cooking water which is then discarded. Preliminary washing may be desirable, but water in which any vegetable is soaked and cooked should be utilized. The amount of water to be used will, of course, depend on the desired consistency of the finished product. All dried products take up water and swell. Generally, water to two or three times the volume of the amount of dry legumes will be sufficient. At least one hour should be allowed after soaking for cooking at simmering temperature.

Twenty-five cents will buy considerably more protein in plant foods than in meat (see Table 5), and whether meat, legumes, or nuts furnish the principal protein of the meal is immaterial in protein metabolism if other foods containing proteins are eaten with the legumes and nuts. All proteins must be reduced to amino acids in digestion before they can be absorbed into the blood stream and carried to the various parts of the body where they are rebuilt into specific proteins. Therefore, even though meat has a more favorable assortment of amino acids for human nutrition than plant food it is useful only to the extent of the quantity of lean eaten. The source of the specific amino acids for the building of the body proteins is immaterial.

For nutritive value of one serving of meat, poultry, fish, legumes, and nuts see Table 11.

Table 11. NUTRITIVE VALUE OF 1 SERVING OF MEAT, POULTRY, FISH, LEGUMES, AND NUTS*

Food	Size of Serving	Energy Value, Cal.	Protein, gm.	Calcium, mg.	Iron, mg.	Vitamin A, I.U.	Thiamine, mg.	Riboflavin, mg.	Niacin, mg.	Ascorbic Acid, mg.
Bacon, broiled or fried	2 slices	97	4.0	4	0.5	...	0.08	0.05	0.8	...
Beef, round, cooked	3 oz.	197	23.0	9	2.9	...	0.06	0.19	4.7	...
Chicken, broiler, raw	½ bird	332	44.4	31	3.3	...	0.18	0.36	22.4	...
Clam, raw	4 oz.	92	14.5	109	7.9	120	0.11	0.20	1.8	...
Cod (fresh), raw	4 oz.	84	18.7	11	0.5	...	0.07	0.10	2.5	2
Eels, raw	4 oz.	183	21.1	20	0.8	2040	0.31	0.42	1.6	...
Haddock, fried	4″ x 3″ x ½″	158	18.7	18	0.6	...	0.04	0.09	2.6	...
Hamburger or Porterhouse steak (cooked)	3 oz.	316	19.0	8	2.4	...	0.07	0.16	4.1	...
Lamb, roast, cooked	3 oz.	230	20.0	9	2.6	...	0.12	0.21	4.4	...
Liver, calf, raw	3 oz.	120	16.2	5	9.0	19130	0.18	2.65	13.7	30
Liver, pork, raw	3 oz.	114	16.7	8	15.3	12070	0.34	2.53	14.2	19
Oyster, raw	½ C.	100	11.7	113	6.7	385	0.17	0.24	1.4	...
Pork, ham, cooked	3 oz.	338	20.0	9	2.6	...	0.45	0.20	4.0	...
Salmon, canned red	3 oz.	147	17.2	220†	1.0	200	0.03	0.14	6.2	...
Sausage, franks	1 (54 gm.)	124	7.0	3	0.6	...	0.08	0.09	1.3	...
Tuna, canned	3 oz.	169	24.7	7	1.2	70	0.04	0.10	10.9	...
Turkey, raw	4 oz.	304	22.8	26	4.3	...	0.10	0.16	9.1	...
Veal, cutlet, cooked	3 oz.	184	24.0	10	3.0	...	0.07	0.24	5.2	...
Legumes, cooked										
Beans, kidney, white, etc.	1 C.	230	14.6	102	4.9	...	0.12	0.12	2.0	...
Chickpeas (garbanzos)	1 C.	250	14.6	64	4.7	230	0.40	0.12	1.1	...
Peas, split	1 C.	230	16.3	22	3.4	75	0.51	0.19	2.1	...
Soy beans	1 C.	232	24.4	160	5.6	...	0.75	0.22	1.6	...
Nuts										
Peanuts	½ C.	402	19.3	53	1.3	...	0.21	0.09	11.6	...
Peanut butter	¼ C.	368	16.8	48	1.2	25	0.08	0.08	10.4	...
Pecans	½ C.	376	5.1	40	1.3	...	0.39	0.06	0.5	...

* Calculated from U.S.D.A. Handbook No. 8.
† If bones are discarded, calcium content would be much lower.

SUMMARY

The proteins of meat, poultry, fish, legumes, and nuts are the most concentrated of any of the natural foods. The proteins of meat, poultry, and fish are complete and rank high in biological value. Some of the legumes and nuts contain complete protein. However, their proportions of amino acids in a given amount of protein are less satisfactory than those from animal sources, and legumes should be supplemented with cereal grains when used as the sources of protein. In addition to proteins, this whole food group contributes substantial amounts of many of the known vitamins and minerals to the diet, particularly vitamins of the B-complex, and phosphorus, iron, and copper. Livers are extraordinarily good providers not only of these nutrients but also vitamin A and ascorbic acid.

Meat inspection and grading are desirable procedures to assure safety and quality of meats. Meat products are perishable items but they can be satisfactorily preserved by freezing, curing, canning, dehydrating, and salting. Both fresh and preserved products are readily available in American markets.

Less tender cuts of meat are cooked by moist heat to soften certain proteins without excessive drying of the whole. Tender meats may be cooked by either moist or dry heat. The browning that occurs in cooking beef and lamb cuts with dry heat enhances their flavors for most people. High heat toughens proteins so that the rule to follow is, "Cook meat low and slow." Legume and nut proteins are improved for human nutrition by cooking.

Food values of both meats and legumes are well retained during ordinary cooking, if drip and cooking waters are utilized.

Reading List

1. Bowes, A. deP. and C. F. Church, 1951, *Food Value of Portions Commonly Used*, Anna dePlanter Bowes, Philadelphia.

2. Bull, S., 1951, *Meat for the Table*, McGraw-Hill Book Co., New York.

3. Clark, H. and G. Van Duyne, 1949, "Cooking losses, tenderness, palatability, and thiamine and riboflavin content of beef as affected by roasting, pressure saucepan cooking, and broiling," *Food Research*, **14**:221.

4. Day, E. J., H. D. Alexander, H. E. Sauberlich, and W. D. Salmon, 1957, "Effect of gamma radiation on certain water-soluble vitamins in raw ground beef," *J. Nutrition*, **62**:27.

5. Food and Agriculture Organization, 1957, *Yearbook of Food and Agriculture Statistics*, Vol. X, Part I, FAO—United Nations, Rome, Italy.

6. Griswold, R. M., 1955, "The effect of different methods of cooking beef round of commercial and prime grades. I. Palatability and shear values," *Food Research*, **20**:160.

7. Halliday, E. G. and I. T. Noble, 1946, *Hows and Whys of Cooking*, University of Chicago Press, Chicago.

8. Hansen, H. (Editor), 1957, *The World Almanac*, New York World-Telegram, New York.

9. Kotschevar, L. H., 1956, "Taste testing frozen meat cooked before and after thawing," *J. Amer. Diet. Assoc.*, **32**:444.

10. Lowe, B., 1955, *Experimental Cookery from the Chemical and Physical Standpoint*, John Wiley and Sons, 4th edition, New York.

11. McGary, V. E. and M. E. Shipman, 1956, "Acceptability of irradiated foods —II." *J. Amer. Diet. Assoc.*, **32**:1059.

12. National Livestock and Meat Board, 7th edition, *Ten Lessons on Meat*, National Livestock and Meat Board, Chicago.

13. Taylor, C. M., G. MacLeod, and M. S. Rose, 1956, *Foundations of Nutrition*, The Macmillan Co., New York.

14. Terminology Committee, Amer. Home Econ. Assoc., 1959, *Handbook of Food Preparation*, American Home Economics Association, Washington, D. C.

15. Tressler, D., C. Evers, and B. H. Evers, 1953, *Into the Freezer and Out*, Avi Publishing Co., New York.

16. United States Department of Agriculture, 1957, Rev. U. S. grades of beef, U.S.D.A. Leaflet No. 310.

17. Winter, A. R. and P. Clements, 1957, "Cooked edible meat in ready-to-cook poultry," *J. Amer. Diet. Assoc.*, **33**:800.

CHAPTER 4 . . EGGS AT ANY MEAL

◀ **Fig. 26.** Chicken eggs represent one of the most nutritious, inexpensive, and versatile foods in the American diet. (Courtesy of Poultry and Egg National Board, Chicago.)

EGGS REPRESENT ONE OF THE MOST NUTRITIOUS, INEXPENSIVE, AND versatile foods in the Daily Diet Guide. Chicken eggs are the most common type used in American meals (Fig. 26), but other eggs, especially duck eggs, also make good products.

An egg is very nearly a complete food. This is in keeping with the plans of nature, which provides in the egg all the essentials for forming the baby chick. Eggs contribute proteins with an unusually favorable amino acid proportion for man, many minerals and vitamins, and some fats for human nutriment requirement.

The chemical composition and physical properties of eggs are such as to allow preparation of an amazing number of dishes. Thus, it would not be unusual for eggs to be used in every meal every day. Surveys show that 75 per cent of the eggs used for breakfast in American homes are fried,[1] but poached or scrambled eggs, omelets, pancakes, and waffles are also popular. Noontime fare may feature a soufflé or perhaps custard, pudding, cream pie, or ice cream. Sandwich fillings may be made of egg or contain salad dressings made of egg. Other products that contain eggs are croquettes, cakes, cookies, and so on *ad infinitum*. It is not surprising to learn, therefore, that statistics show a steady increase in the egg consumption in the United States (Fig. 27). The country averaged 418 eggs per capita in 1955 (World Almanac 1957), which is more than 1 egg per person per day.

THE ROLE OF EGGS IN THE DAILY MEAL PLANS

Diet guides generally recommend including enough eggs in menu plans for each person to obtain at least 4 eggs per week, and preferably one per day. Some people prefer never to eat an egg as an egg, but the same people may use eggs in so many prepared dishes that they actually consume more egg than those eating a daily breakfast egg. The manner of preparation of eggs is not important to their nutritive qualities so variety in menu planning is unlimited. Nutritive values of eggs are shown in Table 12. On a percentage basis (equal weights) the nutritive contributions of eggs are similar to those of lean meat. Eggs have more vitamin A, more bone-building materials (calcium, phosphorus, and vitamin D), more riboflavin, but less protein and niacin than beef round.

---

[1] U.S.D.A. Agr. Info. Bull. 146.

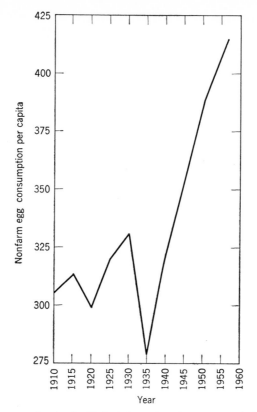

Fig. 27. Egg consumption in the United States has shown a steady increase during the past 57 years. (U. S. Department of Commerce, 1957.)

Proteins

The protein content of whole eggs is consistently 12.8 per cent. In this respect eggs are unlike meat, in which the percentage of protein varies with the fat and bone content. One medium-sized whole egg contains approximately 6 grams of protein. Although this amount meets less than one-tenth of the daily protein allowance for the adult, the amino acids comprising the several egg proteins are those that, according to research findings, are the most suitable and the proportions the most favorable of any single food for human protein needs. Indeed, the amino acids present are in such good balance for human protein needs that their proportions are used as a standard in studies of actual minimum requirements of individuals for specific amino acids.

Another important consideration of egg proteins in human nutrition is their unusually high content of methionine. This essential amino acid is either lacking or is found in low amounts in the cereals and many other foods that may be consumed in large quantity. Thus when egg is mixed with cereal products such as in corn bread, the body is able to use more of the amino acids from the combined proteins than would be possible from the same amount of protein from corn alone. For this same reason the consumption of an egg sandwich or of a baked product containing egg has much merit from the nutritional as well as the palatability aspect.

Vitamins

Although more than one-half of the riboflavin content of the egg occurs in the white, most of the other vitamins are found only in the yolk. The yolk may well be one of the most valuable sources of vitamin A since only milk fats, liver, and eggs contain this vitamin in its pre-formed state. Yolks also contain varying amounts of the yellow carotene pigments—some of which may be partially or completely converted to vitamin A by the human body.

The vitamin A value of egg yolk can be varied by the feed of the hens. The deep yellow color of some yolks is caused by the carotenoid pigments that are present in high concentration in both green and yellow feeds. Feeds high in these colors will produce deep yellow yolks. Not all of the carotenoid pigments are of the right chemical structure to form vitamin A, but highly colored feeds will further the production of eggs rich in usable carotenes as well as in other yellow pigments. The hens also change some of the carotenes to vitamin A, hence the deeply colored yolk may be higher in pre-formed vitamin A than are pale yolks. Producers may add pre-formed vitamin A directly to feeds, in which case egg yolks increase in vitamin A value without becoming more yellow.

There is also some vitamin D present in egg yolk. The quantities are so variable that reliable figures cannot be quoted. It must be remembered, though, that eggs are one of the few natural foods that contain pre-formed vitamin D, a nutrient essential for the absorption and metabolism of calcium and phosphorus. The contribution of eggs to vitamin D requirements depends upon the amount of vitamin D in the feed of the hen and her exposure to sunlight.

Vitamin B_{12}, a vitamin believed to be present only in animal proteins, is found in egg. The amount of vitamin B_{12} in one egg is relatively small and variable (reported to be about 0.028 milligram per egg)

Table 12. THE NUTRITIVE CONTRIBUTIONS OF EGGS*

Part of Egg	Wt., gm.	Water, per cent	Energy Value, Cal.	Pro- tein, gm.	Cal- cium, mg.	Iron, mg.	Vita- min A, I.U.	Thia- mine, mg.	Ribo- flavin, mg.	Nia- cin, mg.	Ascorbic Acid, mg.
Raw											
1 Whole	54	74.8	77	6.1	26	1.3	550	0.05	0.14	tr.	...
1 White	31	87.2	15	3.3	2	0.1	...	...	0.08	tr.	...
1 Yolk	17	49.4	61	2.8	25	1.2	550	0.05	0.06	tr.	...
Dried											
Whole 1 C.	108		640	50.5	205	9.5	4040	0.36	1.14	0.3	...
White 1 C.	56		223	48.1	27	0.9	...	...	1.15	0.4	...
Yolk 1 C.	96		666	30.0	271	13.2	5320	0.48	0.64	0.1	...

*Nutritive values from U.S.D.A. Agriculture Handbook No. 8.

but its presence may be a contributing factor in the high biological value of egg proteins since it is believed that interrelationships exist between vitamin B_{12} and amino acid metabolism.

Other members of the B-complex vitamins are also present. Whole egg should be particularly stressed for its riboflavin content; one medium egg contributes almost as much (0.14 milligram) as one-half cup of spinach or one medium loin pork chop.

Minerals

The minerals of eggs are readily utilized in human nutrition. The percentage of minerals present may not be as high as that of other foods, but because those present are more readily absorbed during digestion eggs actually are one of the best sources. This is true of iron (1.3 milligram from 1 egg) and copper (0.1 milligram), which are essential for the formation of hemoglobin in red blood cells. Eggs are put into the diet of infants early in life (third or fourth month) as a good source of these essential nutrients in order to supplement milk, which is low in iron. An egg also contains appreciable amounts of calcium and phosphorus. Since vitamin D may also be present, eggs are particularly well-suited to the bone-building function of calcium and phosphorus.

Fat and Cholesterol

The entire amount of fat contained in eggs (11.5 per cent) is localized in the yolk. This fat is accompanied by cholesterol. There has been considerable discussion about the cholesterol content of eggs and its effect on blood cholesterol. Research has shown that the cholesterol content of the blood tends to increase only when fat is being accumulated by the body.[2] Thus it would seem not only that persons with normal metabolism could eat eggs without raising their blood cholesterol,[3] but also that they would do well to have eggs in their diets to provide other important substances—vitamins in fat (see Chapter 13 for cholesterol).

---

[2] Stare, F. J., "Research in atherosclerosis," *J. Amer. Diet. Assoc.*, **32**:309, 1956.

[3] Everson, G. J. and H. J. Souders, "Composition and nutritive importance of eggs," *J. Amer. Diet. Assoc.*, **33**:1245, 1957.

The edible portion of an egg is enclosed in three cases. Two thin membranes comprise the inner containers, which are encased in a strong shell shaped to withstand high pressures. A small air sac develops between the two membranes as the egg cools from the body temperature of the hen to that of the environment. Normally this air sac will be found on the large end, which is placed uppermost when eggs are packed. The shell is porous and permits moisture and gases to escape from the egg. The egg contents are generally sterile when laid. A protective film covers the shell when newly-laid. Eventually microoganisms can enter through the pores of the shell, and their numbers are increased by dirt on the shell.

The egg contents are fluid (74 per cent water). When broken out onto a plate, the egg will flatten under atmospheric pressure revealing two distinctly different parts: the *albumin*, or white; and the yolk. The albumin is mostly water (87.8 per cent) with small amounts of protein, which gives the jelly-like quality to the white. Layers of thick white are interspersed with thin white. The yolk is contained in a *yolk sac* with heavy twisted cords at each end called the *yolk anchors*. The yolk sac is usually strong enough to permit easy separation of the yolk and white, a practice that is often desirable in food preparation.

Variations Found among Newly Laid Eggs

Eggs when laid may vary in size, shell color, and shell thickness, and when broken out may vary in the proportion of thick white and in the color of the yolk. Egg size is governed primarily by the age of the hen; young birds produce smaller eggs than old birds. Some breeds of poultry lay somewhat larger eggs than other breeds. Shell color is governed by the breed of the chicken and varies from a stark white through a tint to dark brown. "Rainbow-colored" eggs from small flocks of a new breed have appeared on the market but these are only a novelty and very expensive. Chemical analysis shows the percentage of protein in these eggs to be the same as that of other chicken eggs, although advertising claims a higher concentration.[4]

Shell thickness is largely governed by the diet of the individual hen,

---

[4] Chemical analysis done at University of California at Los Angeles.

however, some breeds normally produce eggs with heavier shells than others.

It is not known exactly what causes variations in the proportion of thick white although it has been found to be partially related to the laying cycle. Workers at Washington State Experiment Station examined 2000 newly laid eggs produced by 2 breeds of chickens and found the albumin index[5] to vary from 40 to 200 with an average of 102.

Variations in the color of the yolk are caused only by substances in the feed. Normally the color varies from pale yellow to deep orange, but occasionally some abnormal colors are produced.

Newly laid eggs may in a few instances have some abnormal defects such as "meat spots" or bloodiness. Candling practices are designed to remove such eggs from the market. Aesthetically these spots may seem undesirable, but they do not affect the eating or cooking qualities of the egg. Germ spots may also be visible if the egg is fertile; however, most of the eggs produced for consumption are infertile.

Changes That Occur during the Holding of Eggs

Changes that occur in the holding of eggs may affect purchase price, appearance of the broken out egg, cooking performance of the eggs, and flavor. The extent of changes that occur over a certain period of time is dependent primarily upon the holding temperature and humidity. Of course the longer the eggs are held, at any temperature, the greater the extent of change. Eggs held three weeks at refrigerator temperature have been found to have less extensive changes than eggs kept three days at room temperature.

During storage, the "bloom" on the shell disappears and the shell becomes shiny. Water may evaporate through the porous shell so that the solids become more concentrated and the size of the air sac will increase. In addition water, which is naturally lower in concentration in the yolk than in the white, slowly passes from the white to the yolk and dilutes the yolk solids. This stretches the yolk sac so that it may break when the egg is handled. If it does not break, the yolk will flatten more than is normal when the egg is broken out onto a flat surface. The thick white thins and will spread when broken out. This is shown in Fig. 28.

Chemical changes take place in the egg during holding. Ammonia may be formed so that there may be an ammoniacal odor when the

---

[5] A method of expressing the amount of thick albumin.

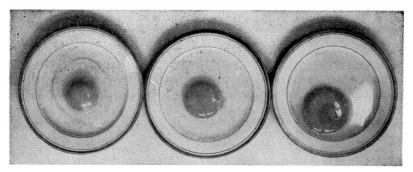

Fig. 28. Eggs aged 0, 21, and 42 days in the shell at room temperature show progressive thinning of the white and flattening of the yolk when broken out.

egg is opened. Carbon dioxide gas is formed and escapes through the shell; the white then becomes more alkaline as well as less viscous. The watery consistency can be noticed while the egg is in the shell, even by an inexperienced person, by gently shaking the egg.

Flavor changes that occur during aging of the egg have been reported from several laboratories. The more predominant the egg is in the recipe, the more noticeable the flavor differences. Some people actually prefer the flavor in the aged egg to that of fresh depending upon what they have become accustomed to having. Alaskans who depend upon eggs from other states have been reported to say: "Keep your fresh eggs and give us something with flavor!"

Surveys of consumer preferences in eggs seem to indicate that the majority of people prefer the eggs as nearly like the newly laid as possible. Many homemakers stated that they were willing to pay a premium for "fresh eggs." It would seem an ideal situation, therefore, to have producers and other egg handlers maintain as much as possible the newly laid qualities of eggs through the marketing process. The few people who prefer aged products could age the eggs to the desired stage themselves.

Grading of Eggs

The practices and laws governing the sale of eggs varies with states and localities. The marketing service of the United States Department of Agriculture has set up standards and definitions for different grades, which some of the states have adopted or use in slightly modified form. Other states do not attempt to grade the eggs sold in their markets.

Clean eggs sold by government grade are designated as Grades AA,

A, B, or C (Fig. 29). The grade designation is dependent upon the factors concerned with sturdiness of the shell and the appearance of the interior contents when the eggs are candled. The grades are determined by candlers who rapidly appraise the eggs for size of the air cell, viscosity of the white, visibility of the yolk, and prominence of germ spot. Eggs containing blood or meat spots are not usually sold on the retail markets. Except for the strength of the shell, these factors could be influenced by aging of the egg; that is, air cell increases in size as the egg is held, white thins, and yolk increases in size and may darken slightly. The yolk of an aged egg is generally more mobile and more visible when swirled before a light than is that of a newly laid egg.

Fig. 29. A patented shield-shaped mark is used to designate clean eggs graded under Federal-State Supervision. (U.S.D.A. photograph.)

Under these grading conditions, if a light-shelled egg has a dark yolk, it could be graded lower than a dark-shelled egg with the same color or lighter yolk just because one can see through the light shell more easily than through the dark one. Even the amount and the source of light in the room, the candler's eyes, or the tint of the candler's glasses might affect the grading accuracy.

Because of all the factors involved, there can be no fine dividing line between grades. Furthermore, a 20 per cent tolerance is permitted. This makes it permissible to have 20 per cent of the eggs in either lower or higher grades than the standards set for the grade designated on the carton. The retailer may hold eggs a week or more before putting them out for sale so that the deviations from the standard may be even greater than 20 per cent when the eggs are purchased.

Electronic grading and other means are being investigated as a possible means of classifying eggs to more nearly accord with characteristics that are so outstanding when the egg is broken out of the shell.

According to the present standards, grade is not synonymous with age of the egg. Only eggs with strong well-shaped shells, air cells no larger than one-fourth inch, very thick whites, outline of yolks barely visible, and contents free of defects are put into top grades. Even newly laid eggs that deviate from these standards are graded as low quality.

U. S. Light Dirty, U. S. Dirty, and U. S. Check or Crack may be available at some markets where graded eggs are sold and may be very economical buys. Clean eggs are preferred if they are to be held for a time because dirt contains many microorganisms that can enter through the pores of the shell and cause mold or rot. In some localities the egg handlers refuse either dirty or washed eggs. Others permit certain washing techniques or sand blasting of dirty eggs.

Factors Affecting Cost of Market Eggs

The market price of eggs may vary with season of the year, grade, size, and in some areas with shell color. Eggs of any size or grade are normally highest in cost in the winter when production is at its lowest. When eggs are graded for marketing, the higher grades will command higher prices than lower grades of the same size. The larger the eggs, the higher the price per dozen of any one grade; however, this does not necessarily indicate a higher price per pound since it must also be remembered that the larger the egg, the greater will be the ratio of edible portion to shell. The federal classification for egg sizes (see Fig. 30) is as given in the table.

Term Used for Size Designation	Net Minimum Weight per Dozen
Jumbo	30 oz.
Extra large	27 oz.
Large	24 oz.
Medium	21 oz.
Small	18 oz.
Peewee	15 oz.

When recipes give egg amounts in count rather than in measure, a medium-sized egg is intended. This is approximately three tablespoonfuls of liquid egg and one could therefore expect to fill a cup with five eggs.

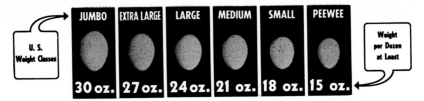

Fig. 30. Eggs are classed according to size and a minimum weight per dozen for each size grouping is specified. (U.S.D.A. photograph.)

Shell color will not affect the price of the eggs unless there is sufficient demand for a specific color. In one area white-shelled eggs may be popular, in another area brown-shelled. Producers either control the color of egg shells by selecting breeds of chickens that produce the desired color, or obtain it by special shell treatments.

Preservation of Eggs

The nutritive value of eggs does not change appreciably during holding in the shell. Although newly laid eggs are generally preferred, the holding of eggs from a few days to several months is often unavoidable and may even be desirable if one is to have eggs in seasons of low production.

Changes that occur during holding of eggs may be delayed by shell treatments. Eggs may be dipped or sprayed with a tasteless lightweight mineral oil that is not noticeable but which plugs the pores of the shell. The eggs are generally then stored at 55° F until they are sold. If they are to be kept for several months, they should be stored near 30° F which is close to the freezing temperature of the egg. Some research workers have reported that flavor differences were more apparent in oil-treated than in untreated eggs stored under the same conditions. It is to be expected that flavor of treated eggs will be more nearly like the newly laid eggs than will that of untreated eggs. Inasmuch as few people have an opportunity to become accustomed to the flavor of newly laid eggs, it must still be determined what the term "fresh egg" really means to the consumer.

The producer who wishes to shell treat eggs for home storage may either oil treat them or immerse them in boiling water for only five seconds; the second treatment closes the pores by coagulating a thin film of white on the interior of the shell. Waterglass solution also closes the pores. Shell treatments should not be regarded as substitutes for low temperatures in egg storage, but as additional aids to retain original properties.

Radiation and pasteurization of shell eggs are being investigated. Both methods have possibilities for prolonging the shelf life of shell eggs.

Liquid egg may be kept for long periods of time by freezing. Eggs cannot be easily frozen in the shell because the shell may burst; they are therefore broken out and frozen whole or separated. One disadvantage of frozen whole egg or yolk is the phenomenon of change in the physical character of the yolk—it becomes irreversibly pasty and then does not blend easily with other ingredients. Additions of sugar or salt to the yolk, or the thorough blending of the white with yolk decreases the pastiness but limits the use of the egg. Whites are not altered during freezing and may be frozen separately. Eggs may be broken out of the shell and frozen in individual containers; this is not practical since cooking does not restore the liquid quality of the yolk desired by many in poached, fried, and soft-cooked eggs, and the extra handling increases costs.

Many industries use frozen eggs even when shell eggs are readily available in order to have the advantages of less handling, no breakage, and more uniform quality than in shell eggs.

The pasteurization of liquid egg before freezing not only decreases pastiness but also gives other advantages. The contents of newly laid eggs may be entirely devoid of microorganisms; however, they become contaminated very quickly when broken out and serve as a good medium for the growth of microorganisms. When temperatures as high as 140° F for four minutes are employed for pasteurization of whole eggs, all of the disease-producing microorganisms and 99 per cent of the nonpathogens are destroyed. Pasteurization is also desirable as a preliminary treatment before the drying of egg products. Not only are microorganisms destroyed, but also the liquid egg is dried more easily.

Dried egg products are not readily available on the retail markets in the United States, but they are processed for use in mixes and other industrial purposes.

Care of Whole Shell Eggs

A chilled egg maintains its original qualities for a relatively long time and no noticeable changes take place in untreated shell eggs during two or three weeks in refrigerator storage. Even trained tasters cannot distinguish a flavor change in less than three weeks of refrigerator storage. The consumer who wishes high quality in eggs will generally be better satisfied if he buys at a store that refrigerates the eggs than if the eggs are held at room temperature. Eggs should then be re-frigerated in the home. The porous shell allows for absorption of flavors, and care should be taken not to have strong-flavored foods such as onions or cantaloupe close to eggs. Even oil-treated eggs can absorb flavors.

PREPARATION OF EGGS AND EGG DISHES

Eggs have so many different uses (Fig. 31), it is no wonder that they are found in every meal of the day and even with between-meal snacks. Eggs should be included in meal plans for all ages from infants to senior citizens. Although at least one egg per person per day is highly desirable, some people may prefer fewer. In using less egg than one per day it may be wise to combine them with other foods so as to have the advantages to be gained by combination of proteins.

No appreciable losses of nutrients occur during ordinary cooking of

Fig. 31. Eggs have so many different uses that they may be included in meal plans for all ages.

eggs. However, if the protein is toughened by high heat or prolonged cooking, a longer time is required for complete digestion. This could mean incomplete absorption during the time the food remains in the alimentary canal. Obviously, under these circumstances high heat or overcooking is undesirable.

Poached eggs may lose some of the water-soluble riboflavin from the white to the cooking liquid but if the liquid is used with toast or other foods, no waste will occur. Eggs scrambled in excessive fat might also lose some of their vitamin A to the fat. However, if only small amounts of fat are used in cooking, they would be consumed with the egg and there would be no loss.

Many variations of cookery make eggs popular in the breakfast menu (Fig. 32). Whether eggs are fried, poached, shirred (baked), cooked in the shell, scrambled, or made into omelets, the principles of cooking are identical. Eggs are cooked for several reasons:

1. To coagulate the proteins, which makes them more palatable and probably somewhat more easily digested.

2. To inactivate avidin, an enzyme which combines with biotin making that vitamin unavailable from raw egg white.

3. To destroy the microorganisms that may be present.

Newly laid or so-called "fresh" eggs usually are preferred for table use where appearance and flavor of the product are important and are not camouflaged by other ingredients. Older eggs may give the most tender omelets, sponge goods, and similar products because their proteins are more extensible than those of newly laid eggs.

General Principles of Egg Cookery

The treatment of eggs in food preparation may be varied according to the desired results. For example, eggs taken directly from the refrigerator will spread less during frying than eggs at room temperature since whites are more viscous at low temperatures. On the other hand, eggs for baked products, omelets, mayonnaise, and other purposes will beat up more easily and blend with other ingredients more satisfactorily if used at room temperature rather than at refrigerator temperature. Salt or acid added to cooking water in which eggs are to be poached, assists in minimizing the spreading of the egg. Sudden changes in temperature for cooked-in-the-shell eggs may crack the shell and permit the contents to leak out. Pricking or prewarming of the egg may prevent bursting of the shell.

Fig. 32. The breakfast egg need not become monotonous fare if the methods of preparation are varied from day to day. For example, foamy omelet (*a*), French omelet (*b*), fried (*c*), baked (*d*), or scrambled (*e*). (Courtesy of Poultry and Egg National Board, Chicago.)

B

C

D

E

Principles of egg cookery are similar to those for fish entailing merely the coagulation of soft proteins. Chicken eggs have several different kinds of proteins, but all egg proteins are soft and heat-coagulable at temperatures no higher than 158° F. Obviously, egg proteins quickly become overcooked at temperatures of 212° F (boiling water) or higher as in frying. On the other hand, if the coagulation is allowed to proceed too slowly, a very undesirable green color is produced. This discoloration is usually more noticeable on the bottom of omelets and around the yolks of hard-cooked eggs than in other types of preparation. The green color is caused by the formation of ferrous sulfide for which the white furnishes the sulfur and the yolk the iron. In the cooking of eggs in the shell, heat drives the sulfur to the yolk where it reacts with the iron. The green deposit can be kept to a minimum by cooling the cooked egg quickly by plunging it into ice water.

Eggs that have been shell-treated to close the pores of the shell soon after they are laid retain the acidic qualities of the newly-laid eggs to a large extent. Such eggs show less green deposit around the yolk when hard-cooked than do untreated eggs, and the proteins remain tender even if cooked at boiling temperatures.

Untreated eggs will not develop the undesirable effects of either too rapid or too slow cooking if they are simmered just long enough to coagulate the egg to the desired stage. Simmering temperature can easily be maintained for poaching and for the cooked-in-the-shell eggs. Also, a simmering temperature may be attained in "pan-cooking" by heating over boiling water. This is especially desirable for scrambled eggs but even fried, omelets, cooked-in-the-shell, and poached as well as steam-poached eggs can be cooked evenly with little attention in the double boiler over boiling water. The heat controlled unit in all cases can be used in place of the double boiler. If pans in which eggs are to be cooked are oiled and heated to the desired cooking temperature before the egg is added, there should be little or no annoyance with sticking to the pan. Beaters and other utensils used with raw egg should be rinsed in cold water rather than hot so that the egg is not cooked onto the utensils.

Ingredients added to eggs change the coagulation temperature of the proteins. Salt and acid hasten the coagulation of egg proteins by lowering the coagulation temperature. Sugar raises the coagulation temperature. Custards therefore require a longer time to bake than do unsweetened egg-milk mixtures. Sugar also delays coagulation in the beating of eggs. These principles and facts are applied in mixing and cooking procedures of various products.

General Uses for Eggs in Food Preparation

The unique physical-chemical properties of eggs account for the variety of roles that eggs play in food preparation. Raw eggs not only mix readily with other ingredients but also impart qualities that allow a great deal of variety in prepared dishes.

The ability of eggs to form stable foams makes possible a wide variety of airy products like meringue, soufflé, and sponge cakes. Usually the whites only are whipped because the yolk interferes with foam formation, and the yolks, if used, are carefully folded into the foam. Meringues, fluffy frostings, candies, kisses, and angel food cakes require whites only.

Freezing or drying preservation of egg whites does not destroy their foaming properties. Dried egg whites, however, may require different techniques in whipping because they may have been given special treatment to increase their shelf life.

Chemical changes that occur during the time eggs are held may affect the ease of foam formation and the volume of the foam, but egg whites can be used for foams just as long as the egg remains edible. The age of the egg is no more important to the volume of angel food cake than is the handling of the foam. Individuals who prefer older eggs for sponge goods than for other purposes base their preferences on familiarity with their responses to foaming.

The gelling of an egg-milk mixture is one of the important functions of eggs, as custards are popular throughout the world. The egg proteins are so liquid-loving (*hydrophilic*) that one egg will gel a cupful of milk. Milk is always used in preparing a custard because it furnishes calcium salts necessary to make a gel. A soft gel can also be formed with broth as the liquid if the broth contains sufficient calcium salts. Newly laid eggs coagulate more readily and give a slightly stiffer gel than older eggs. Sugar tenderizes custards; the more sugar desired, the more egg that will be required to form a strong gel.

One of the most spectacular roles of eggs in food preparation is that of a stabilizer in such emulsions as mayonnaise, Hollandaise sauce, and cream puffs. The term, emulsion, refers to a system in which one liquid is dispersed in droplets throughout another liquid without blending with it. In food, these are oil and water systems. In the absence of an emulsifying agent (stabilizing substance) the two liquids tend to separate as the mixture stands undisturbed.

Eggs may be used in puddings and ice creams to improve color, richness, texture, and flavor. Their proteins help in thickening, but puddings will be most satisfactory if the starch thickener is allowed to swell fully and cook thoroughly before eggs are added.

Eggs are useful as glazes for baked goods. Just a thin film of diluted egg spread over the surface of the product before baking makes the surface shiny. It will also help in the adhesion of seeds, seasonings, and decoration for the gourmet touch.

Broths and coffee are sometimes clarified of suspended particles by adding egg. As the egg coagulates, it enmeshes the suspended material and the strained liquid has more clarity and sparkle. A sufficient amount of white for clarification purposes clings to the shell when an egg is broken out so that the otherwise discarded shell portion can serve a useful purpose.

Other uses made of eggs include those of binding and coating agents. Egg proteins also add strength to structures for baked products. Meat loaf, poultry stuffing, meat or vegetable patties, and croquettes depend primarily upon eggs to hold their ingredients together during cooking. Croquettes are usually dipped in beaten eggs and then crumbs so that the cooked egg will form a film and thus decreases porosity of the food to take up less fat during cooking.

General Methods of Combining Eggs with Other Ingredients

There are no well-defined generalized methods of combining ingredients in preparation of egg dishes as there are in flour mixtures. However, many of the egg dishes are combined in similar sequences. In the interests of simplification and convenience in this text, the methods are classified as (1) basic custard, (2) emulsion, (3) whip-fold, and (4) meringue.

The basic custard method of mixing. This method is used for all types of custard products from the egg-milk custard to bread puddings, noodle rings, corn puddings, and many others that depend upon the gelling properties of eggs (Fig. 33). The raw egg material, usually whole egg, is blended and mixed with sugar, vegetable, or cereal, before the hot milk or cream sauce is added. Constant stirring of the egg mixture will insure even cooking as hot liquids are added. Heating of milk for custard making is not essential but shortens the time required for cooking the custard. Cooking times for these products depend only on the time required to coagulate egg proteins as other ingredients will not require further cooking. It should be remembered that sugar raises coagulation temperature of egg so that when it is used a longer cooking period than for unsweetened dishes such as corn pudding and noodle ring will be needed.

Fig. 33. One of the best known of the basic custard variations is the pumpkin pie. (Courtesy of American Institute of Baking, Chicago.)

Custard products will be more evenly cooked if water rather than air serves as the heating medium. Products to be cooked in the oven should be put into molds which can then be placed in a pan of water to the same depth as the depth of the custard. Preheating of the water used in the baking pan helps to shorten the baking time. During cooking in the oven the mold is not covered so that the surface of the custard may brown. Custard type pies are not cooked in water because it is important to bake the crust at the same time the custard is coagulating. The crust transfers the heat to the custard and maintains uniform heating.

A baked custard is completely gelled (done) when a knife inserted into the center has no custard clinging to it as it is withdrawn. Foods will continue to cook if left in the hot water even after their removal from the oven, and prompt cooling on racks is indicated for products that are not to be eaten while hot. These products should be thoroughly cooled before they are unmolded.

Custards may be cooked in a steamer rather than baked. They must be closely covered to prevent condensed steam from entering the food. Custards that are stirred during cooking will be fluid when cooked as the stirring breaks up the coagulum as it forms. Timing is especially important in cooking stirred custards because there is not much leeway between the coagulating and the curdling temperatures. As soon as the custard coats the spoon, cooking should be stopped. This can be done by promptly exchanging the hot water in the bottom of the double boiler for cold. If some curdling occurs in spite of this precaution, beating or straining may break the curdled particles into smoothness.

Many variations in dessert custard are possible through the addition of other ingredients such as cocoanut, orange, chocolate, and caramel. A caramel syrup increases the tendency of the custard to curdle but a thick caramel syrup may be put in the bottom of the baking dish to make "Creme Caramel." When the custard is turned out a thin caramel sauce will be over the unmolded custard. Extra eggs or only yolks in high proportion to the milk are the usual procedure for Creme Caramel.

Spoon bread, corn custard, and noodle rings are examples of custards used in main dishes. These may be made in many different variations also.

Puddings thickened primarily with starches such as cornstarch, arrowroot, and tapioca are also mixed by the basic-custard method when they are to be enriched with eggs. A portion of the sugar should be added to the blended egg. The hot starch paste, which has already been thoroughly cooked, is added to the egg-sugar mixture with constant stirring. A few minutes of cooking over simmering water will be sufficient to complete coagulation of egg proteins, and the pudding may then be cooled.

The emulsion method of mixing. Mayonnaise and Hollandaise sauce are mixed by this method. The oil of egg yolk does not separate from other constituents in the yolk because it is naturally emulsified. The stabilizing material emulsifying the egg fat can be greatly "stretched" by careful handling, so that a cupful or more of oil can be permanently suspended in one-quarter of a cup of water or less. Powders such as mustard and paprika also assist in the stabilizing phenomenon.

Recipes for making mayonnaise usually call for one egg yolk. One egg yolk is only one tablespoonful of material, and the beater blades can barely reach the surface of this small quantity of egg, even when the smallest possible bowl is used. It is well therefore to add one tablespoonful of acid before beating is begun. Generally the seasonings are added immediately, also, in order to obtain whatever stabilizing effect they can give to the emulsion.

It is important to add only tiny amounts of oil at first. Generally recipes state to use no more than one-fourth teaspoonful portions. As the volume of the finished emulsion increases, larger portions may be added. A constant small stream may be added if the mixing is done electrically. Additional amounts of the acid can be added after all the oil has been used, or during the beating period if the emulsion becomes too thick for easy beating. Emulsions may break during beating usually because the oil has been added too rapidly at some point. If this occurs, no amount of further beating will re-establish the emulsion unless a new start is made. The curdled material should be set aside and a new starter placed in the mixing bowl. If desired, another yolk may be used as the starter but this is not necessary. The most practical ingredient to use is a tablespoonful of the acid unless it has all been previously added. If all of the acid has been used, water can be used, or egg white, but the resultant mayonnaise will be thinner than mayonnaise with less water. The curdled material is added to the starter in the manner as oil would be used for a fresh emulsion. An effort should be made to add as much of the yolk portion as possible at the beginning of this beating period.

The greater the proportion of oil to acid and egg, the stiffer the emulsion. Warm oils emulsify more rapidly than cold oils. Pauses in beating as when oil is added in hand beating, assist in the emulsification process.

Emulsions can be expected to be completed in a few seconds in an electric blender, in 5 to 7 minutes with an electric mixer, and in possibly 10 minutes with a hand rotary beater. Fast beating may whip air into the mixture, but a reasonably rapid rate of beating must be maintained to obtain small oil droplets. The smaller the size of the oil globules dispersed in the water, the stiffer the emulsion will be.

Hollandaise sauce differs from mayonnaise in that the fat portion is butter and the acid is lemon, also more egg yolks and less fat are used so that the emulsion may be more fluid than mayonnaise. The butter must be melted, and generally the emulsion is mixed over hot water to prevent congealing of the butter and also to partially cook the yolks. The sauce should be served as soon as completed.

Cream puffs owe their existence to the emulsifying properties of egg also. However, it is necessary to have a very high proportion of water present in a cream puff batter so that steam can form rapidly and "puff" the mixture. A special procedure, the *roux* or paste method, is used for mixing cream puffs.

In making the roux the other ingredients are formed into a thick paste before the eggs are added. The fat and liquid are heated to simmering and the flour is added quickly and stirred. Cooking is continued until the mixture thickens and leaves the sides of the pan. The fat is thus temporarily emulsified in the paste but would not be retained in baking without the addition of the egg. The eggs may be added unbeaten if desired; the important point is to mix the batter thoroughly so that the eggs will permanently stabilize the emulsion. If too much evaporation of water has taken place in cooking the roux, the emulsion will break during baking, and the paste will not puff. The cooking of the roux makes the batter thick enough to hold its shape when dropped although the proportion of flour to liquid is the same as in the pour batter for popovers. Cream puffs are generally baked but the batter can also be cooked in deep fat as is done for some European delicacies.

Water is commonly used as the liquid for cream puffs, but milk or fruit juices make equally satisfactory sources of liquid. Butter is usually the preferred fat for its flavoring qualities, but other fats of desirable flavors may be used. Bacon drippings make a desirable flavor in a puff to be used as a base for creamed eggs or meat for a main dish. Flour with a strong gluten (all purpose) is preferred to obtain large volume and thin shells.

Whip-fold method of mixing. This procedure is used for egg dishes that employ the foaming properties of eggs. The whites are usually separated from the yolks and beaten to a stiff but soft foam into which other ingredients are carefully incorporated by a gentle lifting of a part of the foam and folding over itself. The formation of a strong but soft foam is very important. A dry foam breaks as one attempts to fold ingredients into it. At optimum stiffness, the cells will be tiny but the shininess will be retained (see Fig. 34). Thorough mixing of the ingredients by folding rather than by stirring is necessary for most of the products mixed with this technique.

The type of product is dependent upon the kind and amount of the ingredients folded into the beaten egg whites. These products are many and varied and include the following:

Fruit whips in which sweetened fruit is folded into the foam.

Puffy Omelets in which only seasoning and egg yolk are added. One tablespoon of liquid may be added to make the omelet more tender, but this liquid is generally not milk since milk might destroy the egg foam unless thoroughly blended with the yolk. Puffy omelets are usually partially cooked in a small amount of fat on top of the range and then finished in the oven.

Fig. 34. At optimum stiffness, the egg white foam will have tiny cells, will hold its shape, and will shine. (Courtesy of Poultry and Egg National Board, Chicago.)

Soufflés are dishes in which a thick white sauce (see Chapter 5) is mixed with the yolks and a main ingredient such as fish, ham, vegetable, or cheese is added. Dessert soufflés are sweetened and contain flavoring ingredients such as melted chocolate, grated orange, and the like. The yolk mixture is folded into the foam and the soufflé is baked in a mold like the custard products (see Fig. 35).

Timbales are similar to soufflés except that the liquid, usually milk, is not made into a white sauce. Timbales are usually molded in individual size portions and are most frequently made with a vegetable.

Fondues are similar to soufflés except that the liquid, usually milk, is thickened with dry bread. The yolks and other ingredients as desired are mixed with the soaked bread and the whole folded into the egg-white foam. They are baked in water as are custards.

Sponge-type cakes in which flour and sugar are added to the foam, may be made by the whip-fold technique. An acid, cream of tartar or lemon juice, and salt are added to increase the stability of the foam before the flour-sugar mixture is folded into it. The mixing is similar to that described under meringue method.

EGGS AT ANY MEAL · 135

Fig. 35. The yolk white-sauce mix of the soufflé is gently folded into the stiffly beaten white (*a*), and the resulting mixture is baked like a custard (*b*). (Courtesy of Poultry and Egg National Board, Chicago.)

Meringue method of mixing. Meringue implies the gradual addition of sugar when beating an egg-white foam. Sugar stabilizes the foam, and less of the incorporated air is lost when ingredients are added than when added to a plain egg-white foam. Meringues may be used alone or made into products after various ingredients have been folded into them. These products include the following:

Soft meringues, which have a relatively low proportion of sugar added to the egg white. Flavoring and salt may be the only other ingredients. They are usually used as a topping on pies and are usually baked onto the pie. These can be very decorative in themselves or served with garnishes such as shaved chocolate, toasted cocoanut, or nutmeats.

Hard meringues, which have a very high proportion of sugar added to the egg-white and are baked at low temperatures for a long time in order for them to be crisp instead of chewy. Different flavors (instant coffee, for example) and colors add variety to meringue shells. The meringue is shaped like a cup so that it may be filled with pudding, fruit, or ice cream after baking (see Fig. 36).

Small kisses or macaroons may be made from meringue. Cocoanut, nuts, prepared cereals, or other ingredients are folded into the meringue, and the mixture is dropped by spoonfuls onto paper and baked in a moderate oven. The baked product can easily be removed by slightly wetting the under side of the paper.

Sponge-type cakes may be made with a meringue by folding the ingredients into the meringue. This has the advantage of a stronger foam than formed in the whip-fold method as the sugar used in producing the meringue prevents the liquid from draining out of the foam. In addition, sugar retards foam formation, and a beginner is less likely to overbeat the egg white than when no sugar is added during beating.

Fig. 36. Hard meringues may be made into tortes and served with fruit. (Courtesy of Sperry Operations, General Mills, Inc., Minneapolis.)

Fig. 37. Angel-food cakes contain no egg yolks and rely on steam and air from the egg white foam for leavening. (Courtesy Sperry Operations, General Mills, Inc.)

Specific Methods for Sponge-Type Cakes

True sponge cakes contain the same number of whites as yolks; sunshine cakes contain more whites than yolks; and angel-food cakes contain no yolks (see Fig. 37). Sponge goods made with yolks only must have additions of liquid and baking powder because yolks do not form stable foams.

The type of egg for sponge goods is not important. Excellent angel cakes were made from duck eggs in the Whittier College laboratories. Miller investigated sponge goods from eggs of different market grades, eggs of varying freshness, frozen eggs, pasteurized eggs, and dried eggs. Except for dried eggs of poor quality, all types of eggs produced sponge cakes of good volume and texture.

In all types of sponge goods, eggs are used as carriers of air, and they also furnish liquid for steam formation during baking. The chief difficulty encountered in making sponge cakes is the retention of air in the beaten eggs while they are being combined with the other ingredients. The air in the egg white alone is not responsible for the leavening. Steam is entrapped in the air pockets and expands them. The steam accounts for two or three times more of the volume increase than does the air, but without the air pockets the steam escapes into the atmosphere instead of leavening.

Air is incorporated into egg white with either a whisk or rotary type beater. The volume may be greater if the whisk is used, but the rotary beater is faster and seems to give cakes with finer texture than the whisk accomplishes. If the rotary beater is electrically driven, care must be taken not to overbeat the white. The gradual addition of part of the sugar in the making of a meringue slows down the coagulation of the egg protein during beating, but even meringue can be overbeaten.

Acids not only help to stabilize the egg foams but also serve to tenderize the cake and to bleach light yellow pigments of egg white and flour. This is especially noticeable in angel food cakes, which are yellow and coarse when acid is omitted. Cream of tartar is the usual acid used in angel food and lemon juice in sponge cakes. Fruit juices other than lemon are not acid enough so that too much liquid might be added in an attempt to obtain sufficient acid. Rind of orange is useful, however, in giving a desirable flavor to these cakes.

Fine granular sugar gives the best grain in cakes, but other sweeteners such as syrup and honey may be used. When syrup is used, consideration must be given to the liquid content.

Cake flour produces the finest grain in sponge-type cakes, but other flours may be used. Cake flour absorbs less moisture than do flours with stronger gluten (see Chapter 6). If it is desired to add cocoa or chocolate, the flour content is reduced to compensate for the thickening action of these products.

Mixing procedures for any type of sponge goods are similar. Better volumes of foam are obtained and whipping is easier if ingredients are at room temperature than if they are cold. Egg whites should be beaten in a bowl large enough to hold the complete cake batter. The acid and salt are added to the egg whites as soon as they are foamy. One-fourth of the sugar may be mixed with the flour to separate the particles thus making incorporation of flour easier.

With an electric mixer it might be well to begin adding sugar as soon as acid and salt are added, but it will be easier when hand beating if the sugar is added after soft peaks are formed. The meringue should be stiff but not dry and will be stiffer than the egg foam without sugar.

In the making of true sponge and sunshine cakes, the yolks will be easier to incorporate into the meringue if they are beaten to lemon-yellow color and blended with the flour-sugar portion of the recipe. Lemon juice and rind may also be added to the yolks. The yolk mixture is then poured over the meringue and blended with approximately fifty to sixty fold strokes. The importance of optimum amount of mixing of flour mixtures is discussed in Chapter 6.

In the making of angel food cakes, the flour is sifted with a portion of the sugar and folded into the meringue in small portions. If the dry ingredients are added in four portions and each sifted over the foam and incorporated with approximately fifteen fold strokes, there should be sufficient blending of ingredients without serious loss of air from the foam.

Tube pans have become traditional for sponge-type cakes so that the delicate structure can "get better hand holds." The tube cuts the wall-to-wall distance to less than half the diameter of the pan. Pans are used unoiled so that the cake can cling and climb on the walls.

Browning of all sides of a cake is considered desirable, and it is therefore baked without water, unlike the other egg products. Sponge and angel foods are more moist if baked at medium temperatures of 350 to 360° F. The sugar content of these cakes is high enough to prevent the egg protein from becoming tough at this temperature.

The baked cake is cooled in an inverted position on a rack to allow the pliable cells to stretch as much as possible while acquiring their full rigidity. The rack should permit circulation of air so that the cake does not steam itself out of the pan.

The flavor of sponge cakes can be varied by additions of poppy seeds, sesame seeds, or nuts, or by serving them with fruit, whips, nuts, and other accompaniments. Nuts, fruits, and whips will also improve the nutritive value of the cake.

Cake rolls such as jelly roll and chocolate roll (Fig. 38) are usually made of a sponge-type batter that is baked in a thin sheet and rolled

Fig. 38. Cake rolls are usually made from sponge-type batters that are baked in thin sheets and rolled while warm. (Courtesy of American Institute of Baking, Chicago.)

while still warm and pliable. Waxed paper in a shallow pan allows quick and easy removal of the cake. It should be rolled as soon as taken from the oven so that it assumes the desired shape when cooled. A flexible material such as a towel, foil, or heavy paper is sprinkled with sugar so that the cake will not stick to it and the hot cake is turned onto this and the baking paper is removed. If the sides of the cake are crusty, they are quickly cut off. Beaten jelly is spread onto the jelly-roll cake and the sheet rolled like a scroll with the jelly inside. The cloth can be a help while rolling the cake and then used as a wrap during the cooling. Rolls that are to be filled later with whipped cream or other material, are shaped and cooled first. They must be opened carefully for filling and then rerolled.

Basic proportions of the various egg dishes and method of mixing, with baking times and temperatures, that the authors have found satisfactory for laboratory use for one student, are summarized in Tables 13 and 14. The nutritive value of these foods is given in Table 15.

PLANNED-OVERS FOR EGGS

No matter how eggs are cooked, no left-overs need be discarded. Scrambled eggs, for example, can be rubbed into a paste, seasoned, and used in hors-d'oeuvres or sandwiches. Fried, poached, and even scrambled left-overs can be used in salads, creamed, or put into casseroles just as hard-cooked eggs in general are used. If extra eggs are hard-cooked and kept refrigerated, they will be handy for garnishes or casseroles. They keep well if left in the shell. However, if one is experiencing difficulty with peeling of hard-cooked eggs, they may be broken out into a mold and cooked out of the shell. A narrow loaf pan makes a satisfactory mold. The eggs should be covered tightly and steamed. The cooked egg can then be sliced to the desired thickness. This type of hard-cooked egg is becoming known as "Egg-wich." Hard-cooked eggs can also be pickled, and beet juice for this purpose adds a delightful color.

Some homemakers frequently have yolks accumulate from products employing only whites. Custards with yolks only have a very good flavor. Two yolks are approximately equivalent in thickening power to one whole egg. The yolks can also be used by cooking them whole in water and they are ready for garnishes or casserole ingredients. Raw yolks can be held over a few days in the refrigerator if desired, but will form a hard crust unless covered with water or oil. Whites may

Table 13. EGG DISHES—GELS AND EMULSIONS: PROPORTION OF INGREDIENTS, METHODS OF MIXING, BAKING TIMES AND TEMPERATURES, YIELDS, AND CHARACTERISTICS OF GOOD PRODUCTS

Product	Eggs		Salt	Fat		Sugar		Liquid		
	No.	Wt. gm.		Meas.	Wt. gm.	Meas.	Wt. gm.	Type	Meas.	Wt. gm.
Gels:										
Custard, soft	1 whole	48	⅛ tsp.	...	...	2 Tb.	25	Milk	1 C.	244
Custard, baked	1 whole	48	⅛ tsp.	...	...	2 Tb.	25	Milk	1 C.	244
Pudding, starch	1 whole	48	¼ tsp.	...	...	2 Tb.	25	Milk	1 C.	244
Pudding, vegetable	1 whole	48	¼ tsp.	...	...	2 Tb.	25	Milk	1 C.	244
Emulsions:										
Cream Puffs	2 whole	96	½ tsp.§	¼ C.	50	...	...	Water or Milk	½ C.	122
Hollandaise sauce	2 yolks	36	⅛ tsp.	½ C.	100	...	...	Lemon	2 Tb.	30
Mayonnaise	1 yolk	18	¼ tsp.	1 C.	200	...	½ tsp.	Vinegar	3 Tb.	45

Product	Other Ingredients	Method of Mixing	Cooking		Yield in Av. Portions	Characteristics of a Good Product
			Time min.	Temperatures* °F		
Gels:						
Custard, soft	½ tsp. vanilla	Basic custard	6–10	210	2 servings (½ C. each)	(1)
Custard, baked	½ tsp. vanilla, nutmeg if desired	Basic custard	30–40†	325 (oven)	2 servings (½ C. each)	(2)
Pudding, starch	1 Tb. cornstarch (15 gm.), ½ tsp. vanilla	Basic custard	15 for starch 2 for egg	210	2 servings (½ C. each)	(3)
Pudding, vegetable	1 C. chopped vegetable (250 gm.)	Basic custard	30–40†	325 (oven)	2 servings (½ C. each)	(4)

Emulsions:

Cream Puffs	½ C. flour (55 gm.)	Roux, cooked eggs beaten in last	2–3 for Roux 45–60 for puffs‡	400 (oven)	6 servings (3 in. diameter)	(5)
Hollandaise sauce	Herbs if desired	Emulsion	2–3	210	5 servings (2 Tb. each)	(6)
Mayonnaise	¼ tsp. dry mustard	Emulsion	. . .	. . .	10 servings (2 Tb. each)	(7)

* 210°F indicates over hot water or the use of a controlled heat source

† Dish containing custard may be placed in a pan of hot water for baking

‡ Puffs may be tested for doneness by taking out one and cooling a few minutes. If necessary, reduce heat in order to dry without excessive browning.

§ Less salt may be used if fat is salted.

(1) Smooth with no separation; consistency of thick cream.

(2) Jelly-like; no seepage; uniform texture with no holes.

(3) Similar to soft custard but thicker; very smooth.

(4) Similar to baked custard; no seepage.

(5) Crisp hollow shell; few moist curtains inside. Golden brown.

(6) Smooth; dark yellow; more fluid than mayonnaise; tart.

(7) Homogeneous; stiff enough to hold shape; smooth; tart.

Table 14. EGG DISHES—FOAMS: PROPORTIONS OF INGREDIENTS, METHODS OF MIXING, BAKING TIMES AND TEMPERATURES, YIELD, AND CHARACTERISTICS OF GOOD PRODUCTS

Product	Eggs		Salt	Fat		Sugar		Liquid		
	No. separated	Wt., gm.		Meas.	Wt., gm.	Meas.	Wt., gm.	Type	Meas.	Wt., gm.
Cake, angel food	½ C. whites	120	1/16 tsp.	...	...	½ C.	100	...	...	...
Cake, jelly roll	2 whites	60								
	2 yolks	36	⅛ tsp.	1 Tb.	15	½ C.	100	Water	2 Tb.	30
Cake, sponge	2 whites	60	⅛ tsp.	...	...	⅓ C.	66	Lemon juice	1 Tb.	15
	2 yolks	36								
Fondue, Tuna	2 whites	60	¼ tsp.	1 Tb.	15	...	...	Milk	⅔ C.	162
	2 yolks	36								
Meringue, hard	1 white	30	⅛ tsp.	...	...	⅓ C.	66	Water	1 tsp.	
Meringue, soft	3 whites	90	¼ tsp.	...	...	6 Tb.	75	Water	1 Tb.	15
Pudding, lemon upside down	1 white	30	⅛ tsp.	...	...	½ C.	100	Milk	½ C.	122
	1 yolk	18						Lemon juice	1½ Tb.	22
Omelet, puffy	1 white	30	⅛ tsp.	1 Tb.	15	...	...	Water	1 Tb.	15
	1 yolk	18								
Soufflé, cheese	2 whites	60	¼ tsp.	2 Tb.	30	...	...	Milk	½ C.	122
	2 yolks	36								
Soufflé, chocolate	2 whites	60	¼ tsp.	2 Tb.	30	⅓ C.	66	Milk	½ C.	122
	2 yolks	36								
Timbale, vegetable	1 white	30	¼ tsp.	...	...	...	...	Milk	½ C.	122
	1 yolk	18								

Product	Other Ingredients	Method of Mixing	Cooking		Yield in Av. Portions	Characteristics of a Good Product
			Time, min.	Temperature, °F		
Cake, angel food	½ tsp. cream tartar, ⅓ C. flour (33 gm.)	Meringue	30–35	350 (oven)	5 servings (1 cake 6 in. diameter)	(1)
Cake, jelly roll	½ tsp. baking powder, ½ C. flour (50 gm.), ½ C. jelly	Meringue	12–15	370 (oven)	5 servings (1 sheet of 8 x 10 x 1 in.)	(2)

Cake, sponge	¼ tsp. cream tartar, ⅓ C. flour (33 gm.), ½ tsp. grated lemon rind	Meringue	30-35	350 (oven)	5 servings similar to angel food	(3)
Fondue, Tuna	3 slices bread, 3 oz. tuna, seasoning desired	Whip-fold	30-40*	325 (oven)	2 servings (1 C.)	(4)
Meringue, hard	⅛ tsp. cream tartar, ¼ tsp. flavoring	Meringue	50-60	225 (oven)	2 servings (3 in. diameter)	(5)
Meringue, soft	¼ tsp. cream tartar, ¼ tsp. flavoring	Meringue	10-15	375 (oven)	1 nine in. pie	(6)
Pudding, lemon upside down	1½ Tb. flour (10 gm.), ½ tsp. grated lemon rind	Whip-fold (leave lumpy with egg white foam)	30-35* (bake in small cups)	325 (oven)	3 servings (½ C.)	(7)
Omelet, puffy	Herbs, pepper as desired	Whip-fold	5 on top range 15-20 oven	350 (oven)	1 serving	(8)
Soufflé, cheese	2 Tb. flour (13 gm.), ½ C. grated cheese (60 gm.)	Whip-fold	30-40*	325 (oven)	2 servings (1 C.)	(9)
Soufflé, chocolate	2 Tb. flour (13 gm.), 1 oz. chocolate, ½ tsp. vanilla	Whip-fold	30-40*	325 (oven)	3 servings (⅔ C.)	(10)
Timbale, vegetable	¾ C. vegetable (200 gm.), seasoning if desired	Whip-fold	30-40*	325 (oven)	2 servings (½ C.)	(11)

* Dish containing product may be placed in a pan of hot water for baking.

(1) Light brown; macaroon-like crust; symmetrical top; tender; moist white crumb; fine grained texture.
(2) Similar to sponge cake but lighter brown and drier crumb.
(3) Similar to angel food.
(4) Golden brown top; moist spongy interior; fully gelled.
(5) Delicately browned; crisp; dry and not chewy.
(6) Delicately browned; not chewy; easy to cut through.
(7) Delicate brown; spongy in upper part with pudding on lower half. Invert when cooled to have fully gelled pudding over a cake. Serve with whipped cream.
(8) Airy, golden brown; tender, moist. (Add jelly, cheese, etc. if desired.)
(9) Golden brown top; moist spongy interior; cheese not stringy.
(10) Golden brown top; moist spongy interior; rich chocolate flavor.
(11) Golden brown top; moist foamy interior but fully gelled.

Table 15. NUTRITIVE VALUES OF ONE SERVING OF THE EGG PRODUCTS MADE WITH THE INGREDIENTS GIVEN IN TABLES 13 AND 14*

Product	Energy Value, Cal.	Pro-tein, gm.	Cal-cium, mg.	Iron, mg.	Vita-min A, I.U.	Thia-mine, mg.	Ribo-flavin, mg.	Nia-cin, mg.	Ascorbic Acid, mg.
Egg, whole	77	6	26	1.3	550	0.05	0.14	Tr.	0
Gels:									
Custard	170	7	157	0.7	470	0.07	0.28	0.15	0
Pudding, corn	150	7	89	1.2	692	0.14	0.26	1.22	0
Pudding, starch	194	8	160	0.8	470	0.08	0.28	0.20	0
Emulsions:									
Cream puff (shell)	140	3	14	0.7	150	0.06	0.07	0.03	0
Hollandaise sauce	220	1	11	0.5	220	0.02	0.02	...	4
Mayonnaise	200	...	2	0.1	55	...	...	...	0
Foams:									
Cake, angel food	113	3	3	0.1	0	0	0.08	0.10	0
Cake, jelly roll	250	3	10	0.6	220	0.02	0.06	0.07	0
Cake, sponge	127	3	10	0.6	220	0.04	0.06	0.04	0
Fondue, tuna	411	24	150	2.1	715	0.19	0.50	6.30	0
Meringue, hard	140	2	1	0	0	0	0.04	...	0
Meringue, soft for 9-in. pie	315	10	6	0.3	...	...	0.24	...	0
Pudding, lemon upside down	197	4	58	0.6	245	0.05	0.13	0.18	3
Omelet, puffy	177	6	26	1.3	550	0.05	0.14	...	0
Soufflé, cheese	355	16	305	1.8	1040	0.11	0.38	0.22	0
Soufflé, chocolate	300	7	77	1.4	440	0.07	0.20	0.32	0
Timble, spinach	65	5	70	1.4	5545	0.07	0.31	0.33	10

* Calculated from U.S.D.A. Handbook No. 8.

also be refrigerated and they keep somewhat longer than yolks; whites require only a tightly covered container. They will keep for a long time if frozen.

Cooked eggs retain their nutritive value as long as they remain edible. Cooked egg dishes, and especially creamed and custard products, should be stored in the refrigerator, however, not only to prolong edibility but also to avoid a type of food poisoning that develops easily in moist nonacid foods.

SUMMARY

An egg is nearly a complete food in itself, qualitatively speaking, but it requires three eggs to equal the caloric value and protein quantity of one four-ounce serving of lean meat. Eggs are especially important to the diet because of their easily assimilated iron and the unusually high biological value of their proteins. They also contribute B-complex vitamins and bone-building nutrients.

Market classes of eggs by both grades and sizes may be available to the consumer and priced accordingly. Cool storage temperatures are necessary to maintain the physical and chemical characteristics of newly laid eggs for the few weeks required for marketing. Cold storage, freezing, and drying successfully preserve eggs for longer storage periods.

The foaming, emulsifying, gelling, and binding properties of eggs make possible a wide variety of prepared products. In addition, eggs supplement the physical characteristics as well as the nutritive value of many flour mixtures. This versatility leads to the possibility of "eggs in any meal."

Reading List

1. Dawson, E. H., C. Miller, and R. A. Redstrom, 1956, "Cooking quality and flavor of eggs as related to candled quality, storage conditions, and other factors," U.S.D.A. *Agr. Info. Bull.* 164.

2. Editorial, 1957, "Cholesterol biosynthesis," *Nutrition Reviews*, **15**:282.

3. Everson, G. J. and H. J. Souders, 1957, "Compositions and nutritive importance of eggs," *J. Amer. Diet. Assoc.*, **33**:1244.

4. Hansen, H. (Editor), 1957, *The World Almanac*, New York World-Telegram, New York.

5. Johnston, F. A., 1956, "Iron content of eggs," *J. Amer. Diet. Assoc.*, **32**:644.

6. Justin, M. M., L. O. Rust, and G. E. Vail, 1956, *Foods*, Houghton Mifflin Co., Boston, pp. 207–231.

7. Miller, C., L. D. Sanborn, and G. F. Stewart, 1957, "Incidence of internal defects in shell eggs," *Poultry Sci.,* **36**:1062.

8. Miller, C., and A. R. Winter, 1950, "The functional properties and bacterial content of pasteurized and frozen whole eggs," *Poultry Sci.,* **29**:88.

9. Ramonoff, A. L. and A. J. Ramonoff, 1949, *The Avian Egg,* John Wiley and Sons, Inc., New York.

10. Sanborn, L. D., C. Miller, and G. F. Stewart, 1957, "Blood spots: To what extent do consumers object?" *Poultry Processing and Marketing,* June 18.

11. Sharp, P. F., 1929, "What a week may do to an egg," *U. S. Egg and Poultry Magazine,* **35**:14.

12. Sherman, H. C. and C. S. Lanford, 1957, *Essentials of Nutrition,* The Macmillan Co., New York, pp. 367–370.

13. Suter, E. A., J. V. Harns, W. J. Stadelman, and B. A. McLaren, 1954, "Seasonal variations in quality of eggs as measured by physical and functional properties," *Poultry Sci.,* **33**:519.

14. Sweetman, M. D. and I. MacKellar, 1954, *Food Selection and Preparation,* John Wiley and Sons, New York, Chapter 11.

CHAPTER **5**

Fig. 39. Modern dairy herds are composed of several breeds of cattle to produce market milk in good volume and of desirable color and richness. (Courtesy of Whittier Sanitary Dairy, Whittier, California.)

CHAPTER 5 . . . MILK FOR ALL AGES

Milk, Cheese, and Ice Cream

MILK, AN IMPORTANT ITEM IN THE
    FAMILY FOOD PLANS

Minerals
Fat
Carbohydrates
Proteins
Vitamins
Fortified Milk

PROCESSED MILK AND MILK PRODUCTS

Pasteurization
Homogenization
Evaporation
Concentration
Dehydration
Fermentation
Cheese
Cream
Butter
Milk Foods
      Ice Cream
      Chocolate-Flavored Milk or Chocolate Drinks
      Malted Milk

GETTING THE MOST FOR THE FOOD MONEY THAT
    IS SPENT FOR MILK AND MILK PRODUCTS

Standards for Dairy Products
The Selection of Milk and Milk Products
      Milk
      Cheese
      Ice Cream and Sherbert
Storage of Milk and Milk Products

PREPARATION OF PRODUCTS RICH IN MILK

White Sauce and Products Made with White Sauces
    Milk Soups
    Milk Sauces
    Milk Gravies
    Milk Puddings
Milk Drinks
Frozen Milk Desserts
Whipped Milk Products
    Cream
    Evaporated Milk
    Dry Milk
Cheese Main Dishes, Appetizers, and Desserts

SUMMARY

READING LIST

MILK AND MILK PRODUCTS ARE NUTRITIONALLY IMPORTANT FOR all ages of our population, and properly require a relatively large percentage of the food dollar. As information has been gained concerning milk—its nutritive value, care, and use—the consumption of milk and milk products in the United States has increased. Also, the consumption of fluid milk has increased as the average family income has risen.

Grocery store, newspaper, and magazine advertisements proclaim the importance of various foods, giving dairy products a paramount place; nutritionists advocate a daily allotment of one quart of milk or its equivalent for each child and one pint for each adult. In spite of this, the per capita consumption of milk and milk products in the United States is not only far below accepted standards but also is below that of many other nations.

Milk is not only nutritious, but it is also a thirst-quenching beverage, and it is useful in many types of food preparation. An important ingredient in soups, casseroles, custards, puddings, baked products, and many desserts, its function is primarily that of furnishing the liquid, but in addition it gives substance and flavor. Milk enhances the browning of baked products. Also, it helps to maintain their freshness qualities, and baked products made with milk remain fresh somewhat longer than products made with water.

Milk can be processed to retain its nutritive value and palatability characteristics over a long period of time. Cheese, the concentrated curd of milk, will also keep well and is widely used in food preparation.

Food preparation principles for milk and cheese are based primarily on their protein content. Low cooking temperatures for products high in milk or cheese content are conducive to maintaining the soft tender quality of their proteins.

MILK, AN IMPORTANT ITEM IN THE FAMILY FOOD PLANS

Milk, although not an entirely perfect food, can serve as the entire diet of mammalian young during the first few months of life. It is a very important food in the diet for all ages because, in addition to fats, carbohydrates, and proteins, milk contains all of the vitamins and minerals known to be needed by man (Fig. 40). Certain of the nutrients, however, are not present in appreciable quantities, notably

A

Fig. 40. Two families of rats demonstrate the need for milk in the diet; family A looks well-nourished on an adequate diet containing milk whereas comparable family B on an isocaloric diet without milk, has poor appearance. (Courtesy of Whittier Sanitary Dairy, Whittier, California.)

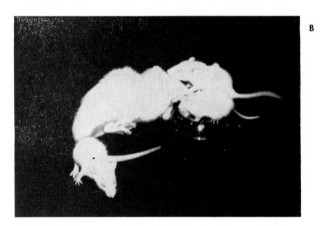

B

iron, ascorbic acid, and possibly vitamin A. For a summary of the dietary contributions made by one quart of milk or its equivalent in milk products see Table 16.

Minerals

The minerals of milk are its most publicized constituents and the word, "milk," usually brings to mind the terms *calcium* and *phosphorus*. This is good, because milk is such an important source of these nutrients that it is difficult to secure the minimum daily recommended

Table 16. THE NUTRITIONAL CONTRIBUTIONS OF ONE QUART OF FLUID MILK AND PRODUCTS DERIVED FROM APPROXIMATELY ONE QUART OF MILK*

Product	Measure	Energy Value, Cal.	Protein, gm.	Calcium, mg.	Iron, mg.	Vitamin A, I.U.	Thiamine, mg.	Riboflavin, mg.	Niacin, mg.	Ascorbic Acid, mg.
Milk, Cow's:										
Whole	1 qt.	666	34.2	1152	0.7	1550	0.35	1.68	1.1	13
Non-fat	1 qt.	350	34.4	1210	0.7	40	0.35	1.75	1.1	13
Evaporated	2 cup	692	35.2	1224	0.8	2020	0.24	1.82	1.0	6
Sweetened condensed	1½ cup	1472	37.2	1252	0.9	1950	0.24	1.82	0.9	5
Dried whole	1 cup	630	33.0	1215	0.7	1790	0.39	1.87	0.8	8
Dried non-fat	1 cup	434	42.7	1560	0.7	50	0.42	2.35	1.4	9
Instant non-fat†	1⅓ cup	358	37.6	1300	0.7	50	0.34	1.85	1.4	9
Chocolate flavored	1 qt.	740	32.0	1090	0.7	910	0.32	1.59	1.0	10
Buttermilk	1 qt.	348	34.2	1152	0.7	40	0.35	1.74	1.1	13
Yoghurt†	1 qt.	666	34.2	1152	0.7	1550	0.35	1.68	1.1	13
Milk, Goat's	1 qt.	654	32.2	1259	1.0	1550	0.39	1.04	2.8	10
Cheese:										
Cheddar	4 oz.	452	28.4	824	1.2	1600	0.04	0.48	Tr.	0
Processed cheddar	4 oz.	420	25.4	764	1.2	1480	Tr.	0.48	Tr.	0
Cheese food, cheddar	4 oz.	368	23.2	648	0.8	1212	0.04	0.64	Tr.	0
Cottage	4 oz.	108	22.0	108	0.4	40	0.04	0.36	Tr.	0

* Values from U.S.D.A. Agricultural Handbook No. 8.
† Values from Bowes, A. deP. and C. F. Church, *Food Values of Portions Commonly Used*, Anna dePlanter Bowes, Philadelphia, 1951.

intake of calcium unless liberal amounts of milk or milk products are included in the diet. Milk not only contains these minerals in high concentration but it also may contain the vitamin D necessary for their absorption. Eleven heads of lettuce; 7 pounds of liver; 44 eggs; or 1 pound of cooked collards would be required to provide, in one food, the 1,152 milligrams calcium contributed by 1 quart of milk.

The relative amount of *iron* in milk is small; however, milk is designed as a food for young mammals, and they are usually born with a supply of iron stored in their livers sufficient to last for several months or until they can eat other foods. The iron content of milk can be supplemented by the use of eggs, especially the yolks. For example, a custard made with 1 cup of milk and 2 egg yolks would contain 2.6 milligrams of iron or approximately one-fifth of the daily recommended allowance for adults.

In some areas of the world milk is an excellent source of *iodine;* however, this is dependent upon the amount of iodine present in the water or the feed of the animal.

Fat

The percentage of fat (average 3.5 per cent) in whole milk varies and is an indication of the energy value of the milk. The carbohydrate content remains relatively constant. Under normal conditions the fat and protein have a definite percentage relationship to each other. That is, as the percentage of fat increases the percentage of protein also increases, and the percentage of water decreases.

The fat of milk is termed butterfat. It is highly emulsified in its natural state, and homogenization serves to further this dispersion, a practice favoring digestion and absorption. Butterfat is made up of larger amounts of those fatty acids believed to be essential in human nutrition than are most other animal fats. It is one of the three natural foods (milk, eggs, liver) that contains pre-formed vitamin A. Milk fat also contains pre-formed vitamin D and precursors of both vitamin A and vitamin D.

It would therefore seem to be good nutritional practice to use whole milk sources—fresh, canned, dried, or soured milk or whole milk cheese—in meal plans. If one prefers nonfat milk for economy, flavor, or convenience, then cream, butter, or fortified margarine should normally be included in the diet. At least one tablespoon of fat should be included for each cup of milk. If this makes the day's total intake of fat too high, meat or other food containing fat might profitably be decreased.

Carbohydrates

Lactose (milk sugar) is the predominant carbohydrate of milk and is considered by some physicians to be superior to other sugars in the diet of infants. Lactose is conducive to the growth of the friendly acid-forming bacteria, and because acid in the intestinal tract is essential for the absorption of calcium and phosphorus, lactose may favor the absorption of these minerals. Lactose is changed also to lactic acid during the production of the various soured or fermented milks. The lactose not utilized by the bacteria in either case is digested and absorbed as are the other carbohydrates in the diet.

A very small amount of lactose is retained with the curd when it is removed from milk during the making of cheese; the remainder is left in the whey, which is frequently put into animal feeds. The small amount that is originally extracted with the curd is changed to lactic acid during an aging process so that cheese contributes little, if any, of this important source of carbohydrate to the diet.

Protein

The proteins of milk are almost completely digested and absorbed, and collectively they contain all of the essential amino acids. These amino acids are in a proportion good for growth and maintenance of body tissues. Because milk protein has this excellent assortment of amino acids, it can supplement the proteins of cereals and other vegetable foods that are known to be low or entirely lacking in certain amino acids.

One quart (4 cups) of whole cow's milk contains approximately 34.2 grams of protein, or one-half of the suggested Daily Recommended Allowance of protein for the average adult. This amount is equivalent to that found in 5 ounces of sirloin, or 2 cups of baked beans.

Vitamins

Milk contains riboflavin in abundance and other members of the B-complex in appreciable quantity. The amount of the fat-soluble vitamins and their precursors is directly related to the amount present in the feed of the animals. Fat-soluble vitamins are carried by butterfat, which is emulsified and therefore readily absorbed from the intestinal tract. The absorption of the B-complex and other water-soluble vitamins is aided by the high percentage of water in milk.

As noted before, pre-formed vitamin A occurs only in foods of animal origin and milk is one of the best sources. The content in milk varies with the amount of carotene found in the feed of the animal, and the concentration of carotene may vary with the season in many sections of the nation. This seasonal variation is caused by feeding dry feeds without adequate vitamin A supplementation during the fall and winter months. The trend toward centralization of milk production to large dairies (Fig. 39) where the feed is very carefully supervised will eliminate much of this seasonal variation. One quart of milk provides approximately 1500 I. U. of vitamin A, which is equivalent to the amount in 3 eggs or 1/10 ounce of cooked beef liver.

Milk is one of four natural sources of vitamin D. However, the amount normally present in milk varies with the diet of the animal. The vitamin D content of milk can be augmented by several methods: (1) animals fed rich sources of this vitamin such as cod-liver or shark liver oil, irradiated yeast, or irradiated ergosterol will produce milk as much as thirty times richer in vitamin D than normally (2) vitamin D concentrates can be added directly to the milk; or (3) the milk can be irradiated by ultraviolet rays which convert 7-*dehydro-cholesterol* to vitamin D. Vitamin D in milk, as noted previously, is advantageous because of the role of this nutrient in the utilization of calcium and phosphorus by the body.

Pasteurized milk is not a reliable source of ascorbic acid, and infants who receive cow's milk should be given a good source of this vitamin.

Fortified Milk

Fortified milks are found in the markets and may contain added amounts of vitamin A, thiamine, riboflavin, niacin, vitamin C, iron, and iodine. Before buying fortified products the cost and the entire diet should be evaluated. The extra vitamins and minerals are generally not needed in diets utilizing all of the foods of the Daily Food Guide.

PROCESSED MILK AND MILK PRODUCTS

Processing treatments such as pasteurizing, homogenizing, evaporating, dehydrating, fermenting, freezing, and the production of cheese, cream, butter, and ice cream should be considered in relation to nutrition as well as in relation to the physical properties of the resulting product. It should be stated that in general processing does not greatly affect the nutritive value of milk. The ascorbic acid content is lowered and possibly the thiamine and vitamin B_{12} content are lowered, also.

Pasteurization

What is meant by pasteurization? It is the heating of a product to destroy both the pathogenic (disease-producing) microorganisms and most of those microorganisms that bring about fermentation (Fig. 41). Two types of pasteurization are commonly practiced: the *long-time, or hold, process* requires that the milk be heated to 143° F and held for thirty minutes; the *short-time, or high-temperature, process* requires that the milk be heated to either 163° F for fifteen seconds or to 175° F and cooled immediately. In each method of pasteurization the milk is cooled quickly. Either the high or the low temperature pasteurization produces safe milk.

Pasteurization by means of *electrical shocks* has been perfected, but this method has not been adopted for general use in the United States.

Fig. 41. Pasteurization produces safe milk. (Courtesy of the National Dairy Council, Chicago.)

Radiation as a means of pasteurization is in the experimental stages, but to date it has not been satisfactory.

The effect of pasteurization upon the nutritive value of milk has long been a controversial subject. Both of the common methods of pasteurization lower the ascorbic acid content and possibly the thiamine and vitamin B_{12} content of the milk. However, the destruction of disease-producing bacteria is without a doubt more important than the preservation of a relatively small amount of vitamins. In the United States health hazards have so decreased that many people have forgotten or have never known the horrors of epidemics of such diseases as diptheria, dysentery, typhoid, undulant fever, and others. Therefore, people may become lax in their insistence upon the use of disease prevention measures. The United States Public Health Service considers pasteurization combined with adequate refrigeration and protection from bacterial contamination during storage and handling as the only measures that will prevent all milk-borne diseases.

Milk that has been pasteurized or that has received other heat treatment forms a soft curd when it is mixed with acid or rennin. This soft curd is more nearly like the curd of human milk, and therefore it may be more easily and completely digested by humans than untreated milks.

Milk that has not been heat-treated is called *raw milk*. It may be sold simply as raw milk or it may be *certified raw milk*. The latter indicates that it conforms to the standards set up by the American Association of Medical Milk Commissions and meets very definite health and sanitation requirements. Certified raw milk is as safe as any raw milk but it is never as safe as pasteurized milk.

Certified pasteurized milk may also be sold. This is milk that conforms to health and sanitation standards of certified raw milk and in addition has been pasteurized.

Homogenization

Homogenization is a process in which the fat globules of the milk or milk product are reduced to approximately one-tenth the original size. The process by which this has always been accomplished is to force the product between metal plates under high pressure. However, the use of supersonics for homogenization is being instituted and has met with some success.

The emulsion that results from homogenization is very stable, and the fat no longer rises to the top of the milk. These smaller fat particles have a greater surface area than the original globules and, unless the milk is pasteurized and properly refrigerated, the fat will become rancid quickly. Homogenized milk has the same nutritive value as non-homogenized pasteurized milk; in addition, the small fat particles may be more readily digested and absorbed than those of the original milk.

Evaporation

Evaporation or the removal of part of the water from whole milk accomplishes two purposes: concentration of the nutrients and pasteurization. Sixty per cent of the water is removed in a vacuum pan at approximately 140° F, and the only change in the nutritive contents is the reduction of ascorbic acid and a slight loss of thiamine. Usually evaporated milk is fortified with vitamin D. When evaporated milk is reconstituted, its composition is very much like whole milk. (See Table 16.)

The evaporated product must be further treated to prevent spoilage, and the most common method is heating to destroy all microorganisms that grow at room temperature. The most widely used procedure is to fill cans, which are then sealed and subjected to relatively high temperatures. The heating results in flavor changes and some browning of the milk. A more recent process termed *aseptic canning* has been used. The fluid milk is rapidly heated and poured into sterilized cans in an aseptic manner. Less browning occurs in the latter method because the heat treatment is not as prolonged.

The heat treatment of the evaporated milk softens the curd. This, plus the fact that the milk is already sterilized, makes it an excellent food for infants. Many older children and adults who are not able to take fresh whole milk may find that evaporated milk will agree with them.

Evaporated milk has a cooked flavor, but this is not disliked by children who were given evaporated milk as infants and who did not have it entirely replaced by fresh milk. Evaporated milks in hot chocolate were preferred to fresh milks by many in a palatability test where the tasters did not know which milk they were given.[1]

In addition to the advantage gained in keeping qualities, the fact that water has been removed makes possible the use of more milk solids in such foods as gravies, mashed potatoes, other vegetables, and puddings, for one need not reconstitute the milk to original water content. Some individuals may prefer to receive their milk in these foods rather than have milk as a beverage.

Milk to which sugar is added before it is evaporated is known as

---

[1] Unpublished data, Cora Miller.

sweetened condensed milk. If this milk is heated after canning, it becomes very thick and brown. Only a few brands of this milk are found in the market, and its use is limited primarily to making desserts. The sugar content is so high (54 per cent) that with today's trend away from the over-rich desserts, it is not favorably received. Sweetened condensed milk should not be used in infant formulas because the sugar content is too high for the welfare of the baby.

Concentration

Pasteurized milk may be concentrated to approximately one-third of its original volume. The milk is concentrated in a vacuum and at a very low temperature, therefore, the flavor is not appreciably changed. This milk may be kept either in the refrigerator or it may be frozen. The advantages over whole fluid milk are in the storage space required, a somewhat longer keeping time, and the fact that, as with evaporated milk, large amounts of milk solids can be incorporated into foods if desired. In spite of these advantages this milk is not widely distributed.

Dehydration

Dehydrated milks may be whole, partially defatted, fat-free, or fermented (buttermilk). Creams also may be dehydrated. The milk is dried to a moisture content not exceeding 5 per cent. The *instant dried milks* are especially processed to make them quickly miscible with water. The only nutrient losses in the dehydration process are similar to those that occur in pasteurization.

Milk in powdered form can be added to baked products with the dry ingredients or it can be reconstituted and used as fluid milk. Quantities larger than the amounts designated may be used for reconstituting if it is desired to increase the concentration of milk solids over that found in regular fluid milk. This is a method of increasing milk in the diet without increasing the volume and might be considered a form of fortification. For many of our senior citizens who never learned to like milk, this can become a pleasant method of obtaining a pint of milk a day. The flavor of dehydrated milk has been greatly improved during the last decade and reconstituted dried milks make suitable beverages for any age.

Fermentation

When acid-forming microorganisms are permitted to grow in milk it is said to be fermented. These microorganisms utilize lactose of the milk and convert part or all of it to lactic acid. Some of the lactic acid unites with calcium caseinate—the protein fraction of the milk—forming calcium lactate and casein. When the acid content of the milk becomes relatively high, the casein forms a gel which makes the milk thick or clabbered.

Milk that is exposed to the air will become contaminated with microorganisms that cause fermentation. Many of these microorganisms produce end products of growth that have undesirable flavors and odors; therefore, most of the soured milks on the market are made from pasteurized milk to which special strains of microorganisms have been added. Each of these strains imparts a specific flavor and by the use of various strains Yami Yoghurt, buttermilk, Leban, Devonshire Cream, and other cultured milk products are developed.

Except for the change in lactose, fermented milks have the same nutritive properties as the original milk from which they are made. Some fermented milks are made from low fat milk (buttermilk) and others may have extra milk solids in them (yoghurt). If extra milk solids have been added this should be noted on the label.

Many health-giving qualities have been ascribed to sour milk. However, the exceptional robust health acquired by groups of people eating soured milk can no doubt be attributed to the use of the milk rather than to the souring of the milk. For those people who prefer milk soured, this should not discourage its use.

Cheese

The calcium caseinate of milk can be coagulated by the use of rennin, the milk-clotting enzyme that is used in the production of cheese. If the curd is left intact as in coagulated milk, the resulting product has the same nutritive value as milk. If the curd is separated from the whey as is done in cheese making, a part of the nutrients remains in each portion. The curd or cheese portion usually contains a high percentage of protein, fat, and fat-soluble vitamins and only a portion of the calcium. The whey or water portion contains almost 75 per cent of all the water-soluble vitamins, much of the minerals, some of the protein, and much of the lactose (see Table 16). A few whey cheeses are made but most of the whey is used for animal feed.

Cream

Cream is made by concentrating milk fat. This can be accomplished by two procedures: (1) whole unhomogenized milk can be allowed to stand and the cream rise to the top; or (2) the milk can be centrifuged to float the cream, which is then decanted from the top. Either method of removing cream is possible because fat is less dense than the remainder of the milk. However, the separator method is the one most commonly used. Cream may vary in its degree of fat concentration depending upon the speed of the centrifuge. *Light cream* is usually 18 to 20 per cent fat, and *heavy cream* may be 35 to 40 per cent fat, with *all-purpose cream* between these two. *Half and half* is made by adding one part light cream to one part low-fat milk making approximately 8 per cent butterfat; it is always homogenized. This last mixture is really little more than a very rich milk.

Calcium, protein, and water concentrations in cream are lower than in whole milk, but there is an increase in fat and vitamin A. The vitamin A concentration is in direct proportion to the fat increase.

Butter

Butter is the fat of milk that is removed by stirring or churning the cream and breaking the emulsion of fat in water. Butter must contain a minimum of 80 per cent fat and the remainder is buttermilk and salt. Butter contains little, if any, calcium or protein. The liquid that remains after the butter is removed from the cream is true buttermilk. However, much of the buttermilk sold in the market is low-fat milk that has been soured with a culture and then churned. Butter and its cooking properties will be discussed more fully in Chapter 7.

Milk Foods

Milks may have various substances added to them for the purpose of changing their use or their flavor. The resulting products are known as milk foods. A mixture of sugar, eggs, flavoring, and milk can be consumed as an egg nog, cooked as a custard, or the mixture can be frozen into *ice cream*. The eggs add both protein and iron to the mix. The sugar provides energy and cream used for part of the milk would also increase the energy value as well as the fat-soluble vitamins. Fresh fruit frozen in the ice cream or used as a topping for plain ice cream makes pleasing and nutritious desserts. A fruit juice concentrate mixed with ice cream also adds to the eating quality as well as the nutritive value. Ice cream makes a pleasant way of adding milk to the American diet.

The calcium content of ice cream is variable and depends upon the amount of ingredients other than milk present. All nutrients in any given volume of frozen product will be less than in a similar volume of the original mix because of the increase in volume caused by incorporation of air during the freezing process. Ice creams made with eggs, fruits and nuts may have a greater variety of nutrients than those ice creams made only with milk or cream. Also products made with synthetic flavoring and coloring will not have the improved nutritional value that the products made with true fruits will have.

Chocolate flavored milk or *chocolate drinks* are available in either fluid or dried form and are very popular—especially with children. Chocolate drinks are usually made from nonfat milk and therefore should not be the sole source of milk in the diet. They contain a relatively large percentage of starch, gelatine, and vegetable gums, which accounts for the thick appearance and which also prevents the cocoa from settling out.

Malted milk is made from powdered milk and barley malt. When malted milk is added to milk drinks, it increases the nutritive value and provides a distinctive and pleasing flavor.

GETTING THE MOST FOR THE FOOD MONEY THAT IS SPENT
FOR MILK AND MILK PRODUCTS

The buying of milk may seem like a routine part of shopping and all too often little thought is given to it. Many people move into a new house and leave a note in a basket on the back porch giving the milk order which they may not change until they move from the house years later. Still other people consider milk a luxury to be curtailed each time the family meets with financial reverses.

Milk and milk products should be selected with the same care that is given to meat or vegetables and the types best suited to the meal plans should be purchased. The box of dry milk solids and the can of evaporated milk need not be considered as emergency shelf items, but they may be used in everyday preparation of food.

Standards for Dairy Products

The first considerations in buying milk and milk products are the sanitary standards. There are many government regulations concerning the price of milk and milk products, but there are no national sanitation regulations for these products. There may, however, be rigid city, county, and state sanitary regulations (see Chapter 12). These health regulations are essential since it is generally conceded that milk and dairy products may carry disease-producing microorganisms. Among the diseases that can be communicated through these products are tuberculosis, typhoid fever, paratyphoid fever, diphtheria, septic sore throat, undulant fever, Q fever, other virus diseases, salmonella infection, and dysentery. Tuberculosis and undulant fever may be transmitted through the milk from the cow to people. The other milk-borne diseases are chiefly the diseases of man and are transmitted by contact of carrier, that is, the milk becomes contaminated from the people who handle it. Pasteurization destroys any pathogenic organisms that may be present.

The United States Health Service has recommended definitions for *grades* of milk based on total bacterial count, but because these are recommendations only, one needs to know the standards for his own community. The lower the grade the higher the bacteria count will be. Also, low-grade milk may have off-flavors and considerable visual sediment. The bacteria count is usually higher in cream because it requires more handling than milk during the processing procedure. Therefore, cream should be refrigerated promptly in order to prevent spoilage and off-flavors.

Dairies that produce high quality products may be as spotless as your kitchen (see Fig. 39). In many dairies the cows are milked by a machine, and the milk goes directly into a large cooling tank, where it is kept at a low temperature. From there it is pumped into a milk tank-truck (see Figs. 42 and 43) and taken directly to the processing plant where it is standardized, pasteurized, homogenized, and bottled. The first chance for contamination occurs when you pour it into your nonsterile drinking glass.

Standards of quality other than sanitation have been developed, and milk and milk foods have been defined by the Food and Drug Administration. For example, the word "cheese" means American cheddar cheese, made from whole milk and containing not more than 39 per cent water and not less than 50 per cent milk fat. The color is not indicated; the cheese may be the golden yellow that looks so rich and inviting, or it may be the creamy white, which looks lean but has only the color omitted—in a blindfold taste test the difference could not be detected.

State laws govern such factors as the butterfat content of true ice cream, the amount of air that may be incorporated during freezing,

Fig. 42. Insulated tank trucks are used to take the cooled milk from producers to the processing plant. (Courtesy of Whittier Sanitary Dairy, Whittier, California.)

Fig. 43. Milk processing plants proudly display their awards of merit for adhering to strict sanitary regulations. (Courtesy of Whittier Sanitary Dairy, Whittier, California.)

the fat content of whole milk, etc. As these laws vary from state to state, no generalizations can be given.

The Selection of Milk and Milk Products

Milk is considered as the foremost contributor of calcium to the diet. Thus in selecting milk or milk products, the cost of this constitu-

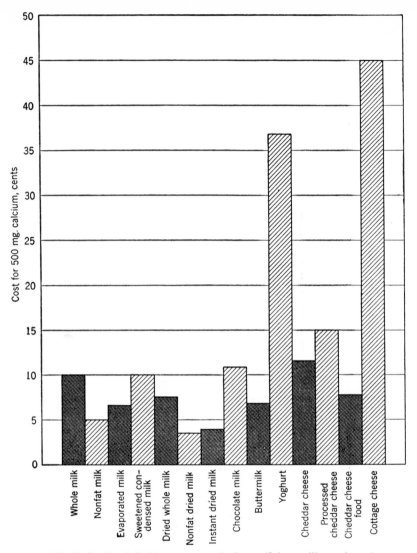

Fig. 44. The Daily Food Guide recommends that sufficient milk products be consumed to obtain approximately 500 mg. calcium (more for children); this graph shows the comparative costs of this amount according to the type of milk product chosen. (Prices—Los Angeles, California, December 1958.)

ent should be of prime importance. The relative cost of calcium from the various milk products available on the market is shown in Fig. 44. In addition to the cost of the calcium there are many other factors that may be considered in the buying of the milk products.

Milk. The price of fresh milk depends upon several factors, but the most influential is the butterfat content. This is not a constant value and varies with the breed of the cow. For example, the milk from Jersey cows is much higher in fat than is milk from Holstein cows. Thus the rich Jersey and Jersey-Blend milks cost more than milk with the standard 3.5 per cent butterfat normally found in the market. Milks from which part of the fat has been removed will be lower in cost than whole milk.

The butterfat content of milk as well as total solids vary with the stage of the lactation period of the cow. Thus, milk from any one cow does not have a constant butterfat or total solids content. It is therefore advisable, in infant feeding especially, to use herd milk rather than the milk from one or two cows because this way there would be less daily variation.

Milks vary in color and flavor. The color is partially dependent upon the feed of the cow, but the breed of cow is an important factor. The dairy herd shown in Fig. 39 is made up of several breeds, each chosen for a specific purpose. Some breeds of cows have a high milk yield with low cream concentration, others have a lower yield but a higher cream content, and still others furnish natural color for the entire lot of milk. Flavor of milk is in part dependent upon the feed of the animal; however, the care given milk is an important factor in flavor.

Prices of milk vary within any given marketing group depending upon the method of dispensing. The convenience of door to door delivery should be evaluated in light of the extra cost. The lowest price for milk will usually be paid at the dairy; however, few dairies are equipped for "dairy-to-you" selling. The next lowest unit price will be paid at the grocery store. The size of the container also influences cost of milk. Like most products, the cost per unit is less if more is purchased in one container.

The various brands of canned and dehydrated whole milks on the market are similar in palatability and nutritive value. They generally sell for less than an equivalent amount of milk solids in fluid milk. The nonfat milks in these categories will naturally have a lower energy value, less vitamin A, and be lower in price than whole milk.

Cheese. Selection of cheese and cheese foods can become a real adventure. Cheese is one of our oldest manufactured food products and its history is unusually interesting. When you visit the cheese section of an import food shop, you can close your eyes and imagine that you see the goat herders and the nomadic tribes who have given us so many of our cheese varieties. The distinct flavors in cheeses are a result of the type of milk used and the processing methods. A few cheeses are eaten as soon as they are prepared; the others are aged with certain molds and/or bacteria under controlled conditions of temperature and humidity. Several months are generally required for the desired flavor changes to develop.

Many of the very flavorful imported varieties of cheese are aged in caves where the conditions are favorable for the growth of the specific microorganisms. These flavors have never been duplicated anywhere but in these caves. However, there are appearing in our markets domestic cheeses similar in flavor, texture, and appearance to many of the products formerly imported, and these domestic cheeses are usually sold at a price lower than that of their imported counterparts.

Imported cheeses are always marked with the name of the country from which they were bought, but often when the cheese is cut in the market this information is discarded, and one must then rely on the integrity of his retailer to determine if it is a true import.

The average American is not a connoisseur of cheese, therefore, he will generally buy a very bland cheese with a rich flavor that is referred to as Cheddar or American Cheese. In spite of this unselectiveness, over a billion pounds of cheese of various varieties are made in the United States each year, and approximately one-tenth of the milk produced is channeled to this purpose.

The aging or ripening is one of the most important processes in cheese-making and it is essential for the characteristic tastes of any specific variety. During ripening one or more of the following changes occurs:

1. The lactose of the milk may be changed by bacterial action to lactic acid.

2. The protein may be partially digested into the usual sequence of soluble proteins and amino acids.

3. Molds may develop and penetrate the cheeses.

4. Carbon dioxide may form causing holes, or the so-called eyes.

5. Putrefactive flavors may develop.

6. The tough rubbery quality of the unaged cheese may be changed to a soft and mellow texture.

7. The fat in the outer layer may become rancid.

The ripening process is slow at low temperatures, and the rate increases as the temperature increases. Changes that occur during ripening not only affect texture and flavor but also affect cooking quality. The increased solubility of the proteins caused by partial digestion increases the ease with which cheese may be blended with other foods, and decreases the danger of cheese becoming stringy during the cooking process.

Aging times and conditions are varied according to the desired results. However, unless cheese is pasteurized or processed, aging will continue in the market or home. Cheddar cheese is often *processed*. That is, the rind is removed, the cheese is ground, and milk and an emulsifier are added. This mixture is heated until it is fluid, and then it is molded. The temperature at which cheese is softened is high enough to pasteurize the food thus destroying the ripening organisms, and the wrapping constitutes an airtight container. In this way the bacteria are destroyed and enzymes are inactivated so that the ripening process is stopped. Despite the loss of many of the original characteristics during processing, at least one-third of all the cheese produced in the United States is processed. Because some liquid is added, the processed cheese is softer and has a slightly lower nutrient concentration than the product from which it was made.

Cheese spreads or *cheese foods* need not meet the definitions of any cheese and are usually sold under brand names. The terms cheese spreads or cheese foods are applied to any packaged cheese that will spread easily at room temperature. The types of cheese foods are: cream cheese mixed with pickles, pimentoes, pineapple, or other flavorings; processed cheeses of such age and moisture content that they are soft and pliable; and processed cheese with concentrated whey or skim milk powder added and of such fat and moisture content that the mixture will spread easily. Desirable spreading qualities may be due to either the moisture content or the fat content or both. Cheese foods and cheese spreads may be of lower nutritive value than the original cheese and may be priced higher. However, some substances added may increase the nutritive quality.

Cheeses are classified by many systems, however, the classification given by the United States Department of Agriculture is perhaps the most informative and useful.[2] The classification is reproduced in the following list.

1. Very hard (grating): Ripened by bacteria—Asiago old, Parmesan, Romano, Sapsago, Spolen.
2. Hard:
    a. Ripened by bacteria, without eyes: Cheddar, granular or stirred curd, and Caciocavallo.

---

[2] George P. Sanders, *Cheese Varieties and Descriptions*, U. S. Department of Agriculture, Handbook No. 54, 1953.

b. Ripened by bacteria, with eyes: Swiss, Emmenthaler, and Gruyere.
3. Semi-soft:
   a. Ripened principally by bacteria: Brick and Münster.
   b. Ripened by bacteria and surface microorganisms: Limburger, Port du Salut, and Trappist.
   c. Ripened principally by blue mold in the interior: Roquefort, Gorgonzola, Blue, Stilton, and Wensleydale.
4. Soft:
   a. Ripened: Bel Paese, Brie, Camembert, Cooked, Hand, and Neufchatel (as made in France).
   b. Unripened: Cottage, Pot, Bakers', Cream, Neufchatel (as made in the United States), Mysost, Primost, and fresh Ricotta.

Cheeses commonly used and found in America are illustrated in Fig. 45.

Ice cream and sherbet. Selection of ice cream and sherbet is usually based on personal taste preferences, and these products are not graded. However, it is generally believed that ice cream of high quality should have a rich, creamy, sweet taste, a smooth body, and a fine texture.

The price variation in frozen milk desserts depends upon: the amount of air incorporated; the percentage of butterfat; the type of flavoring; and the size of the package. Ice creams and sherbet are usually sold by volume; however, in the manufacturing process much air is incorporated, and in some ice creams more than one half of the volume is air. Increase in volume due to air is known as "over-run" or "swell." It is important to compare frozen desserts by weights rather than by volumes when prices are being evaluated.

The percentage of fat is an important factor in pricing. As the fat increases the unit price also increases. When fats other than butterfat are used in making frozen milk desserts, the price is generally lower than for similar products made with butterfat. This is not always so, however, because other factors influence the cost to some extent. Fresh fruits and pure chocolate flavorings usually are more expensive than synthetic flavors. As in other products, as the package size increases the unit price of ice cream and sherbet decreases.

Storage of Milk and Milk Products

Storage of dairy products, especially milk, cream, and ice cream is important to their sanitation, nutritive value, and eating quality. Great

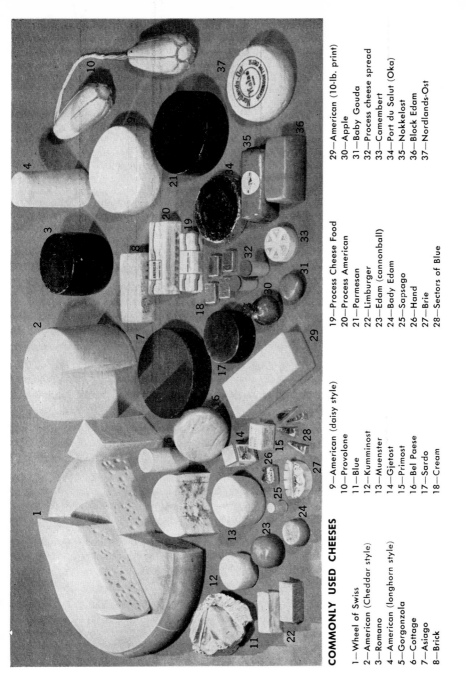

COMMONLY USED CHEESES

1—Wheel of Swiss
2—American (Cheddar style)
3—Romano
4—American (longhorn style)
5—Gorgonzola
6—Cottage
7—Asiago
8—Brick

9—American (daisy style)
10—Provolone
11—Blue
12—Kumminost
13—Muenster
14—Gjetost
15—Primost
16—Bel Paese
17—Sardo
18—Cream

19—Process Cheese Food
20—Process American
21—Parmesan
22—Limburger
23—Edam (cannonball)
24—Bady Edam
25—Sapsago
26—Hand
27—Brie
28—Sectors of Blue

29—American (10-lb. print)
30—Apple
31—Baby Gouda
32—Process cheese spread
33—Camembert
34—Port du Salut (Oka)
35—Nokkelost
36—Block Edam
37—Nordlands-Ost

Fig. 45. The many varieties of cheese result from different ripening organisms and different types and treatments of milks. (Courtesy, National Dairy Council, Chicago.)

care is taken at the dairy to protect the pouring edge of the bottle so that it will not become contaminated. But when the milk arrives in the home, which may have far more bacteria than the dairy, the milk may not be refrigerated immediately, the protective cap is often removed and not replaced, or if a carton rather than a bottle is used, the cap may be left raised.

Milk should be refrigerated as soon as it is delivered and kept covered at all times. If one cannot be at home to receive the milk when it arrives, and if the delivery man is not bonded and therefore cannot enter the house to place the milk in the refrigerator, it would be best to buy directly from the grocery store or dairy.

If milk is purchased in clear glass, it should be protected from light to prevent the inactivation of riboflavin. Amber bottles or waxed cartons are superior to clear glass for this reason.

If a portion of milk or cream is removed from the original container it should not be returned to the container because it will contaminate the milk remaining in the carton. The milk that was removed probably had its bacteria content increased, and this would hasten the spoilage or change the flavor of the entire quantity of milk.

Ice cream should be kept frozen until it is used. If it melts, it should not be refrozen. The low temperature at which it is stored prevents deterioration, but mishandling may result in off-flavors, poor texture, and poor consistency. With few exceptions cheeses also should be refrigerated and kept tightly wrapped.

PREPARATION OF PRODUCTS RICH IN MILK

Milk may be consumed as a beverage—or one may eat at least a part of his daily milk supply. Milk can be made into soups, sauces, gravies, drinks, desserts, cheese, or put into baked products. Many people feel that they do not obtain their 2 cups of milk each day because they have not had that much in a glass. They may have forgotten the ¼ cup they put on the cereal; the 8 tablespoons in the 4 cups of coffee; the ½ cup in the noon bowl of soup; the ¼ cup in the potatoes and gravy; and the ½ ounce of cheese that they had with the apple pie. Why don't you count your hidden milk intake occasionally?

Milk scorches easily and like other foods that contain significant quantities of protein, it should be cooked slowly. It is suggested that milk be cooked over hot water, or over an automatically controlled heat source, or in a very heavy pan. It has been the experience of students in the laboratory that when the inconvenience and longer cooking time involved in using the double boiler is weighed against the time involved in cleaning a burned pan or spill-overs on the range, the double boiler usually wins. If the double-boiler does not win the next class usually comes into the laboratory and finds the burned pan. Whenever milk is heated it is assumed that it will be heated over hot water, in a heavy pan or that an automatically controlled burner or heating element will be used (temperature setting 2° F below boiling temperature of water in the specific locality).

White Sauce and Products Made with White Sauces

The white sauce or cream sauce—milk thickened with cereal—is the basic ingredient for many of our foods. Teachers and students alike may have thought that in the past too much emphasis has been placed upon the white sauce. But a close look at many soups, gravies, sauces, puddings, ice creams, and even milk drinks will reveal the lowly white sauce. Call it by any name you like, but use it and learn to recognize t regardless of its disguise.

White sauces are classified according to their viscosities, that is, thin, nedium, thick, and very thick. The proportions for these are given in Table 17.

Table 17. PROPORTION OF INGREDIENTS USED IN WHITE SAUCES

Consistency	Amount of Milk, C.	Amount of Flour, Tb.	Amount of Fat, Tb.
Thin	1	1	1
Medium	1	2	2
Thick	1	3	3
Very thick	1	4	4

In preparing white sauces flour particles should be separated by some medium so that as the flour takes up water the particles will not stick together to cause lumps in the finished products. Salt may be added at any stage because the quantity is not great enough to interfere with the hydration of the starch.

There are three general methods of combining the ingredients:

(1) The flour is mixed thoroughly with the melted fat and the milk is added gradually during stirring and heating.

(2) A small amount of cool milk is added to the flour to form a

smooth paste, and this is added to the remainder of the milk, which has been previously heated.

(3) The flour and milk are shaken together in a jar or swirl mixer, and then the fat is added.

After the ingredients are combined, the sauce is cooked slowly over hot water or in a heavy pan. The sauce should be stirred constantly until thick. After it is thick the cooking should continue for 10 to 15 minutes to completely swell the starch. If the sauce is to be added to a product that is to be cooked further such as a soufflé, the last 10 to 15 minutes of cooking can be omitted.

Milk soups. Milk soups may be thin, medium thick, and thick. Thin soups are called cream soups and may contain vegetables or meat. Cream-of-tomato soup is one of America's favorite thin soups. It is rather difficult to make because the acid of the tomato may curdle the milk. This can be avoided to some extent if the tomato and the thin white sauce are the same temperature and if the tomato is added slowly to the milk rather than the milk added to the tomato.

Medium thick or thick soups are called chowders. They also may contain vegetables and meats. Chowder is really a milk stew, and it may be thickened with potatoes rather than with a cereal.

Planned-overs as well as freshly cooked foods can be used in milk soups and chowders. Formulas or recipes for these need not be followed slavishly because almost any pleasing combination of foods can be used.

Milk sauces. Milk sauces are usually medium white sauces seasoned with herbs, spices, cheeses, or other flavoring. They may be used with vegetables and meats, or for casseroles. Creamed meats served with toast or hot biscuits make excellent main dishes. Cheese sauce usually contains a high proportion of grated cheese blended into the finished white sauce. The white sauce to be used with cheese may be made without fat as the cheese will furnish sufficient fat to make the sauce palatable.

Milk gravies. Milk gravies are white sauces flavored with meat drippings. This can be a pleasant method of eating milk as well as consuming the drip of cooked meats. Gravies will not be excessively rich if some of the fat is removed from the meat drippings. A good product is produced if the quantity of fat used is less or equal to the amount of flour used for thickening; if fat floats on the top of such gravy, additional milk will be needed to hold the fat in emulsion.

Milk puddings. These are either thick or very thick white sauces to which sugar or other sweetening agents and flavoring have been added.

Eggs are sometimes added, which changes the physical characteristics slightly and improves the flavor. The thickening that is used can be any of the starches, flour, cereals, or bread. Cornstarch puddings to which eggs have been added are often used as fillings for pie shells. These pies may be topped with meringue (see Chapter 4) or served with whipped cream.

Milk Drinks

Milk drinks, served either hot or cold, add variety to the diet. They are made from milk and flavored with chocolate, fruits, flavoring extracts, malted milks, eggs, and so on. The most common examples of milk drinks are hot chocolate, milk shakes, egg nogs, malted milk, and fruit coolers. They are excellent afternoon snacks for children, and they are generally no more costly than soda pops and much more nutritious. Milk drinks are not difficult to prepare since those that are to be served cold need only stirring and shaking. The hot drinks require more preparation time than the cold. Hot chocolate is really a thin white sauce; the starch from the cocoa or the chocolate serves as the thickening agent. Cocoa or chocolate may be added to sugar, mixed with a little water, and cooked over direct heat until a thick syrup is formed. This procedure is desirable in order that the starch of the cocoa or chocolate will be completely cooked and thus to some extent prevent the chocolate from settling to the bottom of the container after the milk is added. The milk is added to the thoroughly cooked chocolate mixture and heating is continued over hot water. If a scum forms during the heating process, it may be broken up by beating with a rotary egg beater.

Frozen Milk Desserts

Frozen milk desserts are often purchased ready to eat, but with the trend to back-yard picnics and do-it-yourself procedures, the home-produced varieties are becoming popular again. There is probably nothing that gives more pleasure to a party than a freezer of ice cream with a dasher to "lick."

Ice creams can be made in the mechanical refrigerator or in a special freezer with an ice-salt mixture as the freezing medium. The freezer usually gives the more acceptable product unless an electrically driven agitator is used for ice cream frozen in the freezer cabinet or refrigerator. Such an attachment is shown in Fig. 46.

The old-fashioned ice-cream freezer consists of five parts: (1) a tub to hold the ice and salt; (2) a container for the mix; (3) a paddle or dasher for agitating the mix; (4) a lid for the mix container; and (5) gears for stirring the mixture during freezing. Such a freezer is shown in Fig. 47. The tub is usually made of wood or other material that is a poor conductor of heat so that heat will not be absorbed from the surrounding atmosphere but from the mix container. The tub must be water-tight so that the salt can be dissolved in water. Then as the ice melts the heat will be absorbed from the mix. Unless there is an open drain hole near the top of the outside container, salt water might seep into the ice-cream mix and ruin the flavor of the ice cream. The mix container must be made of aluminum or other metal that is a good conductor of heat so that the heat will pass quickly into the ice-salt brine.

The paddle should fit tightly in the mix container so that as the mixer is turned, the frozen mix will be scraped from the sides of the container. The paddle is usually made of wood, which should be swollen before use by soaking in hot water. The lid must fit tightly

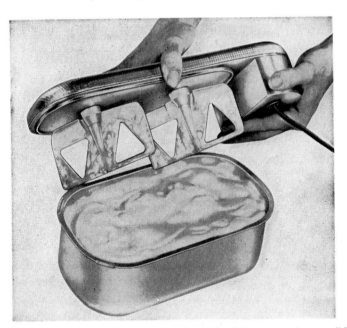

Fig. 46. An electrical attachment for a mechanical refrigerator makes possible the home production of America's most popular dessert—ice cream. (Courtesy of Southern California Edison Co., Los Angeles.)

and overlap the mix container to prevent the salt water from contaminating the ice cream mix. The gears should be so constructed that the mix container will turn in one direction and the paddle in another. It would be well for the inexperienced person to assemble the empty freezer and note its workings before attempting to freeze a product.

If the gears of the freezer are electrically driven, it should be possible to change the speed for two reasons: the ice cream should be stirred very slowly until the temperature falls below 35° F. This will prevent "churning out" the fat particles. And, the thoroughly chilled mix becomes somewhat viscous and at this time it is possible to incorporate a large amount of air by rapid stirring. Agitation during freezing tends to produce small crystals for a smooth fine-textured ice cream.

The crystals that form in frozen desserts are only water. Factors affecting the size of the crystals are: the rapidity of freezing; the rate

Fig. 47. A home freezer can be used to produce velvety ice cream. Freezing temperatures are obtained by means of an ice and salt solution put into the tub into which the can of mix is immersed. (Courtesy of Southern California Edison Co., Los Angeles.)

of agitation during freezing; and, the presence of interfering sub-stances. Products which are not agitated during the freezing process will have smaller crystals if the freezing proceeds rapidly than if the freezing proceeds slowly. Products that are to be agitated are frozen slowly as this permits agitation over a long period of time resulting in small crystals. Milk proteins, gelatine, eggs, chocolate, and fat inter-fere with the development of crystals by preventing the water particles from clumping. The greater the amount of these interfering sub-stances the smaller the crystals will be.

Salt added to water will lower the freezing point, and if enough salt is added the freezing point may be lowered as much as 22° F. The freezing point of water is lowered in direct proportion to the amount of salt added. Therefore the rate of freezing the ice cream will be increased as the amount of salt is increased (see Chapter 2). The ratio by *weight* of salt to ice that is commonly used is: 1 part salt and 8 parts ice for ice cream; 1 to 5 for sherbets; and 1 to 3 for ices.

The mix to be frozen is put into the container and the whole freezer is assembled before the ice is put into the tub. The mix container should be no more than half full to allow for expansion during freez-ing. Unless the salt is thoroughly mixed with ice, it will be more efficient to add all of the salt after the tub has been completely filled with ice since it will dissolve and go down through the ice.

Unless nuts, fruits, chocolate bits, and similar foods can be sus-pended in the unfrozen mix, they should be added after the cream has been frozen to a soft mush. Whenever turning is stopped after freezing has begun, the freezing does not stop and unless care is taken to work quickly, the paddle may freeze to the sides of the mix con-tainer. If this occurs, it is better to use a metal spatula to scrape down the sides of the container rather than putting a strain on the freezer gears.

When the mixture becomes so stiffly frozen that turning is difficult, the effectiveness of continued turning is not appreciable, and the dasher can be removed and freezing permitted to continue without agitation. Ice creams have a smoother texture if they age at least three to four hours after freezing.

If ice cream is frozen in a mechanical refrigerator without an electrically driven agitator, air can be incorporated by adding whipped creams, egg whites, or gelatine just before the mixture solidifies. The texture of the mix is improved if it is stirred several times during the freezing process. The substances dissolved in the mix will lower the freezing temperature of the mix and the refrigerator must be turned to a temperature lower than that used for cooling or the making of ice cubes.

Milk mixes that are used for freezing can vary widely in composition. When milk, or milk and fruit juices are used, the mix is generally referred to as a *sherbet*, if eggs are added to this, they are called *frozen milk desserts*, and when cream or other sources of fat are used, they are termed *ice creams*. *Mousses* are products made with whipped cream that are not agitated during freezing. Ice creams have a better body and a finer crystal if egg, starch, gelatine, or another stabilizing agent is used and if they are cooked before freezing. Also, the use of homogenized milk and cream improves the texture. The finished frozen desserts are lighter in color; milder in flavor, and less sweet than the original mix.

Whipped Milk Products

Cream may be whipped and used as a topping for desserts, or it may be used to incorporate air in products that contain cream. Air bubbles are incorporated in liquid when cream is whipped and they are kept suspended by being surrounded with a protein film. Cream that is properly whipped and that has the correct content of fat will maintain its foam for several days when stored at a temperature below 50° F, or the foam can be frozen and kept for several weeks.

The protein film contains small particles of fat which when cold give permanence to the foam. Most products foam best at room temperature, but cream and gelatine must be at refrigerator temperature to maintain their stability. If cream is properly whipped all of the liquid is held in the films. If it is overbeaten, the films break and lumps of butter are formed.

The volume achieved and ease of whipping cream depend upon many factors: (1) cream that has aged for at least twenty-four hours whips better than freshly drawn cream; (2) the cream must have at least 20 per cent fat to whip, but a higher percentage (30 to 35 per cent) will give a firmer foam; (3) cream with large fat globules will produce a stiffer whip than cream with small fat globules, thus homogenized cream does not whip well; (4) the cooler the cream, the stiffer the foam will be because the fat will be firmer (the best results are obtained if the temperature of the cream is below 45° F); and, (5) sugar decreases the foaming power of cream, therefore, any sugar to be added should be added when the foam is formed. If sugar is added to a whipped cream at a temperature slightly above 45° F so that the foam is not firm, the result will be a lump of sweetened butter.

Evaporated milk, because of the concentration of milk solids and fat, can be whipped if it is cooled to 32° F or lower. This does not produce a stable foam unless acid is added. It is suggested that 2 tablespoons of lemon juice for each cup of fluid milk be added to the whipped milk.

Dry milk when partially reconstituted (1 cup of water to ¾ cup dry milk) can also be whipped. Dried whole milk produces a less stable foam than do nonfat dry milk solids.

Cheese Main Dishes, Appetizers, and Desserts

Cheese adds variety and good eating to any meal. In America cheese is usually served only for lunch, dinner, or supper, but in many of the European countries it is commonly served for breakfast.

Fig. 48. A cheese tray with crackers and fruit accompaniments makes a quick, nutritious, and pleasing dessert for everyday or special parties. (Courtesy of the California Dairy Advisory Board, Los Angeles.)

Cheese may be eaten alone, or it can be mixed with many foods and used as appetizers, main dishes, or desserts (Fig. 48). It may be the major portion of the dish or grated and sprinkled only on the top. When added to vegetables, cereals, and legumes, it improves the essential amino acid ratio of the proteins of these foods and makes true meat substitutes of them. Cheese has long been a favorite for a sandwich, but the same nutritive value is attained if a nippy variety is eaten with crackers at the end of the meal, or if it is used for the topping of a canapé and eaten as an appetizer.

If a cheese is to be cooked, the aged or processed varieties will give the best results because they do not tend to form rope or strings. However, even these cheeses will become tough and rubbery if the cooking temperature is excessively high. Cheese has a high protein content (see Table 16), therefore, its response to heat is the same as that of meat or eggs. In certain foods the cheese is protected from

Fig. 49. Insulating the cheese during cooking insures the soft tender consistency of the proteins. (Courtesy of the Sunbeam Corporation, Chicago.)

the heat of cooking by various types of covers, for example: cheese balls fried in deep fat and cheese straws or cheese biscuits have the cheese diluted and protected by the dough and therefore can be cooked at relatively high temperatures; cheese in the center of a grilled sandwich (Fig. 49) remains soft and tender while the cheese on an open-faced grilled sandwich may become tough; and cheese enclosed in pastry remains soft while cheese on top of Pizza baked at the same temperature becomes stringy.

Cheese can be added to fruits and vegetables and made into salads. These salads may be used either as the main part of the meal or as an accompaniment to the meat course. Cheese may be used in salads in many ways, for example: as the major ingredient—cottage cheese or other soft unripened cheese with fruit; as one of the components of a tossed salad—cheddar or other hard cheese cut into strips or cubes and tossed with the other ingredients; grated and sprinkled on the top—Parmesan or other hard cheese; and, as a part of the salad dressing—Roquefort, other semi-soft ripened cheese, or cream cheese.

Cheese used in main dishes such as soufflés, sandwiches, and sauces, may be any of the bland or nippy varieties. Nippy cheeses are generally used in smaller quantities than the bland cheeses. A cheese soufflé usually has 1 cup of grated cheese (¼ pound) to 1 cup thick white sauce and 4 eggs (see Chapter 4). The cheese is in high proportion, and a mild cheddar gives the best flavor. In sandwiches, mild cheddar is popular. However, cheeses with more distinctive flavors like nippy cheddars, Swiss, and Edam may be used, especially if the bread is made from whole grain as the flavor of the whole grain seems to blend very well with the flavor of the fully ripened cheeses.

Cheese sauces are made by adding grated or chunk hard cheese to medium or thick white sauce. These sauces make excellent additions to vegetables. When vegetables are listed on menus as "au gratin" they will be served with cheese sauce. Baked potato served with cheese sauce and chives makes a pleasing flavor combination. Cheese sauce may also be added to macaroni and other pastes to make main dishes as for example, Italian Lasagna, Greek and Armenian Moussaka, and American macaroni and cheese.

Slices of cheese added to the top of individual casseroles, or allowed to melt over grilled vegetables or hamburgers make food flavor variations and add nutrients. An excellent combination is chili and beans with a slice of cheese melted over the top. In a similar manner bits of cheese added to hot soups may improve flavor. French Onion Soup is served with croutons (toasted bread cubes) and hard Parmesan-like cheese granules.

Cheese pies, cheese cake, and plain cheese with crackers or fruit make nutritious and delicious endings for meals. Cheese pies and cakes are usually made from soft unripened cheeses such as cottage cheese or cream cheese. They are really custards in which cheese furnishes a part of the calcium caseinate that causes the custard to thicken. The custom of serving cheese and fruit at the end of the meal even if another dessert has been served is a Continental practice.

The proportions, and methods of preparation of milk food products which have been found suitable for laboratory use are given in Table 18. The nutritive values of the foods made from these formulas are given in Table 19.

SUMMARY

Milk is an important item in the family food plan. Although it is not an entirely perfect food, it contains fats, carbohydrates, and proteins as well as many of the vitamins and minerals. Milk is such an excellent source of calcium that it is not difficult to meet the daily recommended allowances for this mineral when two cups of milk or the equivalent in milk products are included in the diet. The proteins of milk have an excellent assortment of amino acids, and thus make good supplements to the proteins of cereals and vegetables. The iron content is low, and ascorbic acid, normally low, is likely to be lost during processing. The common methods of processing do not appreciably change the nutritive value of the milk other than in the ascorbic acid content. Pasteurization is considered the only measure that will prevent all milk-borne diseases.

The different forms of milk should be compared in cost, ease of handling, and nutritive value when the family milk supplies are purchased. The fat content influences the cost of milk and milk products. Although low-fat milk is very inexpensive, whole milk should not be omitted completely from the diet unless butter or other foods contributing both essential fatty acids and pre-formed vitamin A are used.

Milk has many uses in food preparation, but its principal role is that of a flavorful liquid for beverages, soups, sauces, puddings, frozen desserts, or baked products. Evaporated, concentrated, and dry milk solids permit the incorporation of a higher concentration of milk solids without excess water than does fluid milk, but these milks may also be fully reconstituted and used as fluid milk. The proteins of milk and cheese become tough and rubbery when they are heated to a high

Table 18. PROPORTIONS AND METHODS OF PREPARATIONS OF COMMONLY USED MILK PRODUCTS

Milk Product	Milk	Cheese	Flour or Starch	Fat	Egg	Salt	Other	Method of Preparation	Cooking Time, min.	Cooking Temp.,* °F	Approx. Yield
Milk, whole	1 C.	...	...	...	...	...	...	...	...	...	1 serving
Cheese, Cheddar	...	2 oz.	...	...	...	...	...	...	...	...	1 serving
Cheese sandwich	...	2 oz.	...	1 Tb. (butter)	...	...	2 slices bread	...	...	...	1 serving
Cheese sauce	1 C.	4 oz. or 1 C. grated	2 Tb.	...	...	¼ tsp.	Paprika, pepper	White sauce	15	210	1½ C.
Cheese soufflé	1 C.	4 oz. or 1 C. grated	3 Tb.	...	4	¼ tsp.	Seasoning	See chapter 4	...	...	4 servings
Cream (20%)	...	...	...	...	...	...	4 Tb. cream	...	...	...	1 serving
Creamed tuna	1 C.	...	3 Tb.	3 Tb.	...	¼ tsp.	1 C. tuna, seasoning	White sauce	15	210	2 C.
Cutlets, beef	1 C.	...	4 Tb.	4 Tb.	...	¼ tsp.	2 C. ground round	White sauce	25	210—sauce 350—fry	5 servings
Egg nog	1 C.	...	...	...	1	...	1 Tb. sugar, nutmeg, vanilla	Shake, thoroughly	...	...	1 serving
Gravy, milk	1 C.	...	2 Tb.	2 Tb.	...	½ tsp.	½ C. meat drippings	White sauce	15	210	1½ C.
Ice cream	1 C.	...	1 Tb.	...	1	1/16 tsp.	½ C. sugar, 1 C. cream	White sauce and freeze	30	210 for sauce 21 for freeze	8 servings
Pudding	1 C.	...	2–3 Tb.	...	...	...	4 Tb. sugar, flavoring	White sauce	15	210	1¼ C.
Sherbet	1 C.	...	...	...	1	...	⅔ C. sugar, 1 C. fruit juice	Mix and freeze	15	Freeze at 18	6 servings
Soup, tomato	1 C.	...	1 Tb.	1 Tb.	...	½ tsp.	1 C. tomato	White sauce	20	210	2 C.
White sauce (med.)	1 C.	...	2 Tb.	2 Tb.	...	¼ tsp.	...	Mix flour with fat (White sauce)	15	210	1 C.

* 210°F indicates over hot water, or controlled heat source.

Table 19. NUTRITIVE VALUE OF ONE SERVING OF COMMONLY USED MILK PRODUCTS MADE WITH THE PROPORTION OF INGREDIENTS IN TABLE 18*

Product	Size of Serving	Energy Value, Cal.	Protein, gm.	Calcium, mg.	Iron, mg.	Vitamin A, I.U.	Thiamine, mg.	Riboflavin, mg.	Niacin, mg.	Ascorbic Acid, mg.
Milk, whole	1 C.	166	8.5	288	0.2	390	0.09	0.42	0.5	3
Cheese, Cheddar	2 oz.	226	14.2	412	0.6	800	0.02	0.24	...	...
Cheese sandwich	1	452	18.3	454	1.4	1260	0.15	0.34	1.0	...
Cheese sauce (med.)	4 Tb.	111	6.2	185	0.3	323	0.03	0.15	0.1	...
Cream (20%)	4 Tb.	120	1.6	60	...	480	Tr.	0.08	Tr.	...
Creamed tuna	½ C.	228	15.0	80	0.8	132	0.07	0.17	5.7	...
Cutlets, beef	4 oz.	344	26.8	67	3.3	75	0.13	0.30	5.7	...
Egg nog	1⅛ C.	291	14.6	314	1.5	940	0.14	0.56	Tr.	...
Gravy, beef	4 Tb.	72	1.6	49	0.2	65	0.04	0.08	0.2	...
Ice cream	½ C.	186	3.6	91	0.2	485	0.03	0.15	0.1	...
Pudding, vanilla	½ C.	144	4.0	116	0.2	156	0.06	0.18	0.2	...
Sherbet, orange	½ C.	237	2.6	84	0.2	212	0.07	0.12	0.4	31
Soup, tomato	1 C.	173	5.7	158	0.8	1465	0.13	0.26	1.5	21
White sauce (med.)	1 C.	414	9.7	290	0.6	390	0.15	0.46	0.7	3

*Calculated from nutritive values in U.S.D.A. Agriculture Handbook No. 8.

MILK FOR ALL AGES · 187

temperature; also milk scorches easily. The general rule for cooking these products is to use a low temperature. Formulas for preparation of foods containing milk and cheese in laboratory portions are given.

Reading List

1. Hughes, Osee, 1955, *Introductory Foods*, The Macmillan Co., New York.

2. Mirone, L. and K. Y. Lee, 1956, "Effect of cocoa and its components on growth and body composition of mice," *J. Amer. Diet. Assoc.*, **32**:1171.

3. Paul, P. C. and P. J. Aldrich, 1953, "Nonfat dry milk solids in food preparation," *J. Amer. Diet. Assoc.*, **29**:234.

4. Sanders, G. P., 1953, "Cheese varieties and descriptions," U. S. Department of Agriculture, Handbook No. 54.

5. Sherman, H. C. and C. S. Lanford, 1957, *Essentials of Nutrition*, The Macmillan Co., New York.

6. Sweetman, M. D. and I. MacKellar, 1954, *Food Selection and Preparation*, John Wiley and Sons, Inc., New York.

7. Taylor, C. M., G. MacLeod, and M. S. Rose, 1956, *Foundations of Nutrition*, The Macmillan Co., New York.

8. Terminology Committee, Amer. Home Econ. Assoc., 1959, *Handbook of Food Preparation*, American Home Economics Association, Washington, D. C.

CHAPTER 6

Fig. 50. Bread, the staff of life. (Courtesy of American Institute of Baking, Chicago.)

CHAPTER **6** . . . BREAD,
THE STAFF OF LIFE

Grains, Cereals, Flours, and Flour Products

NUTRITIONAL CONSIDERATIONS OF CEREALS
AND CEREAL PRODUCTS

Proteins
Carbohydrates
Fat
Vitamins
Minerals

PRODUCTION, BUYING, AND CARE OF CEREALS
AND CEREAL PRODUCTS

Breakfast Cereals
    Ready-to-Eat Cereals
    Partially Cooked Cereals
    Completely Raw Cereals
Flours
    White Flours
    Whole Wheat Flours
    Flours Other than Wheat
Alimentary Pastes
Baked Products Made from Flour

PREPARATION OF CEREALS AND CEREAL PRODUCTS

General Methods for Cooking Cereals
    Rice
    Alimentary Pastes
General Uses for Cereals and Pastes

PREPARATION OF BATTERS AND DOUGHS

Functions of the Ingredients Used in Batters and Doughs
    Flour
    Liquid
    Leavening Agents

Eggs
Sugar
Fat
Salt
Mixing and Baking Batters and Doughs
Temperature of the Ingredients
Kind, Quality, and Proportion of Ingredients
Order, Method, and Amount of Mixing
Size and Shape of Mixing Equipment
Size, Shape, Material, and Fill of Baking Pan
Baking of Batters and Doughs
Staling of Baked Products
Preparation of Specific Products
Quick Breads
Cakes
Bread and Rolls

SUMMARY

READING LIST

CEREALS, SEEDS OF THE GRASS FAMILY, ARE ONE OF MAN'S MOST ancient and highly respected food products. The cereal grains most commonly used in human diets are rice, wheat, corn, oats, rye, and barley, listed in decreasing amounts of total world consumption. Nongrass seeds from which flours are manufactured, buckwheat, soybeans, and peanuts, are often included with the grains.

Grains are grown in almost every country of the world; however, each country may have one that is produced in greater abundance than the others. Those produced in the greatest amount usually become the hub of the food industries. In the United States this cereal is wheat, whereas in the Orient it is rice.

Cereals are good sources of food energy, and they also contribute many vitamins and minerals to the diet. Types and amounts of grains used and methods of using them in the diet are influenced by cultural backgrounds, income, and food habits of the people. "Cereals," it is to be noted, is not a term limited to breakfast foods but applies to the large group of commodities made from grains.

In addition to a vast assortment of breakfast foods, numerous alimentary pastes and countless varieties of baked products are made with flours milled from various grains. Individuals who enjoy food preparation generally find flours and other cereal products to be one of the most interesting and versatile types of food used in cooking.

NUTRITIONAL CONSIDERATIONS OF CEREALS
AND CEREAL PRODUCTS

Cereals and cereal products when eaten in quantity are valuable sources of protein, carbohydrate, thiamine, other B-complex vitamins, and certain minerals. Because of this favorable nutritive composition in conjunction with a low price the cereal products are used extensively in diets of low-income families. Cereals have a bland flavor and this makes it possible to use large quantities without depressing the appetite.

Proteins

The proteins of cereals are of great significance because 24 per cent of the total protein in the average diet is derived from this source, and in many diets cereals furnish a much larger proportion. Although a specific cereal does not contain all of the essential amino acids in favorable proportions for good nutrition, cereal proteins may be supplemented by eating them with other protein sources such as milk, egg, and meat, by combining different types of cereals, or by serving them with certain vegetables such as legumes and nuts. Diets in which the protein is obtained mainly from cereals and other vegetable foods will support body growth and maintenance when approximately only 10 per cent of the total proteins are supplied by milk. This assumes that the proteins are present in adequate amounts. Other animal sources of protein would also make good supplements.

The original protein content and its amino acid make-up vary among the grains. The protein content of true cereal products ranges from 6 to 18 per cent; however, soybean flour is approximately 40 per cent protein, and peanut flour contains almost 60 per cent. The percentage of protein in any one grain crop may be dependent upon species, variety, climate, and soil fertility. Grains produced in a hot dry climate tend to have a relatively high protein content, and grains grown in soils with a high nitrogen content will contain more protein than grains grown in soils with a low nitrogen content.

The nutritive value of cereal protein may be altered during manufacturing processes as well as during cooking. Heat treatment—toasting, puffing, drying, etc.—during processing of cereals may lower the nutritive value of the protein by damaging or changing the essential amino acid, *lysine*. Refining or excessive milling of cereals may change the percentage of protein in the resultant product and thus produce a change in the overall protein value. Such a change could be either an increase or a decrease.

The cereal proteins are relatively inexpensive when compared to animal proteins, and although singly they must be supplemented with protein from other sources, they help to lower the cost of total protein in the diet. One-half cup flour, ⅔ cup whole milk, 1 egg, and 1 ounce of sirloin steak will yield approximately equal quantities of protein. The current cost of the flour is 1¼ cents, the milk is 4 cents, the egg is 6 cents, and the sirloin is 8 cents.

The popover might be cited as an example of the contribution cereal products can make to the dietary protein. The standard recipe of 1 cup flour, 1 cup milk, and 3 eggs will make 6 large popovers and will yield 39 grams of protein. If one person would eat 2 popovers, he would have approximately 1/5 of the day's protein allowance.

Carbohydrates

Cereals are a valuable source of energy because of their relatively high carbohydrate content. The percentage of carbohydrate varies depending upon conditions of growth and how much of the bran coat and germ have been removed in processing. In general, oats have the lowest starch content and rice the highest of all cereals, but the average value is 75 per cent. In areas where humidity is high and soil is poor in nitrogen, the starch content of the grain increases. Most of the carbohydrate is in the form of starch, but small amounts of the sugars maltose and glucose are present. Maltose and glucose have considerable importance in bread-making.

Carbohydrate is a necessary component of our daily diet. Whole-grain or enriched cereal is one of its good sources because the B-complex vitamins and other nutrients that are necessary for the body to utilize carbohydrates are also present.

Fat

On a percentage basis the fats of whole grain and refined cereals are relatively low, but the small amounts that are present are good sources of the essential fatty acids. Oats are comparatively rich in fats (7.4 per cent), and rice is very low (1.7 per cent).

Vitamins

Cereals make their greatest contribution to the human requirement for nutriments with their B-complex vitamins, especially thiamine. It is practically impossible to obtain the recommended allowance of thiamine unless two or more servings of whole grain or enriched cereals are consumed daily. The latest national food guide recommends at least four servings.

Thiamine is essential for the release of energy from carbohydrates to the body. Unmilled cereal grains contain larger amounts of this vitamin than is necessary for the utilization of the carbohydrate contained in these grains. The greatest concentration of thiamine is found in the germ and bran coats. These parts of grain are often removed in whole or in part during many of the processing procedures. This refinement has been encouraged by consumers to decrease the preparation time, to improve keeping quality, and to add variety to the diet.

Because so many highly processed foods have appeared in the markets, the amount of thiamine and other B-complex vitamins in the American diet have become alarmingly low. It was not practical to try to force people to eat whole grains and attempts to encourage their consumption met with failure. Therefore, it has become advisable to encourage fortification of cereal products with these vitamins. This fortification is designated as *enrichment* in the case of breadstuffs and flour, and *restoration* in the case of breakfast cereals. White rice with restored nutrients is, under certain conditions, listed as *converted*. Fortification information is given on the label so that consumers may check to make certain that products they buy are either whole grain or fortified and that they may be assured of obtaining the most nutrients possible from the cereal products.

Enrichment and restoration is required in twenty-eight states including Hawaii, and in Puerto Rico, and is encouraged in all others. Minimum and maximum standards for enrichment have been established by the federal government; some of these are given in Table 20. These

Table 20. MINIMUM AND MAXIMUM ENRICHMENT REQUIREMENT FOR ONE POUND OF BREAD, FLOUR, ALIMENTARY PASTES, AND CORN MEAL AND GRITS*

Product	Thiamine, mg.	Riboflavin, mg.	Niacin, mg.	Iron, mg.
Bread and rolls	1.1–1.8	0.7–1.6	10.0–15.0	8.0–12.5
Flour	2.0–2.5	1.2–1.5	16.0–20.0	13.0–16.5
Macaroni and noodles	4.0–5.0	1.7–2.2	27.0–34.0	13.0–16.5
Corn meal and grits	2.0–3.0	1.2–1.8	16.0–24.0	13.0–26.0

Nutrients and Amounts Required

* U. S. National Archives, Code of Federal Register Title *21*, Food and Drugs. 1955 with supplement to 1957.

standards are based on values found in whole grain, hence this is not to be considered as dietary supplement, but as a restoration measure.

This artificial means of increasing dietary factors is only one of many ways of improving cereal products. The source of cereals could be selected on the basis of genetic constitution for vitamin content. Varieties of wheat, for example, vary considerably in their thiamine content, and certain varieties of corn are much richer than others in niacin. Scientists are experimenting in order that even greater variety improvements can be made.

Other factors influencing the amounts of vitamins obtained from cereal products are the ingredients used with them. Breads made with milk solids or whole milk are better sources of B-complex vitamins than bread made without milk. The liberal use of milk and eggs in home-baked products and the use of milk with breakfast cereal (Fig. 51) can make these foods excellent contributors to the overall thiamine and other B-complex vitamin intake.

Minerals

Minerals, especially phosphorus and iron, in cereals and cereal products are of considerable significance to the diet. The percentage of these substances contained in cereals is relatively low, but the large amount of cereal consumed make their total contribution important. Iron is concentrated in the bran coats and germ, therefore, much of it is removed during the refining processes. Iron is added to refined cereals as a part of the enrichment program. Milk, milk solids, and eggs added to cereals not only increase the amount of vitamins and proteins but also the amount of minerals.

Fig. 51. Enriched prepared breakfast cereal with milk and melon cubes makes an adequate breakfast. (Courtesy of the Kellogg Co., Battle Creek, Michigan.)

Breakfast Cereals

Breakfast cereals are produced in many forms, namely, whole, cracked, flaked, and granular. Any of these forms may be packaged ready to eat, partially cooked, or completely raw. The broken forms may be whole-grain or they may have part or all of the bran coat and germ removed.

All cereals sold in packages will be labeled as to enrichment or fortification, type of grind, whether whole or refined, cooking time required, grain or grains used, and the weight of the product in the package. Labels thus become good guides for purchasing cereals best suited to individual needs and tastes.

When money is limited, it might be advisable to make careful cost analysis before choosing any cereal. The cost per pound is not the only factor involved. One should compare relative costs of the vitamins and minerals, the fuel needed for preparation, and the value of the time of the person preparing the meal. In considering cost of cereals, the concept that "money can generally be traded for time" is very applicable.

Ready-to-eat cereals. These foods are completely cooked during the manufacturing process by puffing, flaking, or baking a dough. Cereals are puffed by subjecting the grain to high steam pressure, then releasing the pressure suddenly. This causes the grains to burst and the contents to inflate. Popcorn inflates easily because of its relatively high moisture content and can be puffed by heating in a closed container. Flaked products are made by cooking a granular cereal with sugar and malt and then rolling it. Dough types are made by grinding cereals very finely, then adding water to form a paste. The paste is forced through tubes of various shapes and then baked. The baked product may be ground, shredded, pressed, or crumbled.

Either flaked or dough types of cereals may contain one or more grains, and also they may have other foods added to them. Mixing cereals, or adding other foods to them, or both, can improve the nutritive quality of the finished product. The amino acid combination may be improved and the vitamin content increased. On the other hand, the resultant product could have a lowered nutritive value.

Ready-to-eat products usually have the best flavor and the best eating qualities when they are crisp. All of these products take up moisture readily from the atmosphere, and to retain their crispness they should be packaged in moisture-proof bags or cartons. After the cartons are opened, the cereal should be kept in a warm dry place and closed as tightly as possible. If the moisture content rises above 7 per cent, the cereal will become tough and rubbery.

The cost of ready-to-eat cereals is more per unit of weight than any other type of cereal. The high cost is caused by processing procedures, bulk, and type of containers used. All of these products require a long manufacturing time and a large amount of labor. The products have a light weight in relation to their bulk, and packaging becomes a major cost. Boxes for these products must be air- and moisture-proof, and often containers may weigh more than their edible contents. Because of their bulk, these cereals require a large storage space and are costly to transport, however, some companies are now decreasing bulk of flakes by compressing them.

Partially cooked cereals. Quick cooking cereals are first partially cooked by steaming, and then they may be rolled and/or dried. Steaming destroys or inactivates the enzymes that cause rancidity in similar unprocessed whole grains.

Partly cooked cereals can be completely cooked in 3 to 10 minutes. Their nutritive value is very like the untreated product. The decrease in cooking time makes it possible for many families to have hot whole-grain cereal for breakfast. Working mothers, for example, have found that cooking untreated cereals takes more time than they have available or want to take for breakfast preparation.

Completely raw cereals. Whole raw cereal grains except for barley and rice are not generally available except in special markets. The absence of such products is probably a result of the lowered demands caused by the long cooking time required. The flavor of whole grains is very desirable, and for those people who use cooking as a hobby, these cereals can add interest to many dishes.

Cracking, flaking, or grinding cereals decreases cooking time and affects texture and appearance but not flavor or nutritional value. These products should be covered and stored in a cool dry place to protect against insect infestation and to prevent development of rancidity.

Flours

Flours in the retail markets of the United States are predominately wheat varieties, however, flours made from other grains and seeds are found in limited quantities. The wheat flours may be enriched—this will be indicated on the label, but the white all-purpose flours must be enriched in certain states. Flours may or may not be bleached. If they are, the word "bleached" must appear on the label. Of varying degrees of fineness, flours may be either steel or stone ground. The method of crushing the grain does not affect the nutritional value of flour.

Wheat flour is the basic substance in forming the framework or structure of baked products. The greatest part of the framework is formed from *gluten*, a complex protein of wheat. The composition and structure of gluten is not definitely known, but it has been thought to be formed from two proteins, *gliadin* and *glutenin*. Gluten, as such, is not formed until flour is moistened and agitated, a procedure referred to as "developing the gluten." Gluten takes up large quantities of water (it may imbibe as much as two hundred times its own weight), can be stretched, and coagulates on heating. The coagulation of stretched gluten strands on heating results in the typical structure found in light baked products.

Wheats are classified as hard and soft. The classification is based upon the strength of the gluten. Hard wheats produce a flour that has a tough, sticky, and tenacious gluten. Soft wheats not only produce a gluten of low strength but also that produced is present in low concentration.

The geographic area affects the type of wheat grown. In the central states hard wheat predominates; in Missouri, the eastern half of the United States, and some western states soft wheat is most plentiful; and in some other sections both types are produced. Climate, rainfall, and condition of the soil seem to affect the quality of wheat and in turn the quality of flour made from the wheat.

White flours. These flours are made from wheats that have been ground and sifted through a silken screen (bolted). Variations in the quality of wheat flours may be due to the type of wheat used, the conditions under which the wheat is grown, the size of the flour particles, the completeness of the milling, and the substances added during the milling process. Grades of flour are designated on the containers and are: patent—first grade; clear—second grade; straight—third grade; and red-dog—lowest.

Cost of white flour is related to color, fineness of grind, size of container, and total amount of wheat produced in any one year. An evaluation of statements given on the label will be of great help in securing the flour best suited to need and money available. If flour is to be used only as a thickening agent, quality and cost may be of no importance. However, if flour is to be used for making the family bread supply, both cost and quality are important factors.

All-purpose or family flour is the white flour most commonly found in the retail market. This may be produced from either hard or soft wheat, or it may be a blend of the two. In the southern states the all-purpose flours are predominately soft, and in the northern states they are generally hard. As the name implies, all-purpose flours can be used for many purposes.

In the southern states mono-calcium phosphate (an acid salt) is often added to flour. This flour is then referred to as a *phosphated flour*. The purpose of the phosphate is to give a better volume and appearance to biscuits when sour milk and soda are used as the leavening agents. Soda is often used in excess of the amount needed to neutralize the acid of the sour milk, and the mono-calcium phosphate can combine with the excess soda and produce carbon-dioxide, the leavening gas. This aids in the leavening process and also prevents the bitter taste and yellow spots caused by unreacted soda.

Self-rising flours contain a complete chemical leavening agent. This is usually a mixture of sodium bicarbonate (soda) and calcium acid phosphate. Either all-purpose or cake flours may be self-rising. Other ingredients such as fat, sugar, dried eggs, and/or milk solids may be added to produce mixes that have specialized uses. These are the so-called *"packaged mixes,"* and they are made for cakes, pie crusts, biscuits, griddle cakes, gingerbread, and many others. Cost, preparation time, and eating qualities of these products can be evaluated by comparing the various brands with each other and with similar products compounded in the home. If a true comparison for eating quality is to be made, the products being compared should be produced at the same time and of similar ingredients, because memory time for flavor and texture is very short. Cost comparisons must be based upon equal weights of the ingredients used.

Many special purpose flours are produced for industry. Except for *cake* and *pastry* flour, they are not available in retail stores.

Whole wheat flours. Flours labeled "whole wheat," "cracked wheat," "entire wheat," or "Graham" are made from the entire wheat grain. They are all identical in composition if not in character. Limited amounts of malt and chemicals for bleaching and aging may be added to any of these. Also, they may be made from either hard or soft wheat.

Flours other than wheat. Flours made from rye, barley, rice, corn, peanuts, buckwheat, soybeans, oats, lima beans, potatoes, sweet potatoes, and cotton seeds are found in some markets. Rye flour is the only one of this group that has a protein similar to gluten. Therefore, when these are the only flours used in baked products they provide poor gas retention, and a heavier product results than can be achieved when all wheat flours are used. When they are used with wheat flours, the resulting products can be very light and if lightness is not important, some of these flours may be used without wheat flour. Small amounts (5 to 10 per cent) of soy flour and peanut flour will not affect the texture of bread, whereas the percentage and nutritive quality of the protein in the loaf will be increased by the relatively high protein and the improved ratio of essential amino acids provided by these special flours.

In American markets flours other than wheat are generally sold in small packages and at a relatively high unit cost. This may in part account for the low demand for them. A second reason for the low popularity may be the standards set for baked products. The average person attempts to duplicate texture and structure of products made with white flour rather than letting other flours stand on their own merits and accepting the variation thus attained. Certain packaged mixes, especially muffin, griddle cake, waffle, and bread may contain one or more of these flours.

Alimentary Pastes

This is the general term applied to flour products of high gluten content such as macaroni, spaghetti, noodles, and other similar products that are stamped into fancy forms. Commercially they are made from *semolina*, a flour milled from very hard durum wheat. The flour is moistened with the smallest possible quantity of boiling water, then thoroughly mixed until it is smooth and very tough. This dough is forced with great pressure out of the bottom of a cylinder through a perforated plate. The size and shape of the holes in the plate determines the pattern of the product. Strands of paste come out as tubes, ribbons, or other shapes. Letters, birds, etc. are sliced with a rotary knife as they emerge from the plate. Pastes are dried before packaging. Examples of various sizes and shapes are shown in Fig. 52.

Pastes properly made of fresh durum-wheat semolina are slightly golden colored and translucent. Color may be added to pastes of less

Fig. 52. Alimentary pastes are made into numerous shapes and sizes, fifteen of which are shown. 1. Spaghettini. 2. Alfabeto. 3. Anellini Rigati. 4. Quadretti. 5. Triangoli. 6. Tufini. 7. Mostaccioli Rigati. 8. Fusilli Tagliati. 9. Cornetti Rigati. 10. Stortini. 11. Fusilli Yolanda. 12. Maruzze. 13. Farfaloni. 14. Margherte. 15. Elena. (Courtesy of the Wheat Flour Institute, Chicago.)

desirable cooking qualities, thus the final test of quality is in cooking. Pastes made from low gluten content flour become mushy or sticky and do not hold their shape even though they have been carefully cooked.

Table 21. THE NUTRITIVE VALUES OF COMMON CEREAL GRAINS, FLOURS, MEALS, AND PREPARED CEREALS*

Cereal Product	Portion Meas.	Wt. gm.	Energy Value, Cal.	Protein, gm.	Calcium, mg.	Iron, mg.	Vitamin A, I.U.	Thiamine, mg.	Riboflavin, mg.	Niacin, mg.	Ascorbic Acid, mg.
Bran flakes (40% bran)	1 C.	40	117	4.3	24	2.0	...	0.19	0.09	3.5	...
Buckwheat flour (light)	1 C.	98	342	6.3	11	1.0	...	0.08	0.04	0.4	...
Corn flakes (enriched)	1 C.	25	96	2.0	3	0.6	...	0.10	0.02	0.6	...
Corn flour (yellow)	1 C.	110	406	8.6	7	2.0	370	0.22	0.06	1.6	...
Corn grits (enriched)	1 C.	160	579	13.9	6	4.6	480	0.71	0.42	5.6	...
Corn-Soya shreds†	⅔ C.	28	105	5.1	19	1.8	...	0.14	0.06	...	...
Crackers (plain)	2	11	47	1.1	2	0.1	...	0.01	0.01	0.1	...
Farina (raw)	1 C.	169	625	18.4	47	1.7	...	0.09	0.10	1.4	...
Macaroni (dry)	1 C.	123	463	15.7	27	1.8	...	0.11	0.07	2.5	...
Noodles (eggs, dry)	1 C.	73	278	9.2	16	1.5	140	0.15	0.08	1.7	...
Oatmeal (dry)	1 C.	80	312	11.4	42	3.6	...	0.48	0.11	0.8	...
Peanut flour‡	1 C.	100	341	59.0	65	10.0	...	0.60	0.30	...	...
Popcorn (popped)	1 C.	14	54	1.8	2	0.4	...	0.05	0.02	0.3	...
Rice (brown)	1 C.	208	748	15.6	81	4.2	...	0.66	0.10	9.6	...
Rice (white)	1 C.	191	692	14.5	46	1.5	...	0.13	0.05	3.1	...
Rice (puffed)	1 C.	14	55	0.8	3	0.3	...	0.01	0.01	0.1	...
Rye flour	1 C.	80	285	7.5	18	0.9	...	0.12	0.06	0.5	...
Soybean flour (low-fat)	1 C.	101	230	45.1	268	13.1	70	1.11	0.35	2.9	...
Spaghetti (dry)	1 C.	94	354	12.0	21	1.4	...	0.09	0.06	1.9	...
Tortillas	1	20	50	1.2	22	0.4	40	0.04	0.01	0.2	...

Wheat flour											
Whole wheat	1 C.	120	400	16.0	49	4.0	...	0.66	0.14	5.2	...
Self-rising (enriched)	1 C.	110	385	10.1	299	3.2	...	0.48	0.29	3.8	...
Patent (enriched, all-purpose)	1 C.	110	401	11.6	18	3.2	...	0.48	0.29	3.8	...
Cake	1 C.	100	364	7.5	17	0.5	...	0.03	0.03	0.7	...
Wheat germ	1 C.	68	246	17.1	57	5.5	...	1.39	0.54	3.1	...
Wheat (puffed)	1 C.	12	43	1.3	6	0.4	...	0.01	0.02	0.6	...
Wild rice	1 C.	163	593	23.0	31	...	...	0.73	1.03	10.0	...

* Nutritive values U.S.D.A. Agriculture Handbook No. 8.
† Nutritive values from container.
‡ Calculated values.

Semolina flour from which the pastes are made may be whole wheat, white, or enriched white. The same nutritional advantages are gained from the whole wheat paste as from other whole wheat cereals. The nutritional value of pastes can be improved by methods of preparation and foods with which they are used. Whole grain or enriched alimentary pastes have the same place in the Daily Diet Guide as bread or other cereals. See Table 21.

Baked Products Made from Flour

Flours of cereal grains and other seeds are made into an unbelievable number of varieties of baked products. The buying of these products may be a hazardous financial adventure because it is very hard to evaluate quality before purchasing. Taste preferences of the population vary to such a degree that standardization of these products becomes an impossible task. The Federal Food and Drug Administration has established definitions and minimum requirements for some baked products. However, the only consistent guides that consumers have are the labels. These labels should be read carefully and the information evaluated. The price of these products is dependent upon ingredients and amount of labor and time required for preparation. Large quantities of eggs, milk, fat, and fruits tend to improve eating quality and nutritive value, at the same time increasing unit cost.

Bread is the one baked product bought consistently by our population. The average daily consumption of bread in the United States is estimated at 5½ slices per person.[1]

Bread is defined by the Federal Food and Drug Administration. It must contain at least flour, water or other specified liquid ingredients, salt, and yeast. However, a loaf of bread usually contains sweetening, shortening, bread improver, yeast, and yeast food, in addition. Bread softeners, mold inhibitors, and other such substances are permitted in bread. They are all nontoxic and harmless, but should be considered when bread is purchased.

Softeners prevent the apparent staling of bread thereby making it very difficult to check for freshness. Freshness in bread is not important to nutrition, but if bread is several days old when it is purchased, mold growth may become a problem if bread is not eaten soon after purchasing. Therefore, if softeners are used, bakers should be encouraged to put the date of baking on bread labels. Bread softeners can be a factor in lowering the cost of bread because staling of bread

---

[1] Federal Register 1955.

has long been a major financial problem to bakers. Consumers have always demanded strictly fresh bread (often judged by softness) at the market although it may be kept in the home several days before it is opened. Because of this demand, in the past bakers have been forced either to discard leftover bread, or to reprocess it, or to sell it at a lowered price.

Bread softeners produce a doughy center in the loaf, which is distasteful to some individuals. As a result of this dislike many bakers are making special breads without added softeners and emphasize the omission in their selling campaigns. Such breads may sell at a higher price than bread that contains a softener because of a lowered shelf life.

Enrichment of bread is also practiced and is compulsory in those areas having enrichment laws. This enrichment is accomplished by adding the so-called enrichment wafers to the bread formula rather than through the use of enriched flour. The riboflavin content of enrichment wafers used in bread with high milk solids (6 per cent) is lower than that for wafers used in breads with little or no milk solids.

Standards for identifying breads have been established for white bread, enriched white bread, milk bread, raisin bread, and whole-wheat bread. The liquid in bread labeled "milk bread" must be milk, or milk solids in the proportions of normal milk. Raisin bread must contain at least 3 ounces of raisins per 1 pound of bread, and if bread is labeled "Butter-Crust" or "Honey-Crumb," it must contain these ingredients. If bread is sold within the same state in which it is made, these federal requirements need not be met. It is advisable to know and understand the laws governing the manufacture and sale of foods in the state of one's residence. This information may be obtained by writing to the state Food and Drug Administration.

The net weight of the bread is given on the wrapper and is a factor in the cost of bread. It is very difficult to use volume as the yardstick for buying because compact heavy loaves which are gaining in popularity may have the same weight, the same ingredients, and the same nutritive value as large light loaves. If consumers are not accomplished "hefters," they can obtain the weight from the label.

Many special purpose breads are found in our markets. These should be carefully appraised before buying. *Low-calorie breads*, for example, may not be as low in calories as one would anticipate. If one eats only 3 or 4 slices of bread per day, what difference can 10 Calories per slice mean one way or the other in a total daily intake of 2500 Calories. Likewise, *high-protein breads* can hardly be considered superior nutritionally in an average diet where only 2 or 3 slices of bread are consumed. If protein were increased 10 per cent, the increase in 2 slices of bread would be only from 6.0 grams to 6.6 grams. This 0.6 grams would be more than covered by drinking 2 tablespoonfuls of milk. Calorie content as well as total overall nutrients of these special breads should be compared to those found in the regular breads, if one is inclined to be influenced by claims of nutritional advantages only.

Low-salt or low-sodium bread is designed for special dietary purposes and should not be confused with the *Salt-Rising Bread*, which is a bread leavened with bacteria and which possesses distinctive texture and flavor qualities. Unless a physician has prescribed a low-sodium diet, one should not make common use of this special dietary bread.

In order to obtain the most food value and personal satisfaction from bread money, one can compare the various ready-made breads with those made at home for (1) kind and amounts of ingredients used; (2) flavor, texture, and other eating qualities; (3) potential nutritive values; and (4) cost per unit weight.

Bread should be stored in covered containers or wrapped carefully to prevent drying and staling. If bread is to be kept several days, mold growth can be inhibited by storing it in the refrigerator. If it is to be kept several weeks or even months it may be frozen. If a "bread box" is used the box should be thoroughly sterilized before fresh bread is added in order to prevent growth of mold.

Bread products such as rolls, buns, coffee cakes, and sweet rolls are sold in many styles and in varying degrees of doneness. The compromise that has been made between home production and the simulation of home production was accomplished by the use of refrigerated raw doughs and so-called "Brown-and-Serve" types. Baking of these products is completed in the home and they have a "just baked" flavor. For those people who lack the skill and patience or the time and facilities to create a roll, these partially prepared products are very satisfactory. They are, however, more costly than home produced products that contain comparable ingredients.

Cakes, pies, cookies, crackers, and pastries can be purchased in any quality and at almost any price. It is difficult to evaluate these products, and caution is the best guide to buying. Products with cream fillings should be refrigerated if they are not to be used immediately. It is well to avoid purchase of any unrefrigerated baked goods with cream fillings especially during warm weather. Cream fillings provide excellent media for the growth of *staphylococci*, the bacteria which produce the toxin responsible for most cases of food poisoning.

Cereals are completely cooked when the starch is translucent and the flavor decidedly changed. The flavor of cooked starch is bland, compared to the sharp dry taste of raw starch. The texture of cooked starch is also different from that of raw. When cooked starch grains are pressed against the roof of the mouth with the tongue, they disintegrate evenly without leaving a hard center. The flavor and texture of thoroughly cooked starch is difficult to describe, and the practical test is relative and subjective, therefore, perhaps the best way for each person to learn to recognize the flavor is by taste experimentation.

The type of cereal used and consistency desired in the finished product influence the amount of cooking water and length of cooking period. Whole grains require a longer cooking time than do cracked or ground products. Also, cereals that have not been heat-treated require a longer cooking period than quick-cooking or partially cooked types need.

General Methods for Cooking Cereals

The original form of cereal can be maintained during the softening process by using a method of cooking that will not require stirring. Cooking over hot water is a practical method, as the starch of cereal reaches its capacity for maximum absorption of water several degrees below the boiling point of water. The dry cereal can be added slowly to rapidly boiling liquid to prevent lumping. If it is allowed to cook rapidly for 2 or 3 minutes, the starch grains will begin to swell and the cereal will not settle to the bottom of the pan. Then the product may be covered and placed over the hot water or another controlled heat source, and the cooking will continue slowly without undue evaporation and sticking. This method of cooking is referred to as "steaming." If cereal is to be cooked over direct heat, a pan made of a heavy metal that retains heat evenly will give a good product. The heat may be reduced to the simmer position after the heavy pan is thoroughly heated, and a slow even cooking will be maintained. Modern ranges have thermostatically controlled units for such slow cooking. Whatever method is selected it should be one in which stirring is not necessary. Stirring tends to destroy the structure of the grain. The result is a sticky and gummy product.[2] (For principles of starch cookery see Chapter 9.)

Salt added to the water at the beginning of the cooking period will inhibit the absorption of water by starch granules slightly, but salt will help to maintain the original shape of the grain, and it will be absorbed into the cooked product. Salt may be omitted if desired since it is used primarily for flavor. The average amount of salt needed to develop maximum flavor is ¾ teaspoon per cup of dry cereal, although this will vary somewhat with each product.

The type of liquid used in cooking cereal influences both the cooking method and the result. Water is the common medium used; however, milk, fruit juices, vegetable juices, or meat stocks may be used. Milk should always be cooked over hot water or another controlled heat source because it scorches easily. A double boiler can be used for top-of-the-range cooking or if cereal in milk is to be cooked in the oven, the baking dish can be set in a pan of hot water. Milk produces a product similar in appearance to that cooked in water. Acid juices and the addition of sugar to the cooking medium will lower the thickening power of starch. Also they will produce opalescent pastes. Rice and wheat for pilaff are frequently cooked in meat stock to which fat has been added. Cooking is carried out in the same manner as when water is used.

If quick-cooking cereals are cooked over hot water rather than direct heat, the time required may be longer than that given on the package. Some authors have stated that the cooking period will improve flavor; however, studies have shown that this time cannot be extended far without breaking down the weakened cell structure of the previously cooked cereal resulting in a mushy, sticky product.

Rice. This is a typical cereal which is commonly cooked without breaking the grain. Rice may be in the form of whole-grain or brown rice, white rice, quick cooking rice, or precooked rice. The most common problem encountered in cooking rice is one of retaining the original form and preventing the grains from adhering to one another. Washing rice before cooking has been suggested as a means of removing excess starch, which when cooked acts as an adhesive to hold the grains together. If rice has been sprayed with vitamin and mineral additives, these would be removed by such a procedure. The suggestion is usually given on the package that rice not be washed either

---

[2] Pans in which cereals have been cooked and dishes in which they are served should be soaked or washed as soon as the cereal is used because it sticks tenaciously.

before or after cooking. Varieties of rice vary in their stickiness, and considerable research is being done at the present time to determine which strains of rice have adhesive qualities and which do not have them.

The amount of liquid used for rice cookery depends upon the method of cooking. The quantity should not exceed the amount that can be absorbed during the cooking process, or eaten with the rice. Excess liquid that is discarded may carry large amounts of water-soluble vitamins and minerals. If rice is to be cooked over direct heat, 2¼ cups of liquid to 1 cup of rice is recommended. This amount of liquid will be completely absorbed and the rice will increase in volume approximately three times. If the rice is cooked over hot water, the liquid may be reduced to 1¾ cups. Oven cooking requires about the same quantity of liquid as is used over direct heat; however, a longer cooking time will be required.

Minerals in some of the hard waters will cause the flavones (yellow pigment) of the rice to darken. If this is considered undesirable, it can be prevented by adding ⅛ teaspoon cream of tartar, or ½ teaspoon lemon juice or vinegar to one quart of cooking water.

Preliminary to cooking, rice may be browned with or without fat in a skillet. Some of the starch is dextrinized by this process, and a very distinct flavor is produced. Swelling of the grain is decreased by this procedure; however, each grain will be very pronounced. Prebrowning is often used for refried rice, Spanish rice, and many Oriental dishes.

Alimentary pastes. These products can be cooked by methods similar to those used for white rice. Again it should be emphasized that washing either before or after cooking should be discouraged, especially if the pastes are made from whole wheat or enriched flour. Because of their very bland flavor, cooking liquid other than water will enhance the eating quality of this product. The cooking liquid chosen should complement the sauce or other foods that are to be served with the pastes.

General Uses for Cereals and Pastes

Cereals and alimentary pastes have many uses other than as breakfast food or main dishes. They may be used as stuffings, desserts, extenders for main dishes, thickening agents, and covers for other foods.

Stuffings for fowl, pork chops, or rolled meats and fish are often made with precooked corn meal (in the form of corn bread), cracked wheat, bulghur, barley, or rice, and these are pleasant changes from traditional bread-sage stuffing. Tomatoes stuffed with bits of chicken and some brown rice that has been cooked in chicken broth make a very desirable luncheon dish.

Desserts made with cereals are innumerable. Puddings in which cereal is used in place of corn starch or flour has an interesting texture. Cereal fruit bars, cereal pie crust, and cereal toppings for apples and other cooked fruits are but a few of the ways cereals can be used in creating desserts. If the cereals used are whole grain, the compounded desserts are very nutritious.

Macaroni and cheese or meat noodle casseroles are common examples of adding cereals to main dishes. Other cereals may be toppings for casseroles; ingredients for casseroles, stews, or soups; made into bread and steamed on top of stews; or thickeners for such cooked vegetables as stewed tomatoes.

Meats, vegetables, and food mixtures may be coated with granular cereals for frying, steaming, or baking. They not only aid in browning but they also hold the liquids in the food and thus prevent drying and aid in the retention of vitamins and other water-soluble nutrients.

Fig. 53. Muffins are an example of a batter that is soft enough to be dropped from a spoon. Cups are only half filled to permit expansion during baking. (Courtesy of the Wheat Flour Institute, Chicago.)

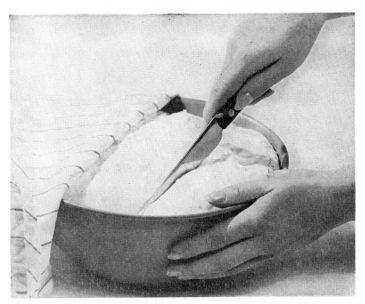

Fig. 54. Doughs are thick flour mixtures that can be cut or rolled. (Courtesy of Sperry Operations, General Mills, Inc., Minneapolis.)

These are only a few of the many possibilities of these versatile products. One needs but a little creative thinking to produce many interesting and nutritious dishes.

PREPARATION OF BATTERS AND DOUGHS

Flours are used as the basic ingredient for that large group of products referred to as batters and doughs. When the ratio of flour to water is such that mixtures will pour or drop easily from a spoon, they are called batters(Fig. 53). Thick mixtures that can be rolled or kneaded are doughs (Fig. 54).

These flour mixtures comprise the most voluminous, complex, and sensitive categories in food preparation. Students working side by side using the same recipe and ingredients often find that their products vary considerably. Small differences in accuracy of measuring, mixing, and baking are not uncommon, and the astonishing part is that among the hundreds of foods prepared by inexperienced students in college laboratories it is estimated that less than 5 per cent would be classed as unacceptable.

The number of ingredients that must be measured in home production of baked goods may be a factor in the growing popularity of prepared mixes. However, in baked goods whether home produced or from mixes, the artistry of the cook need know no bounds and with a little planning and imagination a homemaker can "make her cake and eat it too."

Functions of the Ingredients Used in Batters and Doughs

The fundamental ingredients used in batters and doughs are flour, liquids, salt, and leavening agents. Eggs, sugar, and fat are frequent additions. Each ingredient has a specific function in the various products.

Flour. Gluten of flour forms the framework of baked products. When gluten is moistened and stirred, it forms long strands that become tough and rubbery and have the capacity to hold gases. These gases expand when heated and stretch the strands of gluten to make a fine network.

Starch granules of the flour begin to swell when they come in contact with liquid. These swollen starch granules are entrapped in gluten meshes when they are coagulated, somewhat like bricks in mortar. Cooked starch also helps to strengthen the framework of the baked product.

Liquid. Liquids are necessary for the formation of gluten and the hydration of starch. The baking powder must be dissolved in a liquid before carbon dioxide is released. The moistness or dryness of a baked product is also dependent upon its liquid content. The amount of liquid is an important factor in the manipulation of the batter or dough as well as in the appearance of the finished product.

Gluten strands do not develop easily in large quantities of liquid because as gluten is formed, the particles tend to float in the liquid rather than to adhere to each other. When the quantity of liquid is decreased and the quantity of flour is unchanged the amount of stirring necessary to develop gluten must be decreased because the gluten particles are relatively close together and their chances of meeting and clinging to each other are great.

Leavening agents. Lightness is the distinctive characteristic of products made from batters and doughs. This quality is produced by heat, which expands the air, or by other gases trapped in the elastic gluten and egg proteins. The most common gases are air, steam, and carbon dioxide (CO_2).

Air may be incorporated in a batter or dough by several methods: (1) by folding beaten egg whites into the flour mixture; (2) by fold-

214 ·

ing and rolling the dough; (3) by beating the batter or dough; (4) by creaming fats with sugar; and (5) by sifting the flour. Entrapped air expands rapidly when batters are heated and this causes the products to increase in size. Mere expansion during heating does not account for all of the leavening power of air. Therefore, it would seem that air has a second function. Heat changes some of the water to steam within the trapped air and greater expansion is the result of this formation of water vapor than is caused by the expansion of air.

Steam is responsible for part of the leavening that takes place in all flour-liquid mixtures. When water is converted by heat into vapor, it expands 1600 times its original volume. Steam, as already mentioned, is more effective when air bubbles are present. In leavening such products as pound cake and angel food cake, which contain no baking powder, steam accounts for two or three parts of the expansion and air for one part.

Carbon dioxide in batters may be generated under several conditions: (1) neutralization of an acid by soda; (2) decomposition of chemicals termed carbonates; and (3) fermentation of sugar by yeast or bacteria.

Sour milks and cream, molasses, honey, and chocolate contain acids, and when these products are used with soda, carbon dioxide is evolved. As acidities of these products vary greatly, it is difficult to know how much soda to add to secure the maximum of carbon dioxide or to prevent an excess of soda. If all the soda cannot react, the residual soda produces a bitter flavor and may destroy some of the thiamine and other B-complex vitamins in the flour and eggs (see Chapter 13). Unneutralized acid does not seem to have a deleterious effect on flour mixtures; in fact, it may tenderize the gluten and produce a fine-textured product. Therefore, since baking powder is a more reliable source of carbon dioxide, it might be suggested that the acid ingredients be used for flavor and tenderness, the soda omitted, and baking powder used for the source of leavening gas.

Cream of tartar, an acid salt, can be combined with soda to produce carbon dioxide, and this mixture was extensively used before baking powders were common. Tartrate type baking powders are probably an outgrowth of this mixture.

Baking powders, according to the Food and Drug Administration definition (1906), are leavening agents containing an acid-reacting material and sodium bicarbonate (soda) with or without starch and/or egg white; the powders must produce 12 per cent by weight of their total weight as available carbon dioxide. They all contain some cornstarch as a standardizing and stabilizing aid. The acid-reacting materials may be: (1) tartaric acid or its salts; (2) acid salts of phosphoric acid; (3) aluminum salts of sulfuric acid; or (4) any combination of the foregoing. The chemical reaction that occurs to liberate the CO_2 is typified by the general formula:

$$\text{Acid} + \text{Alkali (soda)} \xrightarrow{\text{(water)}} CO_2\uparrow + \text{Water}\downarrow + \text{Residue}\downarrow$$

The type of baking powders are designated by their acid constituent —tartrate, phosphate, or sulfate.

Tartrate powders react rapidly and completely when cold water is added; therefore, they are known as single-acting baking powders. When tartrate powders are used, a large proportion of CO_2 is produced during the preparation of the batter and is lost in great amounts during mixing. This necessitates using a relatively high proportion of baking powder to flour to produce satisfactory leavening. The residue of tartrate powders is sodium tartrate, which has little effect on flavor.

Phosphate powders commonly contain monocalcium phosphate or monosodium phosphate. The calcium salt is used in powders sold in the retail market, and the sodium salt is used primarily by bakers and for packaged mixes. As much as two-thirds of the carbon dioxide may be liberated when cold water is added but heat is required to liberate the remainder. For some few people the residue remaining in the product has a bitter flavor.

Sulfate powders contain sodium aluminum sulfate (S.A.S.) as the acid salt. This salt is seldom used alone but is usually combined with a phosphate salt. Baking powder thus formed is referred to as a double-acting powder because one of the salts is slow-acting and the other is rapid. The residue from this baking powder may also be bitter tasting to some individuals.

Baking soda (sodium bicarbonate) and baking ammonia (ammonium bicarbonate) will both decompose to give off carbon dioxide gas when heated even though an acid is not present. This method of leavening is seldom used because of the bitter residue that is formed, but some old recipes will still list these as ingredients.

Formation of carbon dioxide by fermentation of sugar with yeast is the common method of leavening bread. Yeast can also be used to make desirable cakes, biscuits, griddle cakes, and doughnuts.

Yeast is a microscopic living plant that produces carbon dioxide during its growth processes. The enzyme, *zymase*, present in yeast activates the fermentation. Sugar is usually added to the flour mixture as yeast food to speed the action; however there is a small amount present in flour and the materials holding the yeast plants, and fermentation could proceed without added sugar.

Like all plants, yeast has three requirements for growth, that is, food, moisture, and warmth. If yeast is to produce an appreciable quantity of gas, these growth conditions must be met. Sugar in the bread formula provides the food, liquid provides the moisture, and the best temperature for growth of compressed yeast is 80 to 86° F but for active dry yeast granules 110 to 115° F is considered optimum. Either temperature can be provided by the use of a water bath, or a gas oven warmed by its lighted pilot will provide the higher temperature suitable for dry yeast.

Yeast may be secured from several sources: the "starter" which is dough or sponge saved from previous "batches" of bread; compressed yeast cakes in which the yeast plants are embedded in moist cornstarch; and dry granular yeast. The last two types may be purchased in the retail market. Some starters impart distinctive flavors to bread and are therefore desirable. Others if kept too long impart undesirable flavors. Compressed yeast cakes must be refrigerated until used, otherwise the yeast plants will grow and produce undesirable flavors or even enough acid to cause the plants to die.

The species of yeast plants that are used by producers of these products are carefully selected for their ability to produce carbon dioxide. Other types of yeast and undesirable organisms may enter the bread through the flour, the milk, and other ingredients. To be certain that these undesirable organisms and the enzymes (*proteases*) are inactivated in the milk source, fresh milks should be scalded. Canned milk and reconstituted dried milks need not be scalded since they have already been sufficiently heat-treated.

Salt-rising bread is leavened with carbon dioxide and hydrogen formed by bacterial fermentation of sugars (*Clostridium welchii*). These organisms were originally isolated from cornmeal to which a relatively large amount of salt was added to inhibit the growth of other bacteria which might give undesirable flavors to the bread, hence the term "salt-rising." Bakers now use cultures of the isolated bacteria. This type of leavening produces the distinctive flavor in this bread which is especially well-liked by some people.

Eggs. Eggs add protein and thereby strengthen the framework of the batter or dough. They contribute to flavor, color, and nutritive value. Eggs also furnish liquid; angel food cakes, for example, have no other source of liquid than egg whites. Stiffly beaten egg whites can serve as a means of incorporating air in the batter.

Sugar. Sugar has several uses in batters and doughs: it adds flavor; it aids in browning by caramelizing on the surface; and it increases tenderness by interfering with the development of gluten. It should also be noted that sugar raises the coagulation temperature of both egg and flour proteins.

Because sugar delays the development of gluten, sugar content must be given consideration when flour mixtures are stirred or kneaded. It can readily be observed that the amount of stirring necessary to develop the gluten increases as the percentage of sugar in the mixture is increased.

Fat. Fat interferes with the development of strands of gluten because an oily coat is formed on the particles, and they do not stick together easily. The strands that are formed are usually short and tender. This accounts for the term, *shortening*, which is applied to fat.

Salt. Salt is used for flavor only. However, in large quantities it does inhibit yeast growth and affects gluten formation.

Mixing and Baking Batters and Doughs

The quality of finished baked products is dependent upon many factors, namely: (1) temperature of the ingredients during mixing; (2) kind, quality, and proportion of the ingredients; (3) order, methods, and amount of mixing; (4) size and shape of the mixing equipment; (5) size, shape and material from which the baking pan is made; and (6) temperature and time of baking.

Temperature of the ingredients. This affects texture, tenderness, and keeping quality of baked products. Methods of mixing are usually given for ingredients that are at room temperature (75° F). Unless methods are changed to fit other temperature conditions, the best results are obtained when ingredients are at this temperature. Fat directly from the refrigerator does not cream well, nor can it be evenly distributed throughout a product. Conversely, fat that is melted or very soft is oily and has a tendency to separate from the batter during baking. The temperature of ingredients to which the fat is added will also change its plasticity. When cold egg whites are whipped, they produce a relatively small volume, which means that the lightness desired in the finished product is not attained. Gluten of the flour takes up water rapidly at temperatures higher than 75° F thus producing tough strands with less mixing.

Kind, quality, and proportion of ingredients. These factors affect not only the finished product, but also some mixing procedures. Baking powders, for example, contain different salts, each of which has a specific effect upon the rate that gluten absorbs water. The combination sulfate-phosphate powders take up the water rapidly and thus delay hydration of gluten. The net result is that batters in which these powders are used are less easily overmixed than those that contain other powders.

Effects that variations in the composition of ingredients have upon the finished product should be considered when substitutions in recipes are made. All-purpose flour is used in smaller amounts than cake flour, and mixing should be decreased because all-purpose flour absorbs more water and has more and stronger gluten than cake flours have; or if honey is used as a substitute for sugar, it should be remembered that it contains liquid and therefore the liquid content of the recipe should be decreased and a lower temperature used in baking to prevent off-flavors from overheated honey.

The proportion of ingredients influences method of mixing, amount of mixing which is optimum, baking time, and keeping qualities of the finished product. When a large amount of liquid in proportion to flour is used, gluten develops very slowly if at all. Starch granules in thin mixtures can swell to a greater capacity than in thicker mixtures, and the interior of the products will have a gelatinous consistency. Sugar and fat in large quantities cause a delay in the development of gluten, and therefore products containing large amounts of fat and sugar must be mixed longer than products with lesser amounts to obtain sufficient gluten strands for structure.

Order, method, and amount of mixing. Order and method of combining ingredients are particularly important in making all baked products. The flake of biscuits and piecrust is the result of both the method of combining fat with other ingredients and the kneading. Cakes in which the flour is added in small portions are finer in texture, but require longer beating than those in which the flour is added all at one time.

The amount of mixing of batters and doughs affects flavor as well as texture. A long mixing period allows for a more thorough blending of ingredients as well as more complete dissolving of sugar and other solutes than does a short mixing period. The amount of gluten development is directly related to the mixing time after the flour is added. Since gluten structure is so closely related to texture and eating quality, this cannot be overlooked. A dry bready product that stales quickly is one of the results of overstirring; tunnels, peaks, smooth crust, and poor browning may also result from this. Sugary crusts, concave tops, and a coarse texture may be the result of understirring. Many times a small error in measuring can be compensated for by adjusting the mixing procedure.

Size and shape of mixing equipment. Large or shallow mixing bowls used for small amounts of batter may be the cause of overstirring. Thus both size and shape of the bowl should both be considered. If batters are mixed with a spoon, size and shape of the spoon are influential. A large slotted wooden spoon will be more efficient than a small spoon. Wooden spoons are usually more efficient than metal spoons because the rough surface of wood has more pull than does the smooth surface of metal, and if stirring is more efficient the stirring time will be reduced. Many people have their favorite mixing bowls for various products and thereby know the amount of stirring necessary for each product.

Size, shape, material, and fill of baking pan. Baking pans vary in material, weight, shape, and size. In general, materials that conduct heat rapidly will give better browning for products that require a short baking time. Tin or aluminum are better suited to baking muffins and biscuits than are iron or glass. When heavy pans made from a material that conducts heat slowly are used, the products have a thick heavy crust and in some cases are misshapen. A lower baking temperature is usually recommended for glass, iron, and enamelware than is used for tin or aluminum. Shiny pans reflect the radiant heat and a longer baking time is required than with dull pans. This may result in a greater volume because the product has a longer time to expand before the crust is formed.

Shape and size of the baking pan are also factors in quality of baked products. Round pans give a more even browning than pans with square corners. The product may be browner at these corners than on the rest of the area. Deep pans, because of increased depth of batter, require lower temperatures and a longer baking time than do shallow pans. The size of the baking pan should be suited to the amount of batter and the shape of the product. Baking heat causes products to rise and this expansion should be allowed for when pans are filled. Generally pans should not be filled more than to half of their depth. For improved volume, pans should be oiled only on the bottoms. This leaves the side areas dry and provides a climbing surface for the batter or dough.

Baking of batters and doughs. Baking of flour mixtures produces many changes that enhance both texture and flavor. The gluten and egg proteins coagulate, which causes a loss of water and a hardening that results in a fixation of the structure. Water that is lost from the gluten is taken up by the starch, with the result that the gelatinized starch holds the greater part of the water. Starch is also a support for baked products. The product dries forming a crust on the surface and baking temperatures are usually high enough to cause some dextrinization of surface starch. Some of the color change of the crust is believed to be caused by a complex chemical reaction between sugar and protein. Other browning may be caused by caramelization of sugar. Flavors associated with these browning reactions are very palatable in baked products.

Optimum baking temperatures are dependent upon the size and type of pan used and the results desired. The first factor was discussed above. Results desired at various times or with different products might include: complete cooking without browning, which requires a low temperature; rapid expansion of steam, which requires a high temperature. If the temperature is too high and a hard crust forms on the surface before the gases have completely expanded, pressure of the expanding gas may break the crust and cracks will be formed. In some cases the uncooked center of the dough may flow out through the cracks.

The baking pan should be placed in the oven so that there is free circulation of heated air around the pan. This means that if two or more racks of the oven are to be used, the pans should be staggered and not placed directly above each other (see Fig. 55).

Fig. 55. Even baking is possible only when air can circulate freely around each pan. Four pans can be baked at one time if they are staggered on two shelves. (Courtesy of Southern California Gas Co., Los Angeles, California.)

Staling of Baked Products

Baked products that have a spongy crumb lose their desirable eating quality quickly after they are baked. Part of this change is caused by staling. The staling process is not entirely understood, but it is reversible by heat, and baked products will regain their freshness by heating. In fact, bread may be freshened several times. Toasting can also be used to restore freshness qualities. This process is amply illustrated by toasting bread products such as biscuit, muffin, or cake slices and even pancakes and waffles.

Proper storage of all baked products will retard staling. Cookies and crackers should be stored in moisture-proof containers. Cakes, bread, and other baked products stale very slowly at freezing temperatures (14° F or less). Muffins, biscuits, waffles, and griddle cakes stale so rapidly that they should be eaten immediately after baking or refreshed before eating.

Preparation of Specific Products

Quick breads. The so-called "quick breads" are cereal products that are leavened with air, steam, or baking powder. They require a

Fig. 56. Dry ingredients for flour products are mixed thoroughly when sifted together. (Courtesy of the Wheat Flour Institute, Chicago.)

relatively short preparation time because they are baked soon after they are mixed. Included in this category are popovers, griddle cakes, waffles, muffins, biscuits, and baking powder breads. Quick breads are commonly mixed by any of three general methods termed: muffin; pastry; and conventional cake.

The muffin method is the so-called "one stage" method. The dry ingredients are sifted together in the mixing bowl. The beaten eggs, milk, and oil are thoroughly mixed and added all at once to the dry ingredients (see Figs. 56, 57, and 58). If plastic fat is used in place of liquid fat it should be added as in the pastry method. The plastic fat can be more evenly distributed if it is blended with the dry ingredients. In either case the liquid and dry ingredients are mixed with the amount of stirring that is consistent with the ingredients used. The thin or pour batters of the popover or griddle cakes can be stirred longer than the thick, low fat, low sugar batters of the waffle, muffin, or coffee cake.

The pastry method is commonly used for pastry and biscuit products. The dry ingredients are sifted together. A plastic fat is cut or blended into this mixture and then the liquid is added and the dough stirred until it is wet. It may then be dropped as for "drop biscuits" or kneaded and rolled as for piecrust and flaky biscuits.

Fig. 57. Eggs are blended before the other liquid ingredients are added prior to the incorporation of liquid into dry ingredients in the muffin method of mixing. (Courtesy of the Wheat Flour Institute, Chicago.)

Fig. 58. Quick breads require little mixing to blend liquid with dry ingredients in the muffin method of mixing, and the finished batter is lumpy but without traces of dry flour. (Courtesy of the Wheat Flour Institute, Chicago.)

The cake method is used not only for making cakes but also for sweet bread products. The fat and part or all of the sugar are creamed together. The beaten eggs are added to this mixture and thoroughly mixed. The dry ingredients are thoroughly mixed by sifting and then are added alternately with the liquid to the creamed mixture. Variations can be made from this by separating the egg and adding the beaten white at the end, or by making a meringue with part of the sugar and folding it in at the end of mixing.

All quick breads are closely related and their methods of preparation do not differ appreciably. It is often difficult to state exactly when a muffin mixture becomes a coffee cake or at what point in adding sugar and fat a coffee cake becomes a cake. Table 22 illustrates this close relationship as well as indicating the proportions and methods that have been found by the authors to be best suited for laboratory use for one person. Smaller amounts than those given are unsatisfactory because unreliable results are obtained, and they are not realistic for families even as small as one or two persons.

The calculated nutritive values of these representative quick breads are given in Table 23. It should be remembered that the nutritional value of the products can be augmented by addition of fruits, nuts, etc., as well as by other foods that are usually eaten with them. A home-mix formula is also given in the Appendix for those interested in compounding their own mixes.

Characteristics of representative products can be evaluated by a study of the illustrations in Fig. 59.

Popovers are made from a very thin batter, which can be beaten for either a short or long time. The fat can be added either to the batter or used in the baking dish to prevent sticking. It is possible to make popovers with less than the 3 eggs per cup of flour; however, the volume will be less because the egg proteins are essential to hold the gluten particles and to increase the extensible protein that will trap the steam. As the steam is formed it will push out the walls of protein, which in turn will coagulate and form a hollow ball.

The oven should be preheated because a hot oven is needed to cause the steam to form rapidly before the walls are too rigid to be extended. The product should be baked until it is very firm, otherwise it will collapse when cooled. Generally a high temperature (425° F) is used for the first 15 minutes of baking and then it is reduced to 375° F for the final baking period. However, good results may be obtained by using a temperature of 400° F for the entire baking period.

The chief causes of failure in popovers are: low oven temperature; insufficient baking; and insufficient egg. Popovers can be made with all-purpose or whole wheat flours.

Griddle cakes are made from pour batters, but they have a higher flour content than does the popover batter. The batter for griddle cakes is mixed by the muffin method. Griddle cakes have many variations and the proportion of flour to liquid may be changed depending on the consistency desired or the type of flour used. If a thin wafer-like product is desired as for cheese blintzes or crepes suzettes, 1 cup of liquid to 1 cup of flour might be desirable; for a thick bready product, the flour may be increased to 1½ cups. All-purpose flour will make a thicker batter than will cake flour.

Thin pancakes may contain no baking powder. Flannel cakes may contain relatively large amounts.

The flavor and texture of griddle cakes can be varied by using one or more types of flour or meal, flaked cereals, various liquids, and addition of such foods as crisp bacon, nuts, dates, sesame seeds, and the like. Flaked cereals such as bran and oatmeal may be added directly to the batter or they may be soaked in the liquid (bran is commonly soaked for 30 minutes). The soaking procedure will cause the product to be soft and light.

The proportions of eggs, fat, and sugar may be varied. They are not essential ingredients for a griddle cake but they add desirable

Table 22. PROPORTIONS, MIXING METHODS, BAKING TEMPERATURES AND TIME, AND CHARACTERISTICS OF GOOD BAKED PRODUCTS

Baked Product	Flour		Baking Powder SAS or Phos.		Salt, tsp.	Fat		Sugar		Liquid			Eggs, No.
	Meas.	Wt., Gm.	Meas., tsp.	Wt., Gm.		Meas.	Wt., Gm.	Meas.	Wt., Gm.	Type	Meas.	Wt., Gm.	
Popover	1 C.	110	...	...	½	2 Tb.	28	...	...	Milk	1 C.	244	3
Griddle Cake	1 C.	110	1½	5	½	3 Tb.	42	3 Tb.	37	Milk	⅞ C.	213	1
Waffle	1 C.	110	1½	5	½	3 Tb.	42	3 Tb.	37	Milk	⅞ C.	213	2
Muffin	1 C.	110	1½	5	½	3 Tb.	42	3 Tb.	37	Milk	½ C.	122	1
Coffee Cake I	1 C.	110	1½	5	⅓	⅜ C.	84	⅜ C.	75	Milk	½ C.	122	1
Cake	1 C.	100*	1½	5	¼	¼ C.	56	½ C.	100	Milk	⅜ C.	90	1
Biscuit	1 C.	110	1½	5	½	¼ C.	56	...	...	Milk	⅜ C.	90	...
Coffee Cake II	1 C.	110	1½	5	½	¼ C.	56	¼ C.	50	Milk	⅜ C.	90	1
Pastry	1 C.	110	...	...	½	¼ C.	56	...	...	Water	2 Tb.	25	...
Bread	3 C.	330	...	...	½	1 Tb.	14	1 Tb.	12	Milk	1 C.	244	
										Water	¼ C.	59	...

Characteristics of a Good Product

Baked Product	Other Ingredients	Method of Mixing	Baking Time, Min.	Baking Temp., °F	Approximate Yield	Crust	Shape	Interior
Popover	...	Muffin	45	400	6—large	Golden brown; crisp	Irregular; rounded	Hollow with moist gelatinous webbing; tender
Griddle Cake	...	Muffin	4	375	9—4 inch	Golden brown	Regular; smooth	Moist, but not soggy; tender; medium fine grain
Waffle	...	Muffin	6-8	375	2—10 x 10 inch	Uniform brown; crisp; tender	Regular	Light; slightly moist; tender
Muffin	...	Muffin	20	425	6—2 inch	Golden brown; pebbled	Rounded rough top	Slightly yellow; slightly moist; uniform medium holes; tender
Coffee Cake 1	Top with sugar, cinnamon, and butter	Muffin	25	375	1—8 inch layer	Golden brown; crisp; tender	Level top	Slightly moist; tender; fine grain
Cake	1 tsp. flavoring	Cake	24	375	1—8 inch layer	Even golden brown	Slightly rounded top	Fine even grain; velvety crumb
Biscuit	...	Pastry	12	425	8—2 x 2 x 1 inch	Pebbley; golden brown; crisp	Straight sides; level top	White; flaky; bready; tender; medium grain
Coffee Cake II	Top with sugar, cinnamon, and butter	Pastry	30	375	1—8 inch layer	Golden brown; crisp	Level top	Slightly yellow; flaky; tender; fine grain; slightly moist
Pastry	...	Pastry	12	425	1—9 inch pie	Blistered; light; even brown	Flat; not shrunken	Flaky; tender
Bread	1 package yeast	Muffin or pastry	45	375	1 loaf	Thin crust; even golden brown	Well rounded symmetrical top	Slightly moist; creamy white; fine texture; resilient; light

* Cake flour.

Table 23. THE NUTRITIVE VALUES OF ONE SERVING OF BAKED PRODUCTS PREPARED WITH THE PROPORTIONS OF INGREDIENTS GIVEN IN TABLE 22*

Baked Product	Serving	Energy Value, Cal.	Protein, gm.	Calcium, mg.	Iron, mg.	Vitamin A, I.U.	Thiamine, mg.	Riboflavin, mg.	Niacin, mg.	Ascorbic Acid, mg.
Popover	2 large	338	12.8	128	2.4	680	0.24	0.38	1.4	...
Griddle cakes	3 4-inch	366	8.4	100	1.5	295	0.20	0.23	1.3	...
Waffle	1 10-inch	597	15.6	161	2.9	720	0.33	0.47	2.0	...
Muffins	2 2-inch	378	7.3	63	1.5	248	0.19	0.21	1.3	...
Coffee Cake I	1 4-inch sq.	340	5.4	47	1.1	186	0.14	0.16	1.0	...
Cake†	1 4-inch sq.	330	5.2	38	1.1	166	0.14	0.15	0.2	...
Biscuit	2 2-inch	225	3.7	32	0.8	36	0.12	0.11	1.0	...
Coffee Cake II	1 4-inch sq.	295	5.7	38	1.1	172	0.14	0.15	1.0	...
Pastry	1/6 of 9-inch crust	140	1.7	3	0.5	...	0.06	0.05	0.6	...
Bread	1 slice 1/2 inch thick	95	2.4	23	0.8	25	0.11	0.08	0.3	...

* Values calculated from U.S.D.A. Agriculture Handbook No. 8 using enriched flour.
† Made with cake flour, unenriched.

characteristics. If fat is used in the batter, the griddle need not be oiled. The sugar is an aid to browning.

A great deal of the success of making griddle cakes depends upon the temperature at which they are baked. If the heat source is thermo-statically controlled, all of the guesswork is removed. A standard griddle or skillet requires a more subjective test. The "water drop" test [3] is fairly reliable. After the griddle has reached the desired temperature, the batter is poured onto it. The cakes will have a better appearance if all the batter to be used in one cake is poured at once rather than spooning it in small portions. It should be necessary to turn the cakes only once. They are ready to turn when bubbles appear at the edges. Thick cakes require longer to bake than thin ones.

Waffles are made from griddle cake batter that contains both fat and eggs. Waffles will have a better texture and will be crisper if the egg whites are beaten stiffly and folded into the mixed batter than if the whole eggs are mixed with the liquids. A waffle is considered most desirable when it is crisp, tender, and evenly browned. To produce a product of this type the batter should not be overstirred and the temperature of the waffle baker should be carefully controlled.

Batter that contains an adequate amount of fat and that is baked at the correct temperature in an "oil seasoned" baker should not stick. The baker should be heated to the baking temperature before batter is added or it may stick even though it contains enough fat. Grids of waffle irons should be left open to cool when baking is finished, so that the "seasoning oils" are not burned off the grids.

Excess waffle batter may be covered and stored in the refrigerator for a few days but it will probably be more satisfactory to bake all of the batter and freeze any excess waffles. Frozen waffles may be heated for use in the toaster or oven.

Muffins are made from a medium batter mixed by the muffin method and the homogeneous mixture of dry ingredients is just moistened by the thoroughly-mixed liquid ingredients. Because muffins have a high flour and a low fat and sugar content, the gluten strands develop with little stirring. Usually ten to twenty-five strokes will be sufficient. The batter is rough and thick and it will drop easily from a spoon.

The basic muffin pattern can be varied by substituting other flours, meals, or flaked cereals for all or part of the all-purpose flour, by using liquids other than milk, by using sweeteners other than sugar, and by

---

[3] A few drops of water are dropped from the tip of the finger to the grill. If the drops sit and boil, the grill is too cool. If they go "pppppppppf" and disappear as steam, the grill is too hot. The temperature is correct when the drops form round balls and glide across the grill.

A

Fig. 59. Representatives of the varieties of quick breads that may be easily prepared in the home are: coffee cake (A), popovers (B), muffins (C), and biscuits (D). (Courtesy of Sperry Operations, General Mills, Inc., Minneapolis.)

B

adding fruits, nuts, crisp bacon, or other ingredients to the batter. When liquids other than milk are used, milk solids added to the dry ingredients will improve the nutritive value.

Muffins are baked in special pans oiled only on the bottom. These pans are made of a metal that transmits heat rapidly and evenly. The recommended baking temperature for muffins is 400 to 425° F, and the average baking time is 20 minutes. If they are allowed to stand undisturbed in the pans a few minutes after baking, the condensation of steam in the pan will facilitate removal of the muffin.

Muffin batters that have the maximum amount of fat and sugar are cake-like in appearance and texture. They may be baked in cake pans and topped with butter, sugar, cinnamon, nuts, strusel,[4] or other topping, and they then become a quick coffee cake. The various muffin batters can be baked in loaf pans to form a loaf of bread. The increase in size will necessitate a longer baking time and a temperature of 375° F is recommended. Products baked in loaf pans often have small cracks on the surface. However, if batter oozes out of the cracks the beginning baking temperature was too high.

Biscuits are made from a soft dough which can be either dropped from a spoon or rolled and cut. In order to form a grain that can be flaked across the biscuit, they are mixed by the pastry method. If the dough is to be dropped onto the baking sheet, the dough is not kneaded. Drop biscuits are coarse and do not have the flaky layers characteristic of the traditional "baking powder biscuit." Crisp and tender dropped biscuits may be used as toppings for desserts, meat pies, or shortcake bases. This dough may also be steamed for dumplings.

Kneading is a folding and turning process in which the dough is worked by the hands. Biscuits require only 10 to 20 folds to obtain a satisfactory product with flaky layers. The kneaded dough may be patted or rolled into the desired thickness and cut into rounds or squares. Care should be taken not to incorporate excessive flour during the kneading or rolling processes since this changes the proportion of the ingredients. A heavy cloth impregnated with flour makes a good rolling surface.

Biscuits should be baked on sheets made from a metal that transmits heat rapidly and evenly. Since biscuits are relatively small they are quickly baked so that a high temperature is used (400 to 425° F). A baking period of 10 or 12 minutes should be sufficient. Larger sizes

---

[4] Brown sugar and cinnamon mixture.

will require longer times and, often, lower temperatures than the small biscuits.

Biscuits may be varied further by using flours other than wheat, by using liquids other than milk, and by adding ingredients such as sugar, cheese, nuts, spices, herbs, wheat germ, and the like. The texture and eating quality can be changed by varying the amount and type of fat used and the extent of kneading. Low fat content gives a bready biscuit, and high fat content gives a rich, tender, compact biscuit with a lowered volume.

Cakes. Cakes are classified into two types—sponge and "butter" cakes (Fig. 60). Sponge cakes do not contain fat, and they do not usually have baking powder added but are leavened with air and steam. Butter cakes contain fat and are commonly leavened with baking powder, steam, and air. The butter cake that contains equal weights of fat, flour, sugar, and eggs is known as a pound cake, and it is leavened only with air and steam.

Sponge-type cakes are made from eggs, flour, sugar, acid, and flavoring. If whole eggs are used, the cakes are termed sponge cakes; however, if only whites are used the cakes are referred to as angel food. True sponge cake has a higher nutritive value than angel food because of the presence of the egg yolk. Sponge cake, more often than butter

Fig. 60. Characteristic of the butter cake is a fine texture and moist velvety crumb. (Courtesy of Sperry Operations, General Mills, Inc., Minneapolis.)

cake, is used for jelly or fruit roll, and shortcake cups. See p. 138, Chapter 4 for preparation of this type of baked product.

The pound cake is so called because it was originally made from one pound of flour, one pound of fat, one pound of sugar, one pound of eggs, and flavorings. This makes a large cake with a compact texture. The pound cake is mixed by the cake method. Its fine texture makes an excellent base for large quantities of dried fruits and nuts and is often the base for Christmas "fruit cakes."

The pound cake is usually baked in a loaf pan, but it can be baked in layers, or in the waffle baker, or in a "krum kaken pan." The last produces a thin wafer-like product that can be rolled or shaped and used as a holder for ice cream, fruits, or whips.

The standard butter cake recipes are many, but the underlying principles for making and baking are all similar. The differences usually occur in flavorings, sizes, methods of combining ingredients, and amounts of sugar and fat used. Although the world could progress nicely without one more cake recipe, here again is a place where each person can put his creative ability into action.

Butter cakes usually contain fat, sugar, eggs, liquid, flour, leavening agent, and flavoring. These ingredients may be combined by the muffin method or the cake method. Variations of these methods are many; however, only four will be discussed here. They are: (1) cake method or conventional method; (2) modified conventional; (3) conventional sponge; and (4) single stage or so-called "quick" method.

The cake method, or *conventional method*, was described earlier (see p. 224). The *modified-conventional* method varies from this only in the manner of adding the eggs. The yolks are added to the fat-sugar mixture during the creaming process and the whites, stiffly beaten, are folded into the batter with the last 50 strokes of mixing.

The conventional-sponge method varies only slightly from the modified conventional. It is sometimes referred to as the meringue method. One half of the sugar is creamed with the fat, and the other half is whipped with the egg white to form a meringue, which is then folded into the batter with the last 50 strokes of mixing.

The single-stage method has been developed especially for use with the mechanical mixer and is a modification of the muffin method. Cakes made by this method require a higher sugar content than is used for other methods. Also fats with added emulsifiers give best results and all ingredients should be at room temperature. The actual mixing is done in two steps but all in one bowl. First all of the dry ingredients are sifted into the bowl, all of the fat, flavoring, and all or half of the milk is added and the whole is beaten for a specified length of time (usually 2 minutes or 300 strokes). In the second step the un-beaten eggs and the remaining liquid, if any, are added and the mixture again beaten for a specified length of time (1 or 2 minutes).

Regardless of the method of combining the ingredients, certain fac-tors are common to all methods. The amount of mixing required after the flour is added to the liquid, depends upon the ratio of sugar and liquid to flour. Flavoring extracts are fat-soluble and will be retained to a greater extent if mixed with the fat. Cake flour will give the finest grain, but very interesting flavors may be developed when whole wheat, part soyflour, part peanut flour, or other flours are used.

Butter cakes may be baked at temperatures of 325 to 375° F. Lower temperatures are used for loaf cakes than for layers. The baking time will depend upon amount of batter, depth of batter, material from which the pan is made, and oven temperature. Cup cakes will be baked in a shorter time than is needed for larger cakes. Cakes should be partially cooled before they are removed from the pan and then allowed to completely cool on a rack.

Comparing products made by the four methods and a comparable packaged mix makes an interesting experiment. The formula used in the experiment should be one that is suited to the single-stage method and also is not unlike the mix. In order to evaluate the methods and to determine the advantages and disadvantages of each, records should be kept. The time required for measuring ingredients, mixing, and washing dishes and quality scores for each product should be recorded. The baking time should be the same for all. Each method has its ad-vantages and disadvantages, and perhaps no person would want to use any one method every time.

Individuals who would like to take advantage of the time-saving afforded by packaged mixes and yet would like to use their own choice of ingredients may find the home-mix formula given in the Appendix satisfactory. Most of the ingredients can be purchased "pre-measured."

Bread and rolls. Bread making is a home skill that is rapidly vanish-ing, but in this do-it-yourself age, it might be well to consider a revival of the art. Bread making is fun, and the results can be very satisfying to one's creative ability. Kitchens are better prepared for making bread than ever before—thermostatically controlled ovens, accurate timers, mechanical mixers, thermometers, adequate heating, and many other improvements are common in many homes. If cooking skill is to pass entirely from the home to the factory, to what use can the homemaker put all of her beautiful kitchen gadgetry?

Bread is made from a very stiff dough leavened with yeast. The flour that will produce the finest texture is made from hard wheat;

however, very desirable bread can be made from all-purpose flours. The amount of flour required to make a dough and the amount of stirring or kneading necessary will depend upon the hardness of the wheat, the condition under which the wheat was grown, the amount of milling, and many other factors. Therefore amount of flour and kneading time are generally not definitely stated and are only approximated.

The liquid most commonly used in bread is milk; however, milk solids with other liquids such as water, vegetable stock, certain fruit juices, or whey may be used. Potato stock is a favorite liquid, and the addition of mashed potatoes to the dough will aid fermentation, retard staling, and add flavor. Breads with milk solids stale less readily than do breads made with no milk.

The amount of yeast used can be varied within wide limits. If one wishes to complete the bread-making process as rapidly as possible, a large amount of yeast (1 or 2 cakes yeast per cup of liquid) can be used. However, if sufficient time can be planned, ½ cake yeast per cup of liquid may be used and the yeast allowed to increase in the dough. The long *proofing* period (fermentation) that is required when ½ cake yeast is used is considered desirable because a by-product of yeast growth is a "butter flavor" which imparts a very desirable flavor to the product. The longer the yeast is allowed to grow the more flavor is developed. After an optimum amount of yeast growth the dough begins to sour. This further changes the flavor of the bread and is occasionally used to produce "sour-dough bread."

Two methods of mixing may be used for breadmaking: sponge and straight-dough. For either procedure the yeast is softened or hydrated after it is sprinkled on the lukewarm water. This mixture need not be stirred but can be left to soften while the other ingredients are measured. If sugar is added to the water, the yeast will start to grow during the softening period.

In the sponge method the liquid, yeast, sugar, and a part of the flour are mixed to form a batter. This batter is set aside, incubated at a temperature suitable for the source of yeast used. Gas production during this proofing period makes the batter spongy, hence the term "sponge." The batter is allowed to ferment until enough carbon dioxide has developed to double the bulk. The remainder of the flour and salt are then added to the sponge, and the dough is stirred until the gluten strands will form complete circles around the bowl, that is, the dough can be stirred without breaking. It is then placed on a floured board or on a cloth impregnated with flour and gently kneaded (Fig. 61) until the gluten is well-developed and the dough has the consistency of putty; the surface is satin smooth and has tiny blisters showing under a skin. From this point it is treated in the same manner as the dough made by the straight-dough method. When kneaded doughs are set to proof, they are lightly oiled or closely covered with a damp cloth to prevent surface-drying and to permit the dough to expand as gas is produced.

The straight-dough method differs from the sponge method in that all ingredients are added in one mixing period without the preliminary proofing period and the dough is kneaded as soon as it is mixed. The kneading time for either method will vary depending upon: type of flour used; thoroughness of the original stirring; and experience and technique of the person kneading.

After doughs are kneaded, they are proofed until they are twice their original size. The carbon dioxide is then pushed out without kneading and the dough is proofed a second time. The gas is again pushed out, and the dough is molded for baking (Fig. 62). The oiled loaf is placed in a baking pan that has been oiled on the bottom, and then the dough is allowed to proof until it has tripled in bulk (Fig. 50).

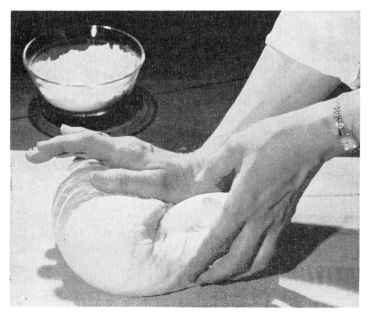

Fig. 61. Kneading of a dough by folding and gently pushing it together is a form of manipulation designed to develop the gluten. (Courtesy of Sperry Operations, General Mills, Inc., Minneapolis.)

A

B

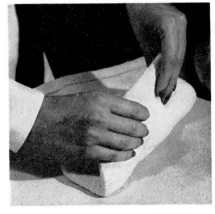

C

D

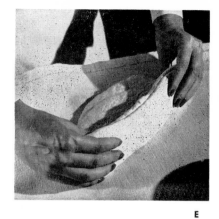

E

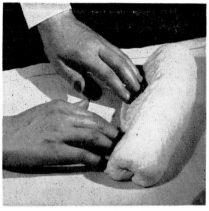

F

G

Fig. 62. Bread dough is
molded after the second
proofing and placed in an
oiled pan for the final proofing before being baked.
(Courtesy of the Wheat Flour
Institute, Chicago.)

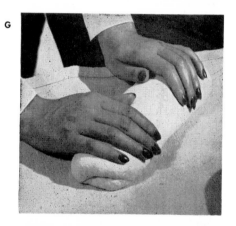

H

The first rising often requires 70 per cent of the total fermentation time. The yeast plants increase in numbers during the proofing periods, and shorter times are required for succeeding fermentation periods. If time does not permit, the second proofing can be omitted, although shortcuts seldom give a good product—bread made from hard wheat, particularly, will be coarse, stale rapidly, and will not have the distinctive bread flavor.

After the initial kneading, the dough should be handled as little as possible. During the fermentation periods the network of gluten has been divided into fine filaments, and if they are pushed together or broken, the texture will be coarse and the bread dry. Doughs that are allowed to overproof until the dough collapses will also have undesirable textures and flavors.

Neither the bowl in which bread is proofed nor the sides of the baking pan need to be oiled as unoiled surfaces give the bread dough a "hand hold" for climbing. Oiling the bottom of the baking pan makes removal of the loaf easier; the sides can be easily loosened with a spatula.

The pan in which bread is baked should be large enough to allow for ample expansion. A rule-of-thumb for judging pan size is that the bread should reach the top of the pan when it has tripled in volume. A shallow pan seems to provide a better loaf than a deep pan.

Loaves should be evenly shaped. Compact spots should be avoided because the finished loaf will be an exaggerated shape of the original. The bread should be placed in the center of the baking pan and baked in the center of the oven. Baking temperatures of 375 to 400° F are recommended.

During the baking process bread will generally double in volume as a result of continued growth of yeast during the first part of baking, expansion of the gases entrapped, and formation of steam in gas pockets. This expansion is known as "oven spring." The greater part of the oven spring occurs during the first 10 minutes of baking as an enclosing crust is being formed and the yeast plants are being destroyed.

Oiling the crust as soon as bread is removed from the oven gives a soft crust. Bread should be removed from the pans a few minutes after it is taken from the oven, thoroughly cooled, and then wrapped. The wrap should be as nearly airtight as possible since exclusion of air will delay staling. As mentioned previously, flour mixtures can be heated and refreshed if they have become undesirably stale.

Roll mixes differ from loaf mixes primarily in the quantity of fat and sugar they contain. Eggs are often added to roll mixes, and the

Fig. 63. Crescents, fan-tans, and pocket-books are only a few of the interesting roll shapes that may grace the family bread basket. (Courtesy of the Wheat Flour Institute, Chicago.)

dough is usually less stiff than bread dough. Eggs add structure to the gluten and give a good flavor and rich color. Roll mixes are usually allowed to ferment only once before they are shaped. After the gas is pushed out of the dough the rolls are shaped and allowed to triple in bulk before baking. Plain rolls are baked at a temperature similar to that used for biscuits (400 to 425° F). Cinnamon rolls or those containing sugar, honey, or molasses will require a low temperature to prevent burning of the sugars before the center is coagulated.

Many variations in the original doughs may be made. Flour and flour mixtures can be varied and liquids and flavoring ingredients can be changed. The real fun in working with yeast doughs is in the shaping (Fig. 63). If the dough is rolled or patted into a thin (¼- to ½-inch) rectangular sheet, various types of "fillings" can be added. Butter, sugar, cinnamon, nuts, peanut butter, candied fruit, dates, prunes, or other ingredients may be spread over the sheet and a loaf obtained by rolling the sheet like a scroll. These ingredients and others can be used singly or in any combination. Many of these additions increase the nutritive value as well as make family and friends happy. If you wish to be the life of a pot-luck party, just take a loaf of your "custom built" bread.

SUMMARY

Cereals, excellent sources of food energy in the diet, are also rich in the B-complex vitamins, especially thiamine, unless highly refined. The proteins of cereal products, also, are important because 24 per cent of the total dietary protein may be derived from this source. These proteins are mainly incomplete, but can be supplemented with milk, egg, meat, and vegetable proteins to produce products containing all the essential amino acids in favorable proportion.

Breakfast cereals can be purchased in many forms—ready-to-eat, partially cooked, and completely raw. Flours in the retail market are predominately wheat varieties; however, flours can be milled from other grains and seeds. Flours may be refined or whole-grain, and they may or may not be enriched with vitamins and minerals. Flours are made commercially into breads, cakes, pies, and other baked products and sold in general markets or bakeries. Of these commercial products, bread is used in largest quantities. Alimentary pastes are made from a very hard wheat and may be white, enriched white, or whole wheat.

Preparation procedures are discussed for cooking of breakfast cereals, alimentary pastes, and baked products containing wheat flours. The classification of batters and doughs with simplified formulas and mixing procedures are given, as well as suggestions for variations in these products. It is recognized that making flour mixtures involves the most complicated procedures of any of the cooking processes. Factors affecting palatability characteristics are discussed.

In the preparation of all cereal products, the major emphasis is on conservation of nutritive value. Palatability is a close second. It is realistic to recognize that no matter how nutritious a dish, unless it is palatable it will seldom be eaten.

Reading List

1. Batcher, O. M., P. A. Deary, and E. H. Dawson, 1957, "Cooking quality of 26 varieties of milled white rice," *Cereal Chem.*, **43**:277.

2. Bogert, L. J., 1960, *Nutrition and Physical Fitness*, W. B. Saunders Co., Philadelphia.

3. Charles, V. R. and F. O. Van Duyne, 1953, "Effect of freezing and freezer storage upon quality of baked rolls, brown-and-serve rolls, and shaped roll dough," *Food Technology*, **7**:70.

4. Charley, H., 1950, "Effect of baking pan material on heat penetration during baking and on quality of cakes made with fat," *Food Research*, **15**:155.

5. *Enrichment of flour and bread; A history of the movement*, 1944, National Research Council Bul. 110.

6. American Medical Association, Council on Foods and Nutrition, 1951, *Handbook of Nutrition*, The Blakeston Co., New York, Chapters XXV and XXVIII.

7. Hartman, R. H. and E. E. Rice, 1959, "Supplementary relationships of proteins," *J. Amer. Diet. Assoc.*, **35**:34.

8. Justin, M. M., L. O. Rust, and G. E. Vail, 1956, *Foods*, Houghton Mifflin Co., Boston.

9. Kik, M. C., 1956, "Nutritional improvement of rice," *J. Amer. Diet. Assoc.*, **32**:647.

10. Kulp, K., O. C. Golosinec, C. W. Shank, and W. S. Bradley, 1956, "Current practices in bread enrichment, nutritive content of enriched bread," *J. Amer. Diet. Assoc.*, **32**:331.

11. Lowe, B., 1955, *Experimental Cookery from the Chemical and Physical Standpoint*, John Wiley and Sons, Inc., New York.

12. Sieburth, J. F., T. Wahl, and B. A. McLaren, 1954, "Effect of added softeners on moisture content of bread," *J. Amer. Diet. Assoc.*, **30**:355.

13. Taylor, C. M., G. MacLeod, and M. S. Rose, 1956, *Foundations of Nutrition*, The Macmillan Co., New York.

Fig. 64. Fats in moderation increase the palatability of each food in the meal. (Courtesy of National Association of Margarine Manufacturers, Lincoln, Nebraska.)

7 . . FATS IN MODERATION FOR NUTRIMENT AND PALATABILITY

RETENTION OF FOOD VALUE OF FATS DURING
FOOD PREPARATION

SUMMARY

READING LIST

THE TERM "FATS" INCLUDES ALL THE EDIBLE OILS AND SOLID FATS extracted from plant and animal sources that are used in food preparation. Sources of plant fats commonly used in the United States include corn, cottonseeds, olives, soybeans, and peanuts; the common animal sources are beef, pork, mutton, chickens, and milk. These vary in flavor, consistency, and somewhat in color.

Fats perhaps more than any other group of foods have been responsible for differences in food preparation among countries and among regions. Some countries, such as those near the Mediterranean, prefer oil, particularly olive oil, for cooking whereas north European countries prefer the harder animal fats such as butter and lard. The types of prepared foods seen in those areas reflect these differences in fats.

In the United States modern technology perhaps has made more changes in market fats than in any other food. These changes have been brought about by deflavoring or adding flavor, removing or adding color, and increasing or decreasing fluidity. American markets today contain wide choices even in this otherwise simple commodity. It is, therefore, possible for the American consumer to obtain all the subtle differences in food preparation afforded by different types of fat, and the cosmopolitan palate need know no boundaries of region or country.

FAT IN THE DAILY FOOD PLAN

Fat, one of the required nutrients in the daily diet, has just as important physiological functions as the more fascinating "micro-nutrients," and is just as important to survival. The uses of fat in nutrition include: (1) providing energy for a portion of the body needs; (2) contributing the essential fatty acids needed for specialized cells and functions; (3) serving as a carrier for fat-soluble nutrients; (4) aiding in the absorption of various nutrients; and (5) assisting in filling the fat depots of the body for reserve energy supplies, for pads, and for temperature adjustment to environmental changes. In addition to the nutritive aspects, moderate amounts of fats give desirable staying quality to meals and improve their palatability (Fig. 64) thereby influencing the intake of other nutrients.

Digestion and Absorption of Fat

Fats leave the stomach slowly, but under normal conditions they are completely digested (95 to 98 per cent). The tolerance for fat varies among individuals, and individual tolerance varies from time to time depending upon physical condition. As with other types of foods, gastric distress may result from excessive fat intake. This distress may be either a full feeling, which results in lowered appetite, or diarrhea. Diarrhea may be influenced by the type of fat as well as the quantity. The fats of lower melting temperature such as oils are absorbed somewhat more rapidly than those of higher melting points and would be expected to be tolerated in somewhat larger quantity.

Quantity and Energy Value of Dietary Fat

The annual average weight of refined fats purchased in the United States was reported to be approximately 48 pounds per person in 1955 (World Almanac, 1957). This does not include fats normally found in foods and consumed without extraction from such foods as milk, cheese, meat, nuts, olives, avocados, and others. This group may be referred to as "hidden fat."

Fat provides approximately 9 Calories per gram or 4000 Calories per pound. The amount of refined fat purchased would indicate an average daily intake of ¼ cupful, or approximately 400 Calories per person per day. It would not be difficult to consume a like quantity in foods such as cheese, meat, nuts, etc. The refined fats consumed by the average American represent approximately 20 per cent of the total required Calories for a sedentary adult. The Food and Nutrition Board of the National Research Council recommends this percentage as a desirable quantity to be obtained from fat by this type of individual.

The Food and Nutrition Board of the National Research Council has suggested a minimum intake of 20 to 25 per cent of total Calories from fat. This provides a condition favoring the absorption of fat soluble vitamins and other substances. For active adolescents and young people, the Food and Nutrition Board indicates that 30 to 35 per cent of the Calories may be derived from fat. These individuals may tolerate fat in quantities even greater than the recommended 30 to 35 per cent, and it is estimated that the American armed forces are ingesting 40 per cent of their total Calories in the form of fat. Other active individuals requiring 4000 to 6000 Calories per day often obtain an even higher proportion of Calories from fat.

Sedentary individuals whose total Caloric requirement may be less than 2000 Calories per day may do well to limit total fat intake to near 20 per cent of the day's total Calories in order to have food from each of the groups of the Daily Food Guide each day. Senior citizens may absorb fats less readily than young people. They should limit total fat intake and distribute that carefully among the meals of the day.

Fat is termed a thiamine-sparing energy food because it is believed that oxidation of fat for energy requires less thiamine than is necessary to oxidize carbohydrate. It would therefore seem especially desirable to satisfy an equitable portion of the energy needs from fat since American diets are frequently low in the thiamine-bearing foods (particularly whole grain or enriched cereals and legumes).

The fat content of meals for family groups composed of individuals of different ages, physical conditions, and activities may need to be given special attention. Children drinking a quart of whole milk are receiving 38 grams (342 Calories) of fat and can hardly be expected to consume vegetables and meats in recommended quantities if these are generously seasoned with fats. For this reason meals planned for young children should have limited amounts of fried foods, salad dressings, pastries, nuts, etc. Families that contain members who are adolescents and young adults requiring high Caloric intake, as well as the young children and senior citizens, can add fatty seasoning to vegetables and salads at the table, and the individual requirements for fat can be considered. Also, desserts and other food preparation can be adjusted for both extremes. Cream pie filling can be left as pudding for children or the aged and made into pie for others. These individualized desserts can fill each person's desire to be like the rest of the family, and no extra work will be involved.

It can be seen that regulating the amount of fat in the meal to fit individual needs may require considerable ingenuity on the part of the homemaker. Methods of preparation may need to be altered and sometimes changes in food consumption patterns may be necessary. Compare, for example, the fat contribution from the two different menus that follow. Each menu has the recommended amounts from each food group of the Daily Food Guide.

This illustrates how easily fat may be varied during the preparation of the foods even when following the Daily Food Guide. Table 24 gives some sources of the so-called "hidden" fat content and energy value of the fats of common foods.

Foods According to the Diet Guide	Menu I Preparation	Grams Fat	Menu II Preparation	Grams Fat
Pork	Braised tenderloin	20	Roast shoulder	26
			Gravy	9
Egg, 1	Poached on toast	6	Fried	9
Milk, 2 C.	1 cup whole—beverage	9	1 cup whole—beverage	9
	1 cup whole—in cooking	9	2 oz. cheese—with pie	18
Cereal, 4	1. Oatmeal (½ C. milk above)	3	1. Oatmeal with ½ C. cream	27
	2. 3 slices bread (butter below)	Trace	2. Flour (in pie)	0
			2 slices toast	Trace
Butter, 2 T.	On bread and in cooking	22	In cooking	22
Orange, 6 oz.	Juice	0	Juice	0
Shred. Cabbage	Slaw—vinegar sugar dressing	0	Cream slaw	5
Carrots	Soufflé (butter above)	. . .	Buttered carrots (butter above)	. . .
Potato	Mashed (butter above)	. . .	French-fried	18
Apple	Baked apple (butter above)	. . .	Apple pie (with cheese above)	15
Total Fat		69		158

Dietary Fat and Essential Fatty Acids

A fat molecule, although made up of only carbon, hydrogen, and oxygen, is considered a complex molecule because the first products of digestive breakdown are always glycerol and fatty acids. The fatty acids are of many kinds, depending on the number of carbons and the proportion of hydrogen; the oxygen content is the same for all fatty acids. The complete molecule, no matter what its fatty-acid constituents, is known chemically as a *triglyceride* (three fatty acids with one glycerol). Since there are many different fatty acids, triglycerides of many different combinations are possible. All fats are mixtures of these triglycerides, and fats from different sources have different triglyceride combinations.

The fatty acids *arachidonic*, exclusively from animal fats, and possibly *linoleic* and *linolenic*, both from plant oils, should be present regularly in the diet. They are termed *essential fatty acids*. The human requirement for these essential fatty acids is not known, but it is believed to be small. If one has some variation in food, there appears to be no difficulty in obtaining sufficient amounts of these nutrients. Menu plans that include the foods suggested in Daily Food Guide with the addition of small quantities of oil dressings, butter or margarine will automatically include sources of all three fatty acids.

Dietary Fat as an Aid in the Absorption of Nutrients

It has been pointed out that vitamins A, D, E, and K, are soluble in fat (see Chapter 13). Not only are these vitamins carried by fat but

Table 24. THE CALORIC VALUE AND FAT CONTENT OF SELECTED FOODS[*]

Food	Measure	Weight, gm.	Food Energy, Cal.	Fat, gm.	Fat Energy, Cal.
Almonds	¼ C.	34	212	19.0	171
Avocado	½	114	279	30.1	271
Bacon, cooked	2 slices	16	97	8.8	79
Bread, white, 2% milk solids	1 slice	23	64	0.8	7
Cake, plain	3″ wedge	100	378	14.7	132
Chocolate, bitter	1 oz.	29	142	15.0	135
Doughnuts, plain	1	32	136	6.7	60
Ham, cooked	3 oz.	88	338	28.0	252
Hamburger	3 oz.	88	316	26.0	234
Ice cream, plain	⅐ qt.	81	167	10.1	90
Olives, ripe	10	65	106	11.6	104
Peanuts	¼ C.	34	200	15.9	143
Pie, apple	4″ wedge	135	331	12.8	115
Potatoes, french fried	8 pieces	40	157	7.6	68
Sausage, franks	1	51	124	10.0	90

* Calculated from U.S.D.A., Agriculture Handbook No. 8 (1950).

also fat participates in their absorption from the intestinal tract. Nutritionists have recommended that the daily diet should include whole milk or at least 2 tablespoonfuls of butter or margarine to provide a source of pre-formed vitamin A unless some suitable substitute is made.

As the yellow and green vegetables, high in precursors of vitamin A and also high in vitamin K, do not contain fat, it is good nutritional practice to serve oil dressings with salads and fatty seasonings with cooked vegetables in order to have fat present during digestion for the absorption of these foodstuffs.

Mineral oil should not be substituted for food fats because it is not absorbed from the intestinal tract. The fat-soluble nutrients dissolve easily in the mineral oil and it not only hastens the food along the intestinal tract and carries with it some of the fat-soluble substances, but it also coats the absorbing surfaces and thereby curtails absorption of other nutrients. Physicians who prescribe mineral oil as a laxative, expect it to be taken at bedtime when the three meals of the day will have had an opportunity to be digested and largely absorbed.

Dietary Fats and Their Relation to the Fat Depots of the Body

Carbohydrates and proteins as well as fats absorbed in excess of the current needs are deposited as fat in the fat depots of the body. Therefore, dietary fat alone is not responsible for these deposits, and before any program for reducing body fat is instigated, a careful study of the overall diet should be made.

A reducing program that leaves fat out of the food intake entirely, and a program for weight-gaining that attempts to include many foods of high-fat content may both be ineffective. Lack of fat could conceivably result in high total consumption of other energy foods to satisfy the appetite, and this could account for the inability of the reducer to lose weight with mere reduction of fat consumption. Conversely, a sudden increase of food fats might overtax the fat tolerance of the individual. Also, fats lubricate the digestive tract. Thus food might be caused to pass through the intestinal tract very rapidly, thereby lowering absorption of all foods. Foods must be digested and absorbed before they can be utilized by the body. Both of these processes must be accomplished before the movements of the intestine push the food beyond the absorptive region of the intestine. Increases in waste caused by undigested food may result from increasing fat consumption. Persons having difficulty gaining weight may be more successful, therefore, if they give attention to a different proportion of the energy foods rather than simply consuming total energy foods greater than their daily requirement.

Dietary Fats and Their Intangible Qualities in Nutrition

Fats aid in the general satisfaction obtained from food by slowing down the rate at which food is digested, thereby retarding the onset of hunger. Diets composed primarily of low fat foods such as cereals, legumes, and vegetables without fat accompaniments do not have the staying quality of *isocaloric* (equal Calories) foods of higher fat content.

The increase in palatability of foods which results from fat is also frequently overlooked, and attention might be given to the distribution of total fat among the different foods. If a salad is served but not eaten because it is unpalatable without dressing, it cannot nourish the body. In this respect food patterns of various cultural groups have been unjustly criticized by uninformed or unthinking individuals who have an entirely different eating pattern. The American tourist, forgetting about the natural fat content of meat, milk, bacon, eggs, cheese, butter on his bread, and other foods in his own diet, may consider excessive the amount of oil used with salads and vegetables in the Mediterranean countries. The food pattern of the average southern European shows a very high bread intake (without butter), little or no other baked goods, and relatively small amounts of meat or eggs. The oil of his salad or of his olives—frequently eaten in quantity—is necessary to make the high-cereal diet acceptable.

BUYING AND CARE OF FATS

Despite the differences in chemical structure, all fats have similarities in physical properties. These include a greasy feel; ease of mixing with each other and with the substances of similar construction such as the yellow and green plant pigments and flavorings; taking up of odors from the atmosphere; and an aversion to mixing with water. There are differences, however, that account for the fact that one fat may be better suited to the preparation of a specific food product than is another fat. These differences in properties include melting temperatures, congealing temperatures, smoking temperatures, susceptibility to oxidation, and flavor.

Classification and Description of Market Fats

The market fats may be separated into four categories for specific purposes in food preparation. These are plastic fats that contain other substances but not less than 80 per cent fat; plastic fats containing 100 per cent fat; soft fats; and oils.

Plastic fats that contain other substances but not less than 80 per cent fat. This group includes butter, margarine, and mixtures of butter and margarine. These fats are primarily for speading on bread, enriching puddings and similar preparations, and seasonings for vegetables.

Butter is concentrated natural milk fat churned from either sweet or sour cream. It may be salted or left unsalted. The unsalted butter is termed *sweet butter* but is made from either sweet or sour cream. Salt acts as a preservative agent against microbial growth, and generally 3 per cent of butter is salt. Some people, however, prefer the flavor of the unsalted butter. Approximately 17 per cent of butter is made up of milk solids and water. Unless there are restrictions at the state or local levels, color and butter flavor may be added to butters without so stating on the label.

It is possible for butter to be flavored from bitter weeds, wild onion, or garlic that the cows may have eaten. This is not a common defect even in isolated areas or roadside markets. In large creameries, the cream with such off-flavors would either not be accepted—or it would be diluted with cream from other sources so that the flavor would not be perceptible.

Federal grades for butter have been established. They are based on flavor, body, color, and salt. The grade is then listed on the carton as either a score or letter grade. U. S. Score of 93 (Grade AA) is considered high quality; U. S. Score 92 is Grade A, and so on. The score is that of the butter at the time it is packaged and may not be the score at the time it is purchased. Butter of low grade may be worked with fresh milk and sold as *reprocessed butter.*

Margarine is manufactured from a mixture of fats and resembles butter in texture, composition, and flavor. It fulfills the need for a low-cost spread for bread and a seasoning fat. Popular demand for a yellow color in the margarine resulted in the repeal in 1950 of a high federal tax on these colored products, but state laws may still limit the sale of colored margarine in some areas. A capsule of yellow coloring is included with each package of uncolored margarine.

This yellow color is in no way indicative of vitamin A value; however, margarines are usually fortified with pre-formed colorless vitamin A. When fortified, margarine must contain 15,000 I.U. of vitamin A per pound. Fig. 65 shows the kinds and proportion of ingredients used in the manufacture of margarines. Margarines may also have vitamin D and minerals added.

Preservatives may be added to margarines so that these fats can be kept at room temperature for relatively long periods without becoming rancid. Thus it is possible to have margarines with good spreading qualities at all times.

Margarine and butter combined is a newcomer to the market. It was planned as a product more nearly like butter in flavor than are the ordinary margarines. Another recent development is a so-called *Soy Lecithin Spread* which may be priced even higher than butter. These products have not as yet proved their value, and their acceptability has not been determined.

There was considerable argument in the past over the comparative nutritive values of butters and margarines, which settled around the

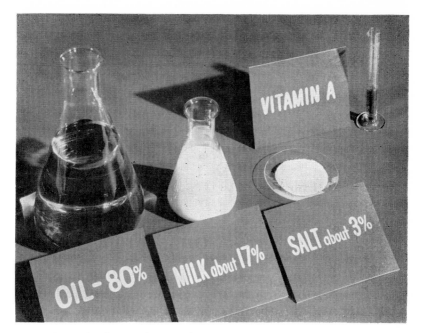

Fig. 65. Margarine is manufactured from hydrogenated oil churned with milk to which salt and 15,000 I. U. of vitamin A per pound are added. (Courtesy of National Association of Margarine Manufacturers, Lincoln, Nebraska.)

vitamin A value. It is true that butter may contain more than the 15,000 I.U. of vitamin A required at present for margarine fortification, but on the other hand, winter butters have been found to contain as little as 5,000 I.U. in some areas. There are no regulations as to the vitamin-A content of butter, so that considerable variation might be found. Under these conditions, it would seem more logical to select spreads from this category of fats on the basis of comparative palatability and price rather than on any nutritive superiority that might or might not exist.

The relative prices of the plastic fats that contain substances other than fat have held the same position for some time. In order of increasing amounts the fats rank: margarines, margarine-butter mix, butter, and Soy Lecithin spread. Butter prices may vary slightly with grade and style; margarine prices vary appreciably with brand.

Plastic fats containing 100 per cent fat. Plastic fats are desirable for making cakes and pastry because they are sufficiently hard to retain a small amount of air but pliable enough so that the fat can be incorporated into other ingredients such as sugar and flour. There are numerous brands of these plastic fats now available on the market. All are similar in composition and pliability, and all except one (Fluffo) are creamy white. These fats are generally made from plant oils that have been treated to decrease fluidity; however, some few may be a mixture of plant and animal fats, and sometimes lard is treated to make a hard fat. The various processes used to obtain the creamy, pliable product found in present-day markets include:

1. *Hydrogenation* in which gaseous hydrogen is bubbled through oils in the presence of a metal catalyst, and the hydrogen is forced into a chemical union with the carbon of the fatty acids. This change in chemical make-up of the fatty acid changes the physical properties from those of the original oils. The most important of these changes is hardness.

2. *Plasticization* or *precreaming* of the hydrogenated fats while they are congealing, which makes them homogeneous and creamy white. This is a whipping action, and a small amount of air is incorporated into the fat. The volume of a pound of precreamed fat would be slightly more than the volume of a pound of oil or other fat without air.

3. *Superglycerination*, which entails the addition of small amounts of monoglycerides and diglycerides to fats to assist in holding moisture and thereby increasing volumes in cakes. (These are some of the same substances which are used commercially as softeners in breads.)

The plastic fats may be colored, which may enhance the appearance of baked products. Carotenes are used for the coloring material, but they are not claimed to be those specific carotenes which have vitamin A value; consequently, the nutritive value of a colored product is not necessarily improved. Also, *antioxidants* are often added to the fats so that they can be stored at room temperature for long periods of time after opening without becoming rancid. Various chemicals are permitted for this purpose, and they will be listed on the label.

Soft fats. *Lard*, animal fat from swine, is prized by chefs for its high shortening power. The composition of the triglyceride molecules of lard makes it especially efficient in tenderizing and separating gluten strands. Natural lard is softer at room temperature than are the hydrogenated fats, but lard is as well suited physically as the harder fats for baked products and frying. People object to the use of lard because (1) at room temperature it becomes rancid more rapidly than do hydrogenated fats, and it may also be very soft; (2) at refrigerator temperature it becomes too hard for easy manipulation in baked goods; and (3) natural lard has a distinctive flavor that, although prized by some, is disliked by many people. Some homemakers buy lard for use only in making pastry; others use it for an all-purpose fat.

The quality of lard is influenced by the location in the animal's body, the method by which the fat is rendered or extracted, and the special treatment it receives. *Leaf lard* is considered choice; it is taken from the kidney region rather than from the carcass. During the rendering, lard may be subjected to deodorizing processes; it is then marketed as *bland lard*. Lards probably contain arachidonic acid, which would normally be missing in hydrogenated products.

Lard is sold under various brand names, but the prices are generally similar. Most lards cost less than equal amounts of hydrogenated fats.

Partially saturated oil has recently become available. This fat is fluid enough at room temperature to pour but contains some congealed fats so that it is cloudy and more viscous than oils. It is suitable for use in making cakes, pastries, and frying, but would generally be too viscous for salad dressings.

Oils. All the fats that remain liquid at room temperature are termed oils. These fats are more suitable for French dressings and mayonnaise than are harder fats since it is necessary to have both phases of an emulsion in the liquid state. It is advantageous to use oils in recipes wherever melted fat is desirable—griddle cakes, waffles, muffins, breads, and the like—as well as in frying because their liquid state is more convenient than the melting of plastic fat.

Processing of oils usually entails deflavoring and decoloring as well as extraction (Fig. 66). However, certain olive oils that are prized for their flavor are sold without treatment and termed, *Virgin Oil.*

Winterizing of oils insures their liquid consistency even at refrigerator temperature. The oils are chilled to low temperatures to congeal some of the triglycerides, and these are removed. Peanut oils are not winterized because they have few triglycerides that would remain fluid at refrigerator temperature. Untreated oils that do congeal when refrigerated become fluid very quickly when warmed to room temperature.

There seem to be no advantages in an oil expressed by any specific method. However, *cold-press oils* might be slightly less desirable than heat-extracted oils as fat-splitting enzymes naturally present in the seed could remain in the cold-press oil and cause acceleration of rancidity in the expressed fat. Except in health food stores, there are few cold-press oils on the market. These oils usually cost more than

A

B

Fig. 66. One source of food oil is corn, which is brought to the processing plant in carload lots (A); the filterable waxes are removed during the refining process by complex refrigeration technique (B); soap stock is removed by centrifuging (C); and the finished product is mechanically discharged into containers for marketing (D). (Courtesy of the Corn Products Refining Company, Chicago.)

C

D

ordinary oils and make no more contribution to the diet than do other oils.

Olive oil commands a consistently higher price than other oils since it is highly prized for its flavor and is produced in relatively small quantities. However, there seems to be no advantage to olive oil other than flavor for either nutrition or culinary purposes.

Comparison of prices among oils can be made very easily—the weight or volume measure is always listed on the container. The weight should be carefully checked because the container may be deceptive as the result of the shape or the thickness of the glass.

Comparison of prices among oils, hydrogenated fats, and soft fats can also be made easily even if oils are labeled by volume and solid fats are labeled by weight. Two cupfuls of oil (1 pint) are equivalent to 1 pound of fat. Salad oils generally are similar in price to the hydrogenated fats. The market order might easily contain choices from each of the fat groups as the amount of fat ordinarily used would not demand an unduly large proportion of the food dollar— even if the more expensive fats were chosen.

Meat Fats

Meat fats that have not been rendered are used for special purposes. These are not pure fats and are sold at the meat counters rather than with the fats. Beef fat, a very hard fat, is known as *suet* and is used for cooking meats and in making mince-meat, plum puddings, and similar products. Pork fat, a soft fat, is either sold as *rinds, salt pork, side pork,* or *bacon.* It is an inexpensive seasoning for baked beans, cooked greens, and other foods. *Chicken fat* may also be available and is used by some people as an all-purpose fat. This fat is somewhat softer than lard, and its response in cooking is similar to that of lard. An economy-minded homemaker could make use of excess fat from stewing hens in cookies, cream sauces, and the like.

Salad Dressings

Commercial salad dressings, found in many flavors and styles, are products with a large proportion of fat. There are three general categories of salad dressings as follows:

(1) *Mayonnaise,* which, by definition of the Federal Food and Drug Act, must contain oil, egg, acid, and optional seasonings.

Fig. 67. Salads will lose crispness if allowed to stand with an oil dressing; combining the salad at the table is a pleasant ritual for either family or company meals. (Courtesy of the Western Growers Association, Los Angeles.)

(2) *French dressings,* which contain no eggs but consist of acid, oil, and seasonings.

(3) *Salad dressings,* which may contain variable amounts of oil and may also contain ingredients other than those permitted for mayonnaise. Generally a starch thickener or vegetable gum is used, and they contain less oil than does mayonnaise.

Food value tables give the average fat content of these products as approximately 78 per cent for mayonnaise and 40 per cent for French dressings and salad dressings. In deciding whether to make these products at home or to buy ready made ones one might well consider the time and energy involved in home food preparation, the cost of ingredients, and the interest of the family members in food production. Some people prefer their own compounded dressings. An electric mixer permits very rapid formation of mayonnaise, and bottles marked for the desired proportion of oil and acid make compounding of French dressing very simple (Fig. 67). Thus they can be made with little time and effort. In comparing the cost of 1 pint of commercial mayonnaise with materials required for home production of the product, the cost of the following ingredients needs to be considered:

⅞ pint salad oil
2 eggs (generally the yolks only are used)
⅓ cup vinegar

One pint of French dressing may be roughly equivalent to the following formula:

⅓ pint vinegar
⅓ pint water
⅓ pint oil

The cost of seasonings for any type of salad dressing is not appreciable.

Care of Fats

Spoilage in fats is confined generally to the development of rancidity except for those fats containing water and milk solids and the meat fats. Any off-flavors in fat are collectively termed rancidity, and therefore the absorption of strong flavors from the atmosphere is generally included in this terminology. True rancidity in fats, however, is confined to the chemical breakdown of the fat molecule. This may occur in two ways:

(1) *Hydrolytic*, in which the fatty acids split from the glycerol molecule in the same manner as during the digestive process.

(2) *Oxidative*, in which the oxygen from the air attacks the fatty-acid portion of the triglyceride molecule and splits off fragments rather than whole fatty acids.

Both reactions can proceed simultaneously, and, once the breakdown of fats has begun, the action proceeds at a rapid rate. Light, moisture, salt, oxygen, and certain metals accelerate development of rancidity, and the higher the temperature, the faster any chemical reaction will proceed. Fat stored in airtight containers in a cool dark place will maintain high quality for a relatively long time. Plasticized fats with preservative added may be stored at room temperature even after they have been opened for use, but care should be taken to keep the surface area at a minimum by taking fat from the entire surface instead of making a pit. Also, air circulation should be shut off by a tight closure. At ordinary room temperature these plasticized fats should be free from rancidity for several months.

Refrigerated storage away from odors is necessary for butter, lard, and the margarines that do not contain preservatives. The paper wraps for these products may be inpregnated with anti-oxidants. These papers, therefore, make better storage wraps for the left-overs from table use than does waxed paper. Whether fat is refrigerated or left at room temperature, a close cover will protect it against not only oxidation but also absorption of flavor from the atmosphere. Fish liver oils and other oils containing vitamin concentrates should always be refrigerated after they have been opened, as their vitamin potency is reduced by oxidation. Also toxic substances may be formed. Unless salad oils are to be used within a few weeks after breaking the seal of the container, they should be refrigerated.

Fats containing moisture and food particles may be subject to mold growth. Butter and margarines are in this category. Salt and other preservatives serve to prevent this type of spoilage although rancidity may be hastened by the presence of salt. Freezer storage prolongs the life of properly wrapped butter and margarine to several years. This type of storage may be used if it is economical to purchase these foods in caselots for school or even family use.

FATS IN FOOD PREPARATION

Fats have many functions in food preparation, and there is seldom any problem in obtaining a sufficient amount of fat in the diet. These functions include:

(1) *Increasing the palatability of other foods* by enhancing flavor and tenderizing. It may be said that with the possible exception of a few raw fruits and vegetables, fats are added to all foods to increase the palatability if for no other reason. Broiled grapefruit and baked fruits such as apples, pears, and peaches may be flavored with butter or margarine. Fruit soups, fruit pies, and tapioca fruit puddings frequently are enriched with fat, and so are cooked vegetables, puddings, etc. Even raw fruits are often served with cream which is a source of fat, and sour cream enriches many types of foods.

(2) *Tenderizing baked products* by shortening the gluten strands. Most baked products have some fatty ingredients, sponge-type cakes and beaten biscuits may be notable exceptions.

(3) *Lubricating foods and utensils.* Foods that are oiled include bread doughs, to prevent drying of the surface during proofing; baked rolls and breads, to obtain a soft crust; potatoes for baking, to maintain soft moist skins; and left-over egg yolks are better protected with a film of fat rather than water. Fats are used to oil baking utensils unless it is desirable for the food to cling to the pan or unless foods can easily be removed, as from a cooky sheet. One usually remembers to

oil the bottom of cake pans, muffin tins, etc, but forgets that oiling jello molds, jelly glasses, and custard cups will aid in removing the contents. Even measuring cups for syrups will have little syrup adhering to them if they are oiled.

(4) *Dispersing undesirable foaming*, as in jelly making or the cooking of certain legumes and vegetables. This use of fat seems to have been forgotten in food preparation although the old adage, "Oil quiets troubled waters," has been quoted for years and practiced outside of the kitchen. Generally 1 teaspoonful of oil is sufficient for a quart of food.

(5) *Transferring heat* in the dry heat cooking of food by French-frying. Many different types of food may be French-fried beginning with appetizers and progressing through dessert: cheese balls, hush puppies, eggplant, cauliflower, potatoes, onions, fish, chicken, dough-nuts, fritters, cookies, pies, and nuts to mention only a few.

(6) *Emulsifying with other liquids.* Since by definition an emulsion is the suspension of droplets of one liquid throughout another liquid without intimately mixing with it, fats must be one phase of all food emulsions because all other liquids occuring in foods are miscible. Typical emulsions in foods are mayonnaise, Hollandaise sauce, French dressings, cream puffs, gravies, white sauce, and some baked products (see Chapter 4).

(7) *Preserving foods* by excluding air. Its usefulness in this respect is limited because the oxygen of the air causes the fat to become rancid within a few months. Before the advent of freezers for farms, however, sausage cakes were cooked and then embedded in hot lard and stored in cold cellars. The cooking destroyed the microorganisms in the meat, and the congealed fat kept the meat from becoming con-taminated during storage. In the same manner, Greek style olives may be immersed in oil instead of brine.

Food preparation techniques involving the uses of fats have for the most part been presented in other chapters. The presentation here, therefore, will be limited to the preparation of pastries and deep-fat frying of foods.

Pastries

Generally one thinks of the common pie or piecrust under the pastry terminology, but puff pastes, Danish style pastry, or the short-paste mix used for tarts might well be included here. Pastries are flour mixtures of relatively high fat content and low moisture. Good flavor, marked tenderness, and flakiness are usually the hallmark of high palatability rating for pastries.

Pastries are easily and quickly mixed. There are various methods of combining the few ingredients required so that one person may develop skill with one technique and another person may prefer a different one. As is true of skills in other areas, food preparation techniques of any kind must be practiced if one is to become adept in them, and pastry making is no exception.

The proportions by volume that are frequently used for a rich pie-crust, tarts, or snack food are one-third as much fat as flour and one-half as much liquid as fat plus some salt for flavoring. The choice of ingredients will affect the palatability characteristics—especially the flavor. White flours are the most popular for pastry making although other flours such as whole wheat or rye are suitable. Pastry flour has less gluten than all-purpose flour. There is less chance of overmixing when pastry flour is used than when a flour with a larger amount of gluten is used. Any type of fat may be used, although lard and hydrogenated fats are the most common. Butter or margarine is used occasionally for flavor in special tarts. The liquid ingredient most commonly used is water although milk or fruit juice gives satisfactory results. Also, for variety special flavoring substances such as sesame seeds, nuts, or chocolate bits might be used, or if the pastry is used for a main dish, cheese, herbs and other seasonings may be desirable.

The four factors that have the greatest influence on tenderness qualities of pastries are:

(1) *Type of fat*—lard gives the most shortening value per unit weight, butter and margarine give the least.

(2) *Proportion of fat to flour*—the larger the amount of fat used for a given amount of flour (the same amount of mixing), the more tender the pastry will be.

(3) *Mixing of the fat with flour*—fat mixed intimately with the flour prevents the development of long strands of gluten and therefore is more efficient in tenderizing than fat left in large pieces. However, it may be desirable to leave some relatively large pieces of fat to obtain flakiness.

(4) *Amount of manipulation of pastry*—there must be sufficient mixing to enable the particles to be equally wetted and to cling together. However, overmixing will decrease tenderness in direct proportion to the amount of agitation given the dough.

Flakiness, a factor in palatability, is thought to be governed largely by the size of the fat particles in the mix. Large particles of fat, coated with flour, are flattened by rolling and thus separate layers of dough rather than mixing intimately with them. It is possible to obtain flakiness without tenderness or tenderness without flakiness. In order to realize something of both of these characteristics, recipes may direct that part of the fat be cut into the flour in very small particles (to tenderize) and the remainder be left in relatively large pieces (to permit flaking).

Mixing methods. There are five common methods of mixing pastry. These methods are usually referred to as pastry, paste, modified puff paste, oil pastry, and hot water.

The *pastry method* of mixing piecrust as described in Chapter 4 has been the standby of cooks for some time. The fat is cut into the flour-salt mixture until the largest particles approximate the size of small peas. Liquid is sprinkled over the surface of the fat-flour mix and the wetted portion tossed aside so that further additions of liquid will wet another layer. The dough is then gathered together and with 10 or 12 kneading strokes is pressed into a cohesive mass (Fig. 68).

The *paste method* was developed to facilitate the distribution of liquid through the whole of the dough. This is only a variation of the pastry method. After the flour has been measured, a quantity sufficient to make a thin paste with the required amount of liquid is removed from the bowl and mixed with the liquid. The fat is then cut into the remaining flour, the paste is added all at once to the fat-flour mixture, and the whole combined with a minimum of stirring. Care must be taken that every bit of paste is used so that there is enough liquid to moisten the dough.

The *modified puff-paste method* may be used if one has a tendency to add too much water in the pastry method. The fat is cut into the total flour as in the regular pastry method; then one-fourth of the fat-flour mix is removed from the bowl before the water is added. The remainder is then moistened and kneaded as in the pastry method and rolled to ¼ inch in thickness. The reserved fat-flour mix is spread over the rolled dough, which is then rolled tightly into a scroll, cut in half, and the thick portion of one piece is pressed onto the thin end of the other piece, thus making a mound of uniform thickness. The dough is then further cut as desired or rolled into the size for use.

Oil-pastry method requires no separate mixing of fat and flour. The oil and water are mixed, added to the flour-salt mix, and the whole stirred with a fork until the mix is blended.

Hot-water method of pastry-making is another easy method. The fat, salt, and water are placed in a round-bottom saucepan over low heat until the water begins to simmer. These ingredients are then blended (a flexible spiral whip is efficient for this purpose), after which the flour is added and the mixture stirred until it forms a ball. The dough must be thoroughly chilled for rolling. If it is patted into a thick round cake before chilling, it will chill more rapidly and roll more easily than if it is left in a ball.

Rolling and baking. Rolling-pin socks and pastry cloths impregnated with flour make it possible to roll pastry without taking up unduly large amounts of flour. Often such pastry cloths will have circles for guides in sizing the pastry for different sized pans (see Fig. 68). One can make such a cloth of heavy muslin if desired, and the rings can be marked with India ink. A child's cotton stocking makes a good rolling pin cover. Another technique for rolling without the addition of flour is to put the pastry between two sheets of waxed paper. However, pastry can be rolled successfully on lightly floured boards if it is remembered that the dough must be "coaxed" rather than pressed. Ball-bearing rolling pins permit easy movement and the dough should be lightly stroked from the center toward the outer edges. Unless the dough is stuck to the board, it will slip slightly with each stroke of the rolling pin. Crusts are usually rolled to about ⅛ inch in thickness and fulled rather than stretched into the pan. Stretched pastry will shrink during baking. Holes are pricked in those crusts that are to be baked before filling so that steam does not force the pastry out of shape. Top crusts of two-crust pies are also given steam vents. Turnovers to be baked may or may not be pricked, but those that are to be deep-fat fried should be tightly encased in pastry to prevent liquid from escaping into the hot fat and causing splatter. It should also be remembered that fruit pies will boil at baking temperatures and will spill over unless the edges are fixed to retain the juices or funnels are put in the steam vents.

The edges of the pies may be decorated in many ways—pinching between thumb and forefinger, pressing with the tines of a fork, or fluting by pushing the dough with the forefinger of one hand and the thumb of another (see Fig. 68). Whatever method is used the object is to securely fasten the top crust to the bottom crust so that juice will not escape around the edges.

Rapid baking of the crust is desirable since there is so little moisture present. An oven temperature of 425° F has been found to be satisfactory except for tart shells containing butter or margarine when a lower temperature must be employed because of the relatively low temperature at which these fats decompose. Pastry shells should be

A

B

Fig. 68. Piecrust prepared by the pastry method entails the use of a plastic fat with high shortening power: the fat is measured (A), cut into the flour (B); the mixture is carefully wetted (C), the dough is pushed into a ball (D), and pastry cloths with guides assist in the sizing of the crust during rolling (E). The crust is then fitted into the baking pan and finished with ornamental edging (F). (Courtesy of Procter and Gamble Co., Cincinnati.)

C

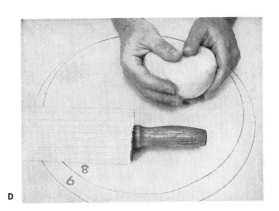

D

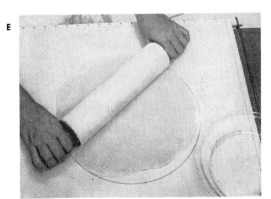

E

F

completely baked in 10 to 15 minutes, and pies with fillings should generally have the temperature lowered after this time except for those in which the filling is already fully cooked. If top crusts become overly brown before the filling is cooked, a heavy brown paper placed over the top of the pie will shield the crust from part of the heat yet permit continued cooking of the filling. If both shelves of the oven are used, it may be well to shift the pies in mid-baking to obtain uniform browning.

Puff pastry. True puff paste is made commercially with a special fat that has an added flavor. Puff paste may be made in the home with butter or margarine from which the milk solids have been washed by working the fat in cold water with a paddle or wooden spoon. After the fat has been washed, it must be pressed free of as much water as possible. The fat must be congealed but pliable enough to flatten easily. The flour is mixed with one-third of the total fat and moistened sufficiently with ice water to make a stiff dough. Two thin oblongs of the remaining fat are formed and kept cold until needed. The dough is then rolled into an oblong somewhat larger than the fat, about ¼ inch thick, and the first piece of fat is placed on the dough and the dough is rolled by hand into a tight scroll. This scroll is then flattened with a rolling pin and again rolled to ¼ inch in thickness. The second oblong of fat is placed on the dough and a scroll is made as before. A few further foldings and rollings enhance puffiness. The finished pastry is rolled to about ¼ inch in thickness, cut, and kept chilled until it is ready for baking. It must be baked at a high temperature (425° F) until puffed, but baking should be finished at low temperatures (325° F) so that the outside of the pastry does not burn before the flour is thoroughly cooked.

Danish pastry. Danish pastry is similar to puff paste except that a yeast dough is used as the base. After the fat has been incorporated, fruit or nut mixtures may be used as fillings or the dough made into fancy shapes without filling. The shaped dough is then allowed to rise before it is baked.

Crumb pastries. Variations of pastries and crumb crusts with high fat contents are also used for desserts. Crumb crusts may be baked or merely chilled. Butter or margarine is preferred to other fats for flavor. Oil is unsuitable for crumb crusts because hardness of the fat must provide the firmness in this type crust. Fine cookie or graham cracker crumbs are mixed with sugar and spices and the melted fat stirred into the mix to moisten the crumbs. The mixture is then pressed firmly into the pie pan and if baked, a second pan is used to hold the crust in place. Baking melts the sugar and makes the crust firm when finished. Crumb crusts are commonly used for cream or chiffon type pie fillings but might also be used for tart shells with fruit fillings. "Convenience foods" in pastry include bakery items, frozen pastries, as well as pastry mixes. These will usually cost more than the ingredients necessary for making similar products at home, and one has no knowledge of the proportion of fat or their composition. A home mix for pastry is given in the appendix.

Deep-fat Frying

Deep-fat frying is a popular method of cooking a wide variety of foods for any meal or for snacks. Careful attention must be given in this type of cooking, however, so that the food is palatable and does not absorb an excess of fat. Both excess fat and products of decomposed (burnt) fat can be unpleasant.

Selection of a suitable fat, control of the amount of fat absorbed in cooking, and care of the used fat, as well as the manipulation are important considerations in this type of cooking.

Selection of fats for deep-fat frying. This is made on the basis of flavor and smoking temperature. Generally a bland or tasteless fat is selected for deep-fat frying. The fat will take up flavors from the food cooked in it. Fish or onion flavor from previous frying may not be objectionable in potato chips but seems out of place in doughnuts.

Although fats are liquids when heated, they do not boil but decompose at varying temperatures depending upon their triglyceride components. The temperature at which decomposition begins is termed the *smoking temperature* (see Table 25). When the fat smokes a volatile substance called *acrolein* is formed. This can be seen as a blue smoke, and it is very irritating to the eyes and throats of persons in the kitchen. It should also be remembered that in spite of good ventilation in the kitchen, one's hair and clothing will become permeated with odors from frying.

The amount of fat absorbed in cooking. This can be controlled to some extent. Some absorption is not only inevitable but also desirable for palatability otherwise some other method of cooking must be chosen. Greasy food, however, soon loses its appeal. Factors having the most influence on the amount of fat absorbed into the food include:

(1) *The surface area.* Absorption of fat increases directly with the increase in surface area. For example, a pound of potatoes cut for French-fries into pieces ½ inch in diameter will absorb less fat than a

Table 25. THE SMOKE POINTS OF SOME EDIBLE FATS*

Kind of Fat	Smoking Temperature,† °F
Shortening	
Crisco	356
Dexo	361
Durkees	370
Fluffo	351
Jewel	448
Mrs. Tucker	363
Natco	356
Royal Satin	358
Snowdrift	356
Spry	356
Swiftning	363
Oil	
Mazola	441
Peanut Oil	450
Lard	
Armours Texturated	365
Black Hawk	376
Boone River	378
Hormel	363
Iowa State College	361
Silverleaf	370
White Clover	403

* Adapted from Justin, Rust, Vail, *Foods*, Houghton-Mifflin Company, Boston, 1956.

† Official AOC Methods used.

like weight cut into thin slices for chips. Or, doughnuts that crack during cooking have more surface area exposed for fat absorption than do those of the same shape and size that do not crack;

(2) *The compactness of texture or nature of the food.* Absorption of fat increases directly with the increase in porosity of the food. This is best illustrated in a flour mixture such as doughnuts. Fat, sugar, moisture, baking powder, and flours of low gluten strength make a porous texture in doughnuts thereby favoring high fat absorption. Chocolate doughnuts absorb more fat than plain doughnuts do because their high fat and sugar content causes them to practically disintegrate in cooking. The extra sweetness and chocolate flavors

could be attained by coating the doughnuts with chocolate frosting after they have been fried.

(3) *The manipulation during preparation.* Increased manipulation increases the amount of gluten developed in flour mixtures, which may decrease fat absorption but the resultant product may have an undesirable texture. Re-rolled doughnuts have a compact texture, for example, and are less desirable than "firsts." Also, it is desirable to permit doughnuts to dry for a time after they have been cut before cooking them. The evaporation makes a compact crust that helps protect against absorption of fat.

(4) *Temperature of the fat when cooking is begun.* Low temperatures permit absorption of fat before the outside of the food is cooked, and the time required for thorough cooking and browning must be increased.

Care of used fat. Fat can be reused for frying many times if reasonable care is taken in using and storing it. Decomposition of fat is accelerated by moisture, by heating, and by particles of food in the fat. Also, each time the fat is used, its smoking temperature is lowered. Logical rules for care of fat so that it may be used many times would include the following:

(1) Avoid adding undue amounts of moisture by thoroughly drying the surface of fish, chicken, potatoes, and other foods.

(2) Keep the food waiting for the fat to heat rather than heating the fat prematurely.

(3) Watch and control the temperature of the fat so that it does not become overheated. Toward this end, thermostatically controlled heating units or fryers are very helpful (Fig. 69).

(4) Remove the heat as soon as possible during the cooking process. Often this can be done while the last portion is finishing its cooking because fat retains heat for some time.

(5) Avoid excess flour, loose cornmeal, or crumbs on the exterior of foods. These drop into the fat and cannot be removed during cooking. In a short time the particles begin to burn; thus they hasten the decomposition process.

(6) Clarify the fat after each use by cooking a few slices of clean raw potato (they need not be pared), which will absorb the finer particles of food suspended in the fat.

(7) Strain the fat when cool enough to handle in order to remove all particles of flour and food. This can be done by straining through a fine meshed cloth or special filter paper.

Fig. 69. An even temperature is maintained in the cooking fat by use of a thermostatically controlled deep-fat fryer thus preventing excessively high temperatures, which hasten the breakdown of fat. (Courtesy of the Sunbeam Corporation, Chicago.)

(8) Store the fat in a cool place; rancidity develops slowly at low temperatures.

(9) Discard fat that has turned brown.

Techniques in deep-fat cooking. These are concerned primarily with the handling of the fat. The first thing for a novice to learn about deep-fat cookery is *safe-handling procedures*. It should always be remembered that (1) the temperature of fat for deep-fat frying is at least 350° F (note—this is much hotter than boiling water at 212° F or steam in a pressure saucepan at 250° F); (2) hot fat is a liquid and spills easily, splashes readily, and drips from the lifted cooked food; (3) hot fat froths when cold moist food is added; and (4) fat is combustible and catches fire easily. One can avoid accidents to himself, his family, or his classmates by observing the following precautions during deep-fat cookery:

(1) Have the depth of the fat no more than half the depth of the container to allow for frothing when food is added.

(2) Make sure that the kettle does not slide easily on the surface unit, and that a deep-fat fryer is set solidly on the counter away from the edge with its drain closed tightly.

(3) Turn handles or containers so that clothing cannot catch on them or children reach them.

(4) Release food close to the surface of the fat to avoid splashing. A pair of tongs for this purpose gives added protection to the hands, and fry baskets are provided with special frying kettles for ease in handling food.

(5) Cook an amount of food consistent with the size of the container. Large amounts of food not only froth more but also cool the fat more rapidly than do small amounts of food even if heat is thermostatically controlled. One must determine the amount of food to be cooked at one time that is compatible with the type of food used.

(6) Turn food by flipping it at the far edge and away from the worker rather than at the close edge and toward the worker. This will minimize danger of splashing.

(7) Permit food in fry baskets, or single pieces of cooked food, to drain into the kettle, then bring the receiving tray to the container rather than swinging the hot food across space to the tray.

(8) Drain food on a rack or absorbent paper to remove excess fat.

(9) Permit the fat to cool before attempting to move the container after cooking is completed.

(10) Make sure there is something within easy reach to smother a fire—a box of salt, canister of flour, chemical fire extinguisher, or a fire blanket. *Never attempt to use water for quenching a fat fire.*

Cooking times and temperatures also are problems in techniques since they depend upon the thickness of the piece and the degree of doneness desired. Foods to be cooked in deep fat are always cut into relatively small pieces (probably less than 2 inches in diameter) so that the exterior does not become excessively browned before the interior is heated and cooked. Heat is transferred from fat to food rapidly but usually does not penetrate to the interior of the food rapidly. It follows that the smaller the size of the piece, the shorter the cooking time at a given temperature. Also if the ingredients, such as in croquettes, are already cooked and need only to be warmed, they can be cooked a shorter time than if the ingredients are to be completely cooked during the frying period. The temperatures usually employed for deep fat frying are 350 to 375° F.

Keeping the temperature of the fat constant is another technique that is difficult. The temperature of the fat usually drops as cold foods are added. Thus, it is important to check the temperature before adding more food to the fat. When cooking doughnuts a rhythm for adding them to the fat can be established, to keep the temperature of the fat constant. If approximately 15 seconds are allowed to elapse between addition of each doughnut for 6 doughnuts and then 15 seconds allowed between each turn, each doughnut will have been given 3 minutes of cooking and a cycle can be maintained until as many doughnuts as desired have been fried. As one doughnut is removed, another is added; when 6 have been added, turning begins, and so on. This technique is much less practical for fish or shrimp that are to be served hot to several people at one time.

Cooking in fat results in loss of moisture, which can easily escape as steam (a gas) through the fat. Excessive drying of some foods is guarded against by "covers." These may be:

(1) Cornmeal, as for fish frying.
(2) Raw egg and crumbs, as for croquettes, appetizers, and the like.
(3) Cover batters (flour-egg-milk mixtures of varying consistencies), as for meats and vegetables to which the egg-crumb cover does not readily adhere or give sufficient protection. If a heavy covering is desired, a thick cover batter is used, and thinner batters for less heavy covering. Chicken, fish, cauliflower, eggplant, onion rings, and many other foods may be dipped in cover batters. These covers provide the diner with the added opportunity of removing most of the fat uptake if he wishes. Flour mixtures such as fritters, doughnuts, and pies provide their own cover batters and permit less loss of moisture than do the other foods. Some foods such as corn "kurls" and potato chips are preferred crisp so are not given covers.

No adjustment needs to be made in cooking procedures as a result of altitude except for potatoes, which may brown excessively unless temperatures are slightly lower than are recommended for sea-level cooking. Proportions of ingredients for products illustrating uses of fat in food preparation are given in Table 26; nutritive values are shown in Table 27.

International dishes cooked by deep-fat frying. Deep-fat frying not only is used for the cooking of a wide variety of foods in the

Table 26. BASIC PROPORTIONS FOR FOOD PRODUCTS HIGH IN FAT

Product	Fat	Sugar	Egg	Salt	Flour	Liquid
Emulsions:						
Mayonnaise	1 C. oil	½ tsp.	1 yolk	¼ tsp.	...	3 Tb. vinegar
Mayonnaise, cream	½ C. mayonnaise	...	...	...	...	...
Salad dressing, French	½ C. oil	...	...	1 tsp.	...	¼ C. lemon, ¼ C. water
Salad dressing, Russian	½ C. mayonnaise	1 tsp. confectioners	...	...	...	...
Salad dressing, Thousand Island	½ C. mayonnaise	1 tsp. confectioners	...	...	...	...
Creaming:						
Frostings, uncooked	2 Tb. butter or margarine	1 C. confectioners	...	⅛ tsp.	...	1 Tb. cream
Sauce, hard	⅓ C. butter or margarine	1 C. confectioners	...	...	...	...
Pastry:						
Crumb crust	⅓ C.	¼ C. confectioners	...	...	...	...
Pie crust	¼ C.	...	...	¼ tsp.	1 C.	water
Puff paste	1 C. butter	...	...	...	2 C.	ice water
Deep-Fat Fry:						
Cover Batters for: Cauliflower, Onion rings, Scallops, Shrimps	1 Tb.	...	2	¼ tsp.	1 C.	¾ C. milk
Doughnuts (cake)	2 Tb.	1 C.	2	⅛ tsp.	3 C.	1 C. milk
Doughnuts (raised)	¼ C. butter or margarine	½ C.	1	1 tsp.	3 C.	1 C. milk
Fritters	1 Tb.	½ tsp.	1	⅛ tsp.	1 C.	1 C. milk
Potato chips	for frying only	...	...	...	...	...

Product	Other Ingredients	Method of Mixing	Cooking Temp., °F	Cooking Time, Min.	Approximate Yield
Emulsions:					
Mayonnaise	¼ tsp. dry mustard	Emulsion	...	...	20 Tb.
Mayonnaise, cream	¼ C. whipped cream	Fold in cream	...	...	12 Tb.
Salad dressing, French	Seasonings	Shake together	...	...	16 Tb.
Salad dressing, Russian	2 Tb. chili sauce; 2 Tb. diced celery; ½ hard cooked egg sieved	Stir together	...	...	12 Tb.
Salad dressing, Thousand Island	Same as above and 1 Tb. chopped stuffed olives; 1 tsp. chopped green pepper; 1 tsp. chopped onion or chives	Stir together	...	...	12 Tb.
Creaming:					
Frostings, uncooked	Flavoring	Cream fat and add sugar	...	...	1 C.
Sauce, Hard	Flavorings and fruit	Cream fat and add sugar	...	...	1 C.
Pastry:					
Crumb crust	1 C. fine crumbs (Graham crackers)	Pastry ...	400 (oven)	10–15	1 9″ crust
Pie crust	...	Pastry	425–450 (oven)	10–12	1 9″ crust
Puff paste	...		425 then lower to 350 (oven)	15 and 25	6
Deep-Fat Fry:					
Cover Batters for:					
Cauliflower, Onion rings, Scallops, Shrimps		Muffin	375–385 (fat)	3	8 servings
Doughnuts (cake)	4 tsp. baking powder; ¼ tsp. cinnamon; ¼ tsp. nutmeg	Muffin	350–375 (fat)	3	24
Doughnuts (raised)	½ oz. yeast; 1 Tb. lemon rind	Modified muffin	350–375 (fat)	3	24
Fritters	3 apples	Muffin	350–375 (fat)	3	6
Potato chips	1 potato—slice thin	...	385–395 (fat)	2	6 servings

Product	Serving	Energy Value, Cal.	Protein, gm.	Calcium, mg.	Iron, mg.	Vitamin A, I.U.	Thiamine, mg.	Riboflavin, mg.	Niacin, mg.	Ascorbic Acid, mg.
Emulsions:										
Mayonnaise	2 Tb.	200	...	2	0.1	55	...	...	...	...
Mayonnaise, cream	2 Tb.	150	0.3	5	0.08	110	0.01	0.01	...	...
Salad dressing, French	2 Tb.	125	0.1	4	0.02	...	0.01	0.01	...	...
Salad dressing, Russian	2 Tb.	144	0.9	5	0.22	190	0.05	0.02	...	...
Salad dressing, Thousand Island	2 Tb.	155	0.9	8	0.26	200	0.05	0.02	...	...
Creaming:										
Frostings, uncooked	2 Tb.	146	0.1	4	...	130	...	...	...	...
Sauce, hard	2 Tb.	130	...	2	...	310	...	...	...	...
Pastry:										
Crumb crust	⅙ pie	200	0.9	5	0.30	311	0.06	0.03	...	...
Pie crust (2-crust pie)	⅙ pie	140	1.7	3	0.50	...	0.06	0.05	...	...
Puff Pastry†	2 x 3 x 1½ in.	302	3.1	10	0.80	925	0.12	0.70	...	...
Deep-Fat Fry:										
Cover batter, cooked†	1 serv.	280	5.0	48	0.90	230	0.14	0.14	...	...
Doughnuts, cake†	2	400	5.8	34	0.90	120	0.13	0.15	...	...
Doughnuts, raised†	2	335	4.0	41	1.00	260	0.11	0.11	...	...
Fritters, apple†	2	330	4.6	58	0.90	166	0.26	0.16	...	...
Potato chips	3	54	0.6	...	...	...	...	...	...	...

* Calculated from U.S.D.A. Agriculture Handbook No. 8.
† Made with enriched flour.

Fig. 70. Apple fritters and a glass of milk make a nutritious after-the-game snack. (Courtesy of General Mills Corporation, Minneapolis.)

United States (Fig. 70) but it is also a universally popular method of cooking. A few examples of these follow:

Swedish Rosette is a delicate cooky made with a specially shaped metal form—a rosette iron. The rosettes are made very thin and crisp. The batters are prepared and allowed to stand several hours before cooking in order for them to be free of bubbles. The iron is thoroughly heated in the hot fat, allowed to drain briefly, and then is dipped into the batter to within ⅛ inch of the top of the iron. It is held in the batter a few seconds until it becomes coated, and the coated form is then returned to the fat for frying and browning. The tiny rosettes are sprinkled with powdered sugar for serving. *Timbale cases* are very similar to rosettes but are made deeper to hold creamed chicken or other similar food.

French Rissoles are made of puff paste, usually enclosing a meat filling although they may be of many varieties. A round of the puff paste ¼ inch thick is heaped with a seasoned forcemeat and covered with a second round. If the edges are wetted slightly, the pastry will seal easily when the two pieces are pressed together. The rissole is then cooked in hot fat in a manner similar to doughnuts. Rissoles may be served as appetizers, soup or salad accompaniments, or as snacks.

Greek Loucomades are made of a yeast dough, and they are very puffy. A soft dough is made and permitted to proof before cooking. It may then be cut out of the bowl with a wet spoon into small balls for cooking. Care must be taken to retain as much of the gas as possible to give the characteristic puffiness of the product. They are served hot with a thin syrup poured over them.

Mexican Sopapilla is also a puffy bread served with honey or syrup. It is made with a strong flour and kneaded, but it contains no yeast. The kneaded dough is rolled ¼ inch thick and is cut into squares about 2 inches on a side and allowed to stand 10 to 15 minutes. The pieces are then dropped into very hot fat and held submerged until they puff.

Western Spudnut is a raised doughnut containing some potato. The dough is fermented, rolled, cut, and again allowed to rise. Generally the doughnuts are glazed by dipping the hot doughnut into a thin powdered sugar-water mixture.

Cantonese Shrimp are common in Chinese eating establishments. They are prepared by dipping jumbo shrimp into a medium cover batter before frying. A pungent mustard sauce is served with them.

Italian Mussels are also deep-fat fried. These tiny mussels are popular throughout all of the Mediterranean countries. They are rolled in flour and fried crisp in a manner similar to the fried clams popular in the New England States. The crisp mussels are served with lemon.

RETENTION OF FOOD VALUE OF FATS
DURING FOOD PREPARATION

Food values from fats can be lost in discards, or by oxidation and decomposition. It should be obvious that discarded portions of any food cannot nourish. Oxidative losses would normally occur only after a period of storage rather than in the preparation processes. Generally any decomposition of fat is limited to that used in deep-fat frying and sautéing. Not only does the burning decrease the nutritive value of the fat but also the food itself may become too unpalatable to eat. This is not likely to become a major problem in the home, but it can be a problem in restaurants, especially if the fat is used over a long period of time.

The fat that is absorbed in deep-fat frying must also be considered as a source of fat in one's diet. Some people may prefer other methods of cooking to decrease fat intake, but there is usually no other reason why a normal person should not include properly cooked fried foods occasionally in his meal plans.

SUMMARY

Fats are necessary constituents of the diet and also have many uses in food preparation. Fats provide essential fatty acids and energy, and aid in the absorption of other nutrients. It is recommended that fats make up 20 to 35 per cent of the total daily caloric requirements and that at least 30 grams (2 tablespoons) of this be consumed as butter, other milk fat, or margarine to provide a source of pre-formed vitamin A.

Few natural foods are rich in fats, but processed market fats are available in plastic, soft, and fluid consistencies. Generally bland and colorless, a few fats are prized for their distinctive flavors, and a few are yellow in color. Fats vary in cost with source, flavor, and size of the market unit. Spoilage is confined to development of off-flavors, termed rancidity, due to absorption of flavors, hydrolytic breakdown, and oxidative changes in the fatty acids. Storage in a cool, dry, dark place in airtight containers is conducive to reasonable shelf life.

Fats have many uses in food preparation. Detailed discussion is given in the preparation of pastries and in use of fat for deep-fat frying of foods. Nutritive losses during preparation are generally confined to discards because fat decomposed by overheating is unpalatable and is not likely to be eaten.

Pastries and deep-fat fried foods are as digestible as equal quantities of fats from other sources, meats, malted milks, and olives, for example.

Reading List

1. Arenson, S. W., 1950, "Shortenings for frying and baking," *Food Industries*, **22**:1015.

2. Griffith, W. H., 1957, "Fats in the diet," *J. Amer. Med. Assoc.* (Council on Foods and Nutrition) **164**:411.

3. Hansen, H. (Editor), 1957, *World Almanac*, New York World-Telegram, New York.

4. Jacobs, M. V. (Editor), 1951, *The Chemistry and Technology of Food and Food Products*, Vol. II, *Edible Fats and Oils*, Interscience Publishers Inc., New York.

5. Justin, M. M., L. O. Rust, and G. E. Vail, 1956, *Foods*, Houghton Mifflin Co., Boston.

6. Lips, H. J., 1952, "Oxidative deterioration in fats and oils," *Food in Canada*, **12**:9.

7. Proudfit, F. T. and C. H. Robinson, 1955, *Nutrition and Diet Therapy*, The Macmillan Co., New York.

8. Sherman, H. C. and C. S. Lanford, 1957, *Essentials of Nutrition*, The Macmillan Co., New York.

9. Stare, F. J., 1956, "Research in atherosclerosis," *J. Amer. Diet. Assoc.*, **32**:309.

10. Sweetman, M. D., and I. MacKellar, 1954, *Food Selection and Preparation*, John Wiley and Sons, Inc., New York.

Fig. 71. Fruits and Vegetables are no longer seasonal and the markets today present a remarkable display of these products. (Courtesy of All American Market, Downey, Calif.)

I T IS NO LONGER NECESSARY TO LIVE IN FLORIDA OR CALIFORNIA TO HAVE fresh fruits and vegetables the year around. Fast freight, refrigerated cars, air express, an agricultural system supplying fresh foods during all seasons of the year, as well as improved packing methods, have created a situation where these commodities have ceased to be a novelty in any part of the United States. The domestic supplies of the so-called out-of-season fresh fruits and vegetables are augmented by shipments from Cuba, Mexico, Bermuda, Jamaica, Puerto Rico, Spain, and other producing countries. The source of supply varies as the seasons change and as local products become available. Even if fresh products of some varieties are not readily available, the canned, frozen, dried, or salted products permit many choices. Therefore, varied selections of fruits and vegetables are available to the consumer at all times (Fig. 71).

The variety in fruits and vegetables found throughout the world is very large. Many of the same kinds of fruits and vegetables are grown in different parts of the world although they may be of different varieties. White tomatoes and white eggplant may be difficult to recognize as the same vegetables we know, however, they are only different varieties of the same species.

The traditional methods for preparation or use of foods of vegetable origin may differ among countries. The Mediterranean countries use tomato sauce or nutmeg with cream sauce as vegetable seasonings. The vegetables of India are frequently served raw with "curds" (similar to cultured milk), and Oriental cooking is typically "wilted" rather than fully cooked vegetables. Common English preparation seems to be fully steamed vegetables, and German vegetables are often prepared with a sweet-sour sauce.

Fruits and vegetables might well be called the protective foods of the diet, because their chief nutritive contributions are vitamins, minerals, and bulk (cellulose and protopectin). A few plants are eaten in their entirety, but usually only selected parts are considered edible. Generally speaking, the manufacturing centers (the leaves) and the storage organs (seeds and tubers) may be expected to contribute a greater number and amount of nutrients than equivalent weights of other portions of the plants.

Many fruits and vegetables can be used without cooking, thereby affording the quick preparation so frequently stressed in present-day living. Cooking produces desirable changes in many of these foods, however, and provides for variation in menu planning. There are

A

B

C

Fig. 72. Many choices are available in each of the five groups of fruits and vegetables—citrus fruits and other plants rich in ascorbic acid (A), leaves (B), dark green and yellow (C), starchy (D), and others (E).

relatively few methods of cooking fruits and vegetables, and these require only simple techniques. Variations in seasonings for both raw and cooked fruits and vegetables added to the large number of plant foods available make it possible to have practically an endless variety in the finished food.

THE ROLE OF FRUITS AND VEGETABLES
IN THE FAMILY FOOD PLAN

It is possible, by careful selection, to meet the entire nutritional demands of the human body by a diet containing only foods of plant origin. Not only would fruits and vegetables be included in such a diet, but also cereals and legumes. This diet is neither practical nor desirable, and the majority of vegetarians include milk products and eggs in their diets.

The importance that is placed upon plant foods in the daily diet is attested to by the fact that of the four groups of foods in the Daily Food Guide (p. 15), only one, milk, contains no plant foods. One group is fruits and vegetables (Fig. 72). A second group (cereals) is of plant origin, and legumes and nuts are a part of a third group.

Variations in Vitamin and Mineral Content

The amount of each vitamin or mineral present in any fruit or vegetable, as well as the amount of any one of these constituents that can be absorbed and utilized by the body, may vary. The degree of variability will depend upon: (1) the inherent factors within the plant; (2) the variations in the growth conditions; (3) the treatment during marketing; and (4) the storage and preparation conditions. The nutritive values given for a specific vegetable in tables of nutrients are averages of many analyses and are not to be construed as exact values. Some of the causes for variation in nutrient content are important to the diet and merit detailed discussion.

Inherent factors within the plant. The part of the plant that is used, the variety within each species, and the genetic background of the plant are inherent factors that cause nutritional variations.

The part of the plant—root, leaf, stem, fruit, seed, or flower— that is used (Fig. 73), will determine the nutritive contribution of the plant. Each part of the plant makes its own unique contribution, and these contributions vary from plant to plant. For example, the word "beets" does not specify tops or roots. The tops of the beet plant have an entirely different nutritive make-up from the root sections.

Leaves, stems, fruits, and flowers are often very high in water content (90 to 95 per cent), and this results in a low energy value. However, these parts may be exceptionally valuable sources of vitamins, minerals, and bulk. Only a few of the fruits are good sources of iron —blackberries, raspberries, strawberries, and some of the dried fruits such as apricots, prunes, dates, raisins, and figs are among the few exceptions. Leaves and flowers generally contribute more calcium than do other portions of the plant, and leaves, flowers, and fruits may all be good sources of ascorbic acid.

The immature seed portions are excellent sources of thiamine, and other B-vitamins. These seeds may also contain a fair amount of minerals, fats, and proteins. The ripe seeds of berries and tomatoes have a firm outer coat that prevents them from being digested, therefore, the nutrients cannot be absorbed unless the seeds are broken by grinding or by chewing.

Roots, tubers, and bulbs such as carrots, potatoes, and onions are relatively high in carbohydrate. They are usually satisfactory sources of the B-vitamins and in some instances of ascorbic acid. They are listed as "satisfactory" not because their percentage content is high, but because large quantities of the vegetables are used in many diets and because there are consistent amounts of the vitamins in each vegetable.

Similar parts of the different *species* of plants vary widely in the kinds of nutrients they contain. For example, yellow peaches and apricots contribute large amounts of carotene (potential vitamin A) but are poor sources of ascorbic acid; and citrus fruits are good sources of ascorbic acid but they are low in carotene content. There is also variation within each type of food in amounts of any one nutrient: lemons and tangerines are both citrus fruits, but 1 tablespoon of lemon juice will contain more ascorbic acid than one tablespoon of tangerine juice. Yellow-fleshed peaches such as Rio-Oso Gem or Hale will have a higher carotene content than the white-meated Babcock peaches will have.

The *genetic* constitution of a plant is also important to its nutritive contribution. It has been established that certain genetic lines of cabbage have a higher ascorbic acid content than do other lines or even the parent stock. Research workers are constantly trying to breed plants with improved nutritive and palatability characteristics.

Variations in growth conditions. The climate and soil fertility conditions under which the plants are grown affect the quantity as well as the quality of the crop. Variations in the general climatic conditions which include rainfall, sun, and wind contribute to variations in the

A

B

C

Fig. 73. Nutritive contributions are dependent upon the part of the plant that is eaten such as the leaves (A), roots (B), and fruits as represented by melons (C), squash (D), and others (E).

development of the plants. It is generally believed that fruits and vegetables will have a high nutritive value if they are well-developed and have a good size, shape, and color for the variety. The fertility of the soil does not seem to affect the vitamin content of individual roots, fruits, or flowers, but it does affect the amount of the plant produced per acre. A soil low in minerals may be a limiting factor in the growth and development of the plant and therefore affect the size of the crop rather than the actual mineral content.

Vine or tree-ripened fruits are usually richer in ascorbic acid than the fully developed fruits that are not ripe at the time of harvest, and which are allowed to develop certain characteristics of ripening in storage or while subjected to ethylene gas. The gas will develop such qualities as color and texture, but the vitamin content does not increase as it does in a comparable fruit that is allowed to ripen on the vine.

The *shape, color, and size* of fruits and vegetables are indicative of the conditions under which they are grown. A fruit that has these qualities well developed for its variety is probably a better buy than poorly shaped, off-colored, or under- or oversized fruits.

Treatment during marketing. Fresh fruits and vegetables are *highly perishable.* Some deterioration that might affect the nutritional value can occur between the time the food is harvested and the time that it is purchased. This deterioration depends upon many factors: (1) the conditions when harvested; (2) the number of handlings; (3) the temperature during the marketing period; (4) the length of time since harvesting; and (5) the care that is given the fruit or vegetable in the retail store.

A connoisseur once coined a brief rule for retention of freshness qualities in vegetables by saying, "Let no more than one hour elapse from plot to pot." The United States has a large urban population, which makes it impractical to consider quite such a rapid delivery of foods. Therefore means of retaining freshness qualities during marketing must be found.

Fresh vegetables except tomatoes are considered to be best when harvested at a slightly immature stage. The maturing action continues after harvest so that immaturity in vegetables at harvest is desirable. Also, firm plants have better keeping qualities than do plants bruised by harvester, insects, or rodents; so healthy intact vegetables are most desirable.

The fewer the number of handlings necessary to move the vegetable from the growing plot to the cooking pot, the fewer will be the chances of bruising the plant tissues or exposing them to unfavorable atmospheric conditions. The producer may crate his produce and transport it to a wholesale distributor, who may take it to a storage depot before moving it into the retail markets. The bruised portions of the plant are generally removed at each point along the way to increase sales appeal, but this practice also exposes fresh portions of the plant to bruising. Retail market workers further increase bruising by sorting, trimming, and resorting. Finally consumers in self-service markets contribute their bit by pinching and sorting. These handlings take their toll in losses of total amount of food, and many times the portions of plants removed are those highest in nutritive concentrations. Bruised portions retained deteriorate more rapidly than unbruised parts.

The extent of deterioration of the vegetable as finally offered to the consumer depends also upon temperature, humidity, and time lapse between field and market. Aside from the total losses caused by trim, partial nutrient losses occur in the vitamin content during transit and holding periods. As pointed out in other chapters these losses are caused primarily by oxidation, therefore the lower the temperature, the shorter the time, and the less exposure to oxygen during transportation and storage the smaller the losses will be. Ascorbic acid is inactivated much more easily than are other vitamins, and leaves, rich in this nutrient generally have the greatest surface area. Therefore leaves may lose 30 to 50 per cent of their original ascorbic acid content during the marketing period. Potatoes and tomatoes have little surface area exposed and retain their ascorbic acid to a remarkable extent. Green peas, beans, and other immature seeds retain ascorbic acid to a greater extent if they are marketed in the pod rather than shelled. Similarly, cabbage in a solid head will retain its ascorbic acid longer than cabbage preshredded and packaged into a so-called convenience food.

A high humidity helps to prevent ascorbic acid losses during holding of vegetables at any temperature and in some markets produce in display trays is sprayed. Wilting, therefore permits serious losses of ascorbic acid in the succulent vegetables. The practice of displaying fruits and vegetables in the sun or toward the front of an open market is a very poor one.

Some losses of vitamin A value might also occur prior to marketing, but if practices designed to retain crispness and ascorbic acid values are followed, no appreciable losses in other nutrients will occur.

Home storage and preparation conditions. Storage in the home should protect the fruits and vegetables from wilting and also provide temperature and humidity conditions compatible with the preservation of ascorbic acid. Vegetables, except bananas, avocados, potatoes, and dry onions, may be protected from wilt by storing in closed containers or plastic bags and stored at refrigerator temperature (normally 45° F).

A great deal of nutritive value can be lost during *preparation*. Excessive trimming or the removal of thick parings will result in the loss of vitamins and minerals in direct proportion to the amount of the food discarded. Vegetables that are pared or cut into slices and then allowed to soak in water before cooking may lose water-soluble vitamins and certain of the minerals to the water. If they are not covered with water but allowed to remain in the air, some of the ascorbic acid may be lost by oxidation. Therefore, it is advisable to prepare vegetables just before they are to be cooked, or if they are to be used for salad, they should be prepared just before serving. Exceptions to this general rule might be such vegetables as cucumbers, radishes, and garnishes that furnish little to the nutritive value of the meal, but are used for their contribution to appearance and crisp texture (Fig. 74).

Vegetables cooked in water may lose large quantities of the water-soluble vitamins and certain minerals to the cooking water. If this

Fig. 74. Cucumbers and radishes are used for color and crispness, not for nutritive values. (Courtesy of Western Growers Association, Los Angeles.)

water is not evaporated or recovered and used in soups, gravies, or other foods, much of the vitamin and mineral value contained in the vegetables will be wasted.

By eating a variety of fruits and vegetables one can be assured of a variety of vitamins and minerals in good quantity because nutrients low in one will likely be contributed by others. Tables 28 and 28A may be used as guides to quantities of these nutrients found in an average serving of the common fruits and vegetables, which have been given reasonable care since harvesting.

Proteins, Carbohydrates, and Fats in Fruits and Vegetables

Fruits and vegetables are relatively low in protein inasmuch as they have a high water content. The proteins present in plant tissues may not be used well by the body because many are low or entirely deficient in certain of the essential amino acids. When these plant foods are used with egg, milk, or meat, the deficient amino acids are supplied and the vegetables can become extenders of proteins. In the average diet there are enough other sources of protein, and one need not be concerned with obtaining large amounts of this nutrient from fruits and vegetables.

The carbohydrate content of fruits and vegetables is very important, and this is one of the factors often considered in making food groupings. Carbohydrate is present as starch, sugars, cellulose, and pectic substances. Some of the starch may be changed to sugar during storage by hydrolysis. This is illustrated by the changes which occur in stored apples. When the apples are harvested they are usually juicy and firm; however, during storage they become mealy and much sweeter than they were originally. The part of the carbohydrate that is in the form of cellulose cannot be digested, but it does contribute to the quantity of bulk, and this aids the digestive processes. The *protopectins* are the intercellular cementing substances of plant tissues; they are also bulk formers.

Except for olives and avocados, the parts of plants that are usually classified as fruits and vegetables contribute little to the fat content of the diet. Some states stipulate a minimum oil content for avocados permitted to market. Vegetable oils are a by-product of cereals and other seeds, and are considered elsewhere in the book (see Chapter 7).

Table 28. THE VITAMIN AND MINERAL CONTENT OF AN AVERAGE SERVING OF THE COMMON FRESH VEGETABLES*

Product	Size of Serving	Energy Value, Cal.	Calcium, Mg.	Iron, Mg.	Vitamin A, I.U.	Thiamine, Mg.	Riboflavin, Mg.	Niacin, Mg.	Ascorbic Acid, Mg.
Asparagus (green)	½ cup	18	16	0.9	910	0.12	0.15	1.1	20
Avocado†	½ peeled	279	11	0.7	330	0.07	0.15	1.3	18
Beans (green lima)	½ cup	76	23	1.3	230	0.11	0.07	0.9	12
Beans (green snap)	½ cup	13	22	0.5	415	0.05	0.06	0.3	9
Beets	½ cup	34	17	0.6	15	0.02	0.04	0.3	5
Beet Greens	½ cup	20	85‡	2.3	5395	0.04	0.11	0.3	11
Broccoli	½ cup	22	97	1.0	2550	0.05	0.11	0.6	55
Brussel Sprouts	½ cup	30	22	0.9	260	0.03	0.08	0.3	32
Cabbage†	1 cup	24	46	0.5	80	0.06	0.05	0.3	50
Cabbage	½ cup	20	39	0.4	75	0.04	0.04	0.3	26
Carrots†	1—5½ x 1"	21	20	0.4	6000	0.03	0.03	0.3	3
Cauliflower	½ cup	15	13	0.6	54	0.04	0.05	0.3	17
Celery†	1 cup (diced)	18	50	0.5	…	0.05	0.04	0.4	7
Chard	½ cup	15	76‡	1.8	2255	0.03	0.05	0.3	12
Corn (yellow)	1 ear	84	5	0.6	390	0.11	0.10	1.4	8
Cowpeas	½ cup	75	29	2.0	310	0.23	0.06	0.6	16
Cress, water†	2 oz.	10	110	1.1	2680	0.05	0.09	0.4	45
Cucumbers†	6 slices	6	5	0.2	…	0.02	0.02	0.1	4
Dandelion Greens	½ cup	40	169	2.8	13650	0.11	0.11	0.6	15
Endive†	2 oz.	12	45	1.0	1700	0.04	0.07	0.2	6
Kale	½ cup	22	124	1.2	4610	0.04	0.12	0.9	28
Kohlrabi	½ cup	23	35	0.5	…	0.03	0.03	0.1	28
Lettuce†	2 large leaves	7	11	0.2	270	0.02	0.04	0.1	4

Food	Measure								
Mustard Greens	½ cup	15	154	2.0	5025	0.04	0.12	0.5	32
Okra	4 pods—3 in.	14	35	0.3	315	0.03	0.03	0.3	8
Onions†	1 Tb. chopped	4	3	⋯	⋯	⋯	⋯	⋯	1
Onions (green)†	6 small	23	68	0.4	30	0.02	0.02	0.1	12
Parsnips	½ cup	47	44	0.5	⋯	0.04	0.08	0.2	9
Peas (green)	½ cup	55	17	1.5	575	0.20	0.11	1.8	12
Peppers (green)†	1 medium	16	7	0.3	400	0.02	0.04	0.2	77
Potatoes	1 medium	97	13	0.8	20	0.11	0.05	1.4	17
Pumpkin	½ cup (canned)	38	23	0.8	3875	0.02	0.07	0.6	⋯
Radishes†	4 small	4	7	0.2	10	0.01	⋯	0.1	5
Rhubarb (sugar added)	½ cup	191	56‡	0.6	35	0.01	⋯	0.1	8
Rutabagas	½ cup (cubed)	25	42	0.3	270	0.04	0.05	0.6	16
Spinach	½ cup	23	111‡	1.8	10600	0.07	0.18	0.5	27
Squash (summer)	½ cup	17	16	0.4	275	0.04	0.07	0.6	11
Squash (winter)	½ cup	50	25	0.8	6345	0.05	0.15	0.6	7
Sweet Potatoes	1 medium	183	44	1.1	11410	0.12	0.08	0.9	28
Tomato†	1 medium	30	16	0.9	1640	0.08	0.06	0.8	35
Tomato	½ cup	23	14	0.7	1270	0.07	0.04	0.8	20
Turnips†	1 cup	43	54	0.7	⋯	0.07	0.09	0.6	38
Turnip	1 cup (diced)	42	62	0.8	⋯	0.06	0.09	0.6	28
Turnip Greens	½ cup	21	188	1.8	7690	0.05	0.28	0.5	44

* Nutritive values according to U.S.D.A. Agriculture Handbook No. 8 (1950).
† Raw.
‡ Calcium may not be available.

Table 28A. THE VITAMIN AND MINERAL CONTENT OF AN AVERAGE SERVING OF THE COMMON FRESH FRUITS*

Product	Size of Serving	Energy Value, Cal.	Calcium, mg.	Iron, mg.	Vitamin A, I.U.	Thiamine, mg.	Riboflavin, mg.	Niacin, mg.	Ascorbic Acid, mg.
Apples	1 medium	76	8	0.4	120	0.05	0.04	0.2	6
Apricots	3	54	17	0.5	2990	0.03	0.05	0.9	7
Bananas	1 medium	88	8	0.6	430	0.04	0.05	0.7	10
Blackberries	⅔ cup	54	30	0.8	185	0.04	0.09	0.4	20
Blueberries	⅔ cup	55	14	0.8	260	0.02	0.02	0.3	15
Cantaloupe	½—diam. 5″	37	31	0.7	6190	0.09	0.07	0.9	59
Cherries (pitted)	1 cup	94	28	0.6	960	0.08	0.09	0.6	13
Cranberries (raw)	1 cup	54	16	0.7	50	0.03	0.02	0.1	13
Currants	1 cup	60	40	1.0	130	0.04	…	…	40
Figs	3 small	90	62	0.7	90	0.06	0.06	0.6	2
Gooseberries	½ cup	30	16	0.4	220	…	…	…	25
Grapefruit	½ medium	75	41	0.4	20	0.07	0.04	0.4	76
Grapes (European type)	1 cup	102	26	0.9	120	0.09	0.06	0.4	6
Guavas	1	49	21	0.5	180	0.05	0.03	0.8	212
Lemons	1 medium	20	25	0.4	…	0.03	…	0.1	31
Lemons	1 Tb. juice	4	2	…	…	0.01	…	…	7
Limes	1 medium	19	21	0.3	…	0.02	…	0.1	14
Loganberries	1 cup	90	50	1.7	280	0.04	0.10	0.4	34
Mangos	1 medium	87	12	0.3	8380	0.08	0.07	1.2	55
Oranges	1 medium	70	51	0.6	290	0.12	0.04	0.4	77
Papayas	1 Cup ½″ cubes	71	36	0.5	3190	0.06	0.07	0.5	102
Peaches (yellow)	1 medium	46	8	0.6	880	0.02	0.05	0.9	8
Pears	1 medium	95	20	0.5	30	0.03	0.06	0.2	6
Pineapple	1 cup (diced)	74	22	0.4	180	0.12	0.04	0.3	33
Plums	1—2″ diam.	29	10	0.3	200	0.04	0.02	0.3	3
Raspberries	1 cup	100	54	1.2	…	0.03	0.09	0.4	32
Strawberries	⅔ cup	36	28	0.8	60	0.03	0.07	0.3	59
Tangerines	1 medium	35	27	0.3	340	0.06	0.02	0.2	25

*Nutritive values according to U.S.D.A. Agriculture Handbook No. 8 (1950).

Consideration of the Nutritional Value of Processed Fruits and Vegetables

Each year many fruits and vegetables are produced in such large amounts that they cannot be consumed during the production or fresh season. It is economically advantageous to preserve the excesses either by canning, freezing, cool storage, drying, salting, fermenting, radiation, or a combination of these methods.

Many changes occur during the preservation process and the storage period, but these changes do not necessarily lower the nutritive value. Nutrient content can be enhanced by concentration, by additions of other food or specific nutrients, or as a result of heating. When water is removed (as in the drying process), the nutrients are concentrated. The addition of syrups to fruit increases the energy value, and the addition of ascorbic acid to frozen fruits to prevent browning may result in a higher amount of this vitamin in the frozen product than in the fresh fruit. These are a few examples of instances in which nutritional value is increased. It is well to remember that properly processed food may be of higher nutritive value than comparable fresh fruits and vegetables that have been marketed under adverse conditions.

Many packers are taking their processing plants directly into the field, and only a few minutes elapse between harvesting and canning or freezing. This procedure helps to insure canned and frozen fruits and vegetables of the highest quality.

When nutritive losses occur, the amount and kind will depend upon many factors: (1) type of processing; (2) type of food and its condition at the time of processing; (3) trimming losses or wilting; (4) ingredients added during the processing; and (5) storage of the processed food. In general these are the same factors that were discussed in preparation procedures and in other phases of food processing.

THE BUYING OF FRUITS AND VEGETABLES FOR GOOD MEAL PLANNING AND THE WISE USE OF THE FOOD DOLLAR

Fresh Fruits and Vegetables

Intelligent and efficient buying of fresh fruits and vegetables is aided by an understanding of the quality standards and a knowledge of general marketing procedures.

Quality standards. The United States Department of Agriculture has designated and described grade and size standards for many fruits and vegetables (Fig. 75). A description of these may be obtained upon request from that agency.[1] It should be understood that because all federal grade descriptions give the minimum quality that is permissible within a grade, there is a possibility of differences in quality between crops of fruits and vegetables of the same grade designation. However, the buyer may feel assured that vegetables marked *U.S. No. 1* will meet a certain minimum standard at the time of packing.

Use of the federal grading and sizing system is optional, yet these standards form the basis for trading in wholesale markets regardless of the terminology used. The size may be indicated by weights, dimensions, number in the container, or generalizations (large, medium,

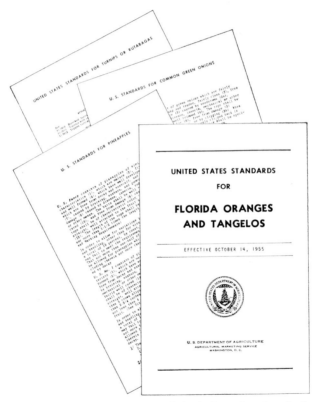

Fig. 75. The United States Department of Agriculture has described grade and size standards for many fruits and vegetables.

[1] Inquire at the local Agricultural Extension Service.

small). The quality may be designated by descriptive term, letter, number, brand name, or some unrelated term. The designation for quality may also imply size. The grocer will be able to give the grade equivalent for the brands or other terms to the buyer. *The consumers may ask for this information.*

Descriptive terms such as Fancy, Choice, and Good may be used. Because these terms bring a very definite quality picture to the mind of the consumer, they are more meaningful than the brand name. These descriptive terms may be replaced by the letters, A, B, and C. The descriptive terms or letters may also be used in conjunction with the brand name. The combination can be a very effective guide to selection if they are understood by the buyer. The letter grades are used most often by packers for the cooperative associations and for certain chains of markets.

Numbers are used to designate the federal grades for potatoes and other root vegetables. An explanation of these grades may be secured from the Department of Agriculture. They should be thoroughly investigated, because they are deceptive—"No. 1" may not be the highest quality but only an acceptable product. Descriptive words may be used with the number to indicate higher quality.

Brand names are registered trade marks and can be used only by the

Fig. 76. Quality designation may be made by an unrelated term stamped on fruit; for example, "Sunkist" represents first quality. (Courtesy of Sunkist Growers, Los Angeles.)

specific producer or distributor who owns the name. A producer usually has one or more brands for each grade or size. The names are not necessarily descriptive of the product, and few consumers realize their significance. Some packers use unrelated terms that are not brand names to designate quality (Fig. 76). For example, oranges packed by the California Fruit Growers Exchange that are marked "Red Ball," are choice.

The grades or terms designating quality may be stamped on the fruit or on the container or both. The distinguishing mark should be available to the buyer as well as to the retailer, therefore, the mark should be on the food whenever possible or the food should be displayed in the original container that bears the stamp.

Grades that are given at the time of packing may not be reliable consumer guides for the more perishable products. For these products or in the absence of any grading system, the consumer may learn to judge quality by inspection. General signs of quality are:

(1) *Freshness*—the product should not show signs of wilt, browning, mold, rot, or over-maturity.

(2) *Size*—vegetables and fruits that have a normal size for the variety usually have good flavor, high nutritive value, and little waste.

(3) *Color*—plant products should have a color that is normal for the specific stage of their development; for example, broccoli flowers should be the green buds rather than the yellow flowers. In some cases it is difficult to evaluate color since the product may be treated to enhance the appearance. For example, oranges may be dyed; or the color of tomatoes may have been improved by exposure to ethylene gas.

(4) *Weight for size*—citrus fruits and melons in particular can be hefted or weighted. Fruits that are light-weight for their size will be lacking in juiciness.

General marketing procedures. Fresh fruits and vegetables are usually least expensive and of highest nutritive value when they are most plentiful. When the nearby supply is abundant, fruits and vegetables are said to be "in season." The length of this period depends largely upon the proximity of the market to the producing section, the method of distribution, and the growing season in the district in which the market is located. Information concerning the market supply and demand may be obtained from the daily newspaper, the radio, or from the Market News Service. These agencies usually obtain their information from the *Market News Service of the United States Department of Agriculture.*

The informed consumer will study the local market conditions carefully, and also he will learn the buying habits of the green grocer. Buyers for large markets will go to the wholesale center daily, whereas small or isolated markets may receive new supplies only every other day, or even weekly. It is advisable to know where, how often, and in what quantities the market purchases the basic supply. If the market receives fresh supplies infrequently and has poor storage facilities, the best selections will be displayed the first day the food is in the market. If the foods are refrigerated or kept in cool-storage, the market storage conditions may be better than those in the home.

Processed Fruits and Vegetables

It is often advantageous to purchase processed foods when the quality of fresh fruits and vegetables is questionable, when the supply is low, or for the convenience in storage and preparation.

Grading systems for processed fruits and vegetables are similar to those described for the fresh. If consumers are to buy canned, frozen, or dried foods intelligently they must understand the meaning of whatever grading system is used. Grade A usually means that the fruit is of uniform dimension and has a desirable flavor. Grade B is a very acceptable product, but may be more mature or somewhat less well shaped than Grade A. The regulations governing the sanitary conditions under which foods are packed and the safety precautions used in processing are the same for all grades. The grade seldom reflects the nutritive value (Fig. 77).

The style of pack in processed foods, particularly canned and frozen products has a bearing on both price and the use to be made of the foods. Nearly all products are packed in two or more styles, for examples: (1) asparagus may be in whole spears, or cut into pieces; (2) snap beans may be whole, halved, quartered, sliced, or diced; and (3) pineapple may be sliced (whole or broken), crushed, or cubed. Selections in canned pineapple illustrate how the style of pack affects price and use—the cubed pineapple may be made from trimmings and represent salvage material from whole slices. Although the quality is as high as the sliced product, the price will be lower than it is for slices. The use may be limited because the cubes may be used only in products where the pineapple is to be cut or broken into pieces.

Frozen fruits and vegetables. The preservation of fruits and vegetables by freezing methods has been developed within the last three decades. It might be said that this processing method is in the developmental stages. Frozen foods seldom have the grade given on the

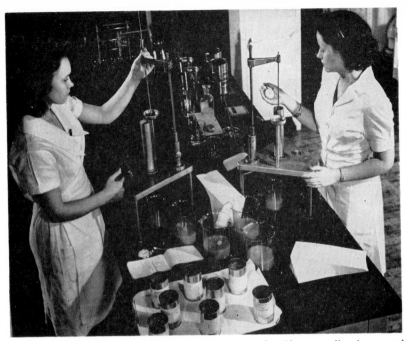

Fig. 77. Packers and processors assure consumers of uniform quality in canned goods by various physical and chemical analyses. (Courtesy of H. J. Heinz Co., Pittsburgh.)

container. However, the United States Department of Agriculture has established tentative standards for many of these products. If the grading system were more commonly used, it would simplify the selection of frozen foods, but in the absence of such a system, the consumer must rely on brands and packer grades. The majority of packers have standardized the quality for each brand so as to retain the good will of their customers.

Frozen foods are packed in a variety of container sizes so that the quantity selected may fit the family need. The package size is not an adequate guide to the amounts in a package as packages of similar size may contain quite different amounts. Whole broccoli, for example, is bulky and many-branched, whereas chopped broccoli can be made more compact without injuring or changing it; thus the container for a pound of uncut broccoli will usually be larger than that for a pound of the chopped vegetable. The weight of the contents is given on the label and may be noted before buying. This weight indicates the approximate amount of edible foods since there is a relatively small amount of liquid added; the entire package contents are edible.

The cost per unit weight decreases as the amount packaged in each container increases. If the consumer is to take advantage of the low unit price for the large package, plans for any excess need to be made. The food should not be thawed and refrozen unless it has been cooked prior to refreezing. Desired amounts may be cut from the package but unless the remainder is securely wrapped in moisture-proof vapor-proof materials, it will not retain its high quality during the next storage period.

All frozen foods must be stored near 0° F if they are to retain a high percentage of their nutrients and good eating quality. Even mold growth is possible at temperatures above 15° F, which is a lower temperature than that required for freezing water. The type and amount of deterioration that occur at higher temperatures than 0° F will vary with the kind of fruit or vegetable. In some cases only color and flavor are lost, but under other conditions nutritive losses also occur. Peas stored above 15° F will quickly lose their desirable bright green color, acquire a yellow-brown tinge, and have a haylike flavor. Not only should the market have desirable storage conditions, but it is equally important for the home to have adequate storage for frozen foods. A temperature near 0° F is recommended as practical to maintain and sufficiently low to protect the desirable qualities of the food.

Discounts in price (often 10 per cent) are given for purchasing frozen foods in caselots. The consumer may take advantage of this type of buying if the home has sufficient storage space or if a rented frozen food locker is available. The length of the time the frozen foods may be stored without palatability changes is limited. Therefore, quantity buying should be confined to the amount that can be used within a practical storage period. Vegetables may acquire a haylike flavor after a year. When the new crop is ready for processing, packers may give a discount on the price of the frozen food that remains from the previous season. Before this food is purchased in quantity, its remaining freezer life should be considered if the consumer is to have satisfactory products at future dates.

Canned fruits and vegetables. Canned fruits and vegetables are easy to store, and they have much the same nutritive value as the fresh or frozen products (Fig. 78). There is some research evidence to indicate that the carotene of the canned product may be more available than in the fresh varieties possibly as a result of the softened texture of the food.

The label on the container will give information regarding quantity, style of the pack, seasoning or syrup used, and quality—as indicated by grade or brand—so that canned goods may be selected to suit the

Fig. 78. Vegetables for soups are carefully selected and prepared before canning. (Courtesy of H. J. Heinz Co., Pittsburgh.)

family need. The type and size of container are important factors when canned fruits and vegetables are purchased. The containers may be of either metal or glass, however, unless dark storage can be provided the metal container is to be preferred. The clear glass container enables the purchaser to see the product before buying, but riboflavin is destroyed and many food colors are changed by light. Metals may change some of the food colors, therefore, most of the packers use lacquered cans for sensitive pigments and in this manner prevent the food from contacting the metal. The sizes of the containers are designed to fit various needs—single servings, multiple servings, and so forth. The unit price of the food decreases as the can size increases, and if the excess food can be used, it is good economy to buy in the larger containers.

Cool, dry storage is required to minimize deterioration. Any color, flavor, or nutritive losses that might occur in canned food will be speeded if the storage temperature is high. Refrigerator space is generally not available but temperatures of 60 to 65° F should be possible. Metal containers and the metal ring or lid used to seal glass containers will rust if the storage atmosphere is damp. The rust may progress through the metal of the can and cause leaks, or the seal may break and allow air to enter the container.

It is well to avoid purchase of dented or damaged cans unless they are to be used immediately because a small amount of pressure during handling may cause them to leak. All food from bulged cans should be discarded. The rounded end typical of a bulged can is caused by gas pressure. This bulge is natural and necessary for carbonated beverages that are canned in metal containers but indicates spoilage for fruits and vegetables. The shelf life of canned fruits and vegetables is several years if properly stored. For this reason the price advantage offered by caselot buying and year-end sales can be profitable.

If the can contains more food than is needed at one meal, it is more than a safe practice, it is advisable to store the excess in the original container. The container is sterile, or it was when the food was opened, therefore, it is more sanitary than the questionably sterile dishes found in the average home. Tight-fitting covers are now available for cans in order that consumers will be encouraged to use this method of storage. Lacquer treatment of metal containers will prevent the metallic flavor that many people find undesirable. In spite of the lacquer treatment, acid food stored in opened metal containers for longer than three or four days may take on a metallic flavor. This is not harmful but may be disagreeable.

Dried fruits and vegetables. These foods are nutritious, keep for long periods, are available the year around, and require relatively little storage space (Fig. 79). They are less expensive than other processed forms of food because the packaging, storing, and transportation costs are considerably reduced.

If dehydrated products are properly treated before drying, the flavor, color, and most of the nutritive value will be well retained. Many fruits are sulfur-treated to prevent the browning of light colors that results from oxidation, and sulfur treating also results in protecting, to some extent, the ascorbic acid and vitamin A. However, the sulfur will inactivate the thiamine. As fruits are poor sources of thiamine but are reliable sources of vitamin A (prunes, apricots, peaches, etc.) and may also contain some ascorbic acid, the sulfured products are to be preferred. Other fruits and vegetables may be blanched prior to dehydrating in order to inactivate the oxidative enzymes that would cause poor flavor, color, and texture. Prunes may be lye-dipped to "crack" the skins to permit drying.

The label on a package of dried foods will give grade, treatment prior to dehydrating, tenderizing, weight of food in the package, and

Fig. 79. Apricots, peaches, pears, prunes, apples, dates, and raisins are commonly preserved by dehydration.

directions for reconstituting. This information is given to enable the buyer to make wise selections and satisfactory usage of the products.

Salted. Salt acts as a preservative when it is used in high concentrations—15 to 20 per cent (see p. 43). At this concentration microorganisms cannot grow and fermentation is prevented. This concentration makes the food too salty for eating, and only a few foods are preserved in this manner. In weaker concentrations of salt (3 to 5 per cent), lactic acid bacteria develop rapidly, and the growth of other undesirable organisms is inhibited. The salt will draw water and water-soluble substances from the food, and the sugars thus extracted serve as food for the friendly bacteria. When adequate sugar is present, the fermentation will proceed to the point where the acid concentration will stop practically all bacterial action. At this point the color, flavor, and texture of the products are changed to the "pickle" stage. Sauerkraut is fermented cabbage and is used extensively in this country. Turnips, yellow string beans, and other vegetables may also be fermented. These foods with the juices may be good sources of ascorbic acid. The Chinese and Japanese style "salad" may be slightly fermented special vegetables. Cucumbers are extensively fermented, and some may have spices or herbs added, as for example, the dill pickle. In many of the commercial pickle manufacturing processes, the vegetables are pretreated by heavy salting (15 per cent), which serves to draw out some of the water content and crisp the product. The brine is then removed, the product refreshed, and the desired vinegar, sugar, and spices added. Olives may also be packed in brine after processing.

Radiated. The energy from the stockpiles of atomic research may be useful in the area of food preservation. This process is in the developmental stage, and it has interesting possibilities for the future. Radiation plants for vegetable processing are being built, and radiated foods may soon be on the market. Sterilization involves the introduction of radiant energy into the food in sufficient amounts to destroy spoilage microorganisms. This is easily accomplished, but inactivation of enzymes is also frequently necessary and requires additional treatments that may cause undesirable changes in other aspects. Radiation inactivates some of the vitamins, notably ascorbic acid and vitamin B_{12}. At the present time some irradiated foods are of poor color, flavor, and odor.

This method of preservation will permit containers that are economical to produce, light in weight, and require reduced storage space. Also, it will prolong storage of food without refrigeration.

Juices. Canned and frozen juices in many varieties are available on present-day markets. Most of these will be found to be acceptable. Fruits and vegetables that are good sources of ascorbic acid provide juices that are high in ascorbic acid, and these include all of the citrus fruits, tomato, guava, and papaya. Some fruits that are not notably good sources of ascorbic acid may be fortified with this vitamin. Information concerning fortification will be given on the label.

Concentrated frozen juices retain their ascorbic acid very well, and they have a flavor not unlike fresh fruit. These frozen products will retain their full ascorbic acid value for three or four days after they are reconstituted if they are covered and stored in the refrigerator.

Dried citrus juices are in the experimental stage. These should not be confused with synthetically flavored powders for drinks. The latter contain acids of minor nutritional value and unless fortified do not contribute either vitamins or minerals.

PREPARATION OF FRUITS AND VEGETABLES TO INSURE
GOOD NUTRITION AND GOOD EATING

Many fruits and vegetables may be eaten raw, while others, for example, potatoes, are more palatable after cooking. Cooking serves to soften protopectins and cellulose and in many instances permits more complete digestion and absorption of nutrients than results from raw products. Cooking may also be employed to give desirable flavor and color changes and serves to "pasteurize" those plants whose growing and handling conditions might permit transfer of disease-producing microorganisms to the consumer, for instance, dysentery.

Preparation Preliminary to Serving

Preparation preliminary to serving or cooking of plant food is an important factor in the eating quality of the finished product. This preparation may include washing, trimming, paring, slicing, other cutting, mashing, chilling, or marinating. Any of these procedures, unless carried out with reasonable care, may bring about undesirable changes in the color, flavor, texture, or nutritive value.

Washing. Plant foods are washed only to remove dirt, sprays, insects, and other contaminates. Roots and stem portions may require scrubbing with a stiff brush. Leaves may need to be washed through several waters. Seeds and fruits probably should remain in the water long enough to soften any soil so that it can be removed without bruising the product. Loose flowers (cauliflower and broccoli) are excellent traps for insects, but a short soaking period in a large quantity of salt water will "float out" the insects.

The practice of washing before cutting, paring, or other partitioning will minimize the loss of water-soluble nutrients as well as the loss of flavor-giving substances. Cold water is best for all washing processes because warm or hot water will cause wilting, which may interfere with the final use to be made of the food as well as increase the nutritive losses.

Trimming. Some of the nutrients concentrated in the outer leaves, cores, skins, and parts not commonly used as food may be obtained if trimming is kept to a minimum. The dark, loose, outside leaves of lettuce, cabbage, and endive have a higher carotene content and a more distinctive flavor than the bleached compact inside portions have. Only the bruised or dried leaves of these plants need to be discarded. The remaining leaves that are undesirable for salads or for cooking alone may be cooked with stews, green peas, greens, onion, or other vegetables. The heavy, but not woody, stems of asparagus, broccoli, and celery may require longer cooking than the more tender portions, but they have a good nutritive content and could be used separately. The stem ends can be removed from the more tender portions and cooking started before the tender tops are added. If desired, the tough portions may be puréed and used for cream soups.

Paring and partitioning. Paring must be kept to a minimum if the maximum amount of nutrients is to be retained. Many vegetables may have their flavors enhanced by cooking without paring. Potatoes, carrots, beets, eggplant, and apples are especially good when cooked unpared. If, because of the use to be made of the cooked vegetable, the skin is undesirable, a very thin layer can be slipped off after cooking or the raw food can be scraped or pared with a "floating blade" or knife with a guard.

Slicing or other partitioning of plant materials should be done just before they are to be used because the oxidative changes that occur at the surface may be great as a result of the large area of surface exposed. If a cube is acceptable for the selected method of preparation, this is more desirable than a slice of the same volume because a cube has less surface area than a slice. This is illustrated in Fig. 80.

Grinding and mashing of uncooked products that oxidize readily permit the greatest losses of flavor, color, and ascorbic acid. An antioxidant can be added to bananas or avocados before they are mashed; this does not produce undesirable flavors and it does protect the color. Potatoes and apples may be dipped or soaked in salt water to delay browning. Some research indicates that less ascorbic acid is lost when salt is used than when salt is omitted. If a food is valuable for its content of water-soluble nutrients, soaking should be discouraged even for color retention.

The sharpness of the knife or grinder blades and the metal from which they are made are also factors in retention of nutrients and palatability. If cutting edges are not sharp, the food is bruised, and bruised vegetables lose color and flavor rapidly. It has been shown that cabbage shredded with a sharp knife will retain ascorbic acid longer than cabbage cut on a shredder or with a dull knife. Iron and copper in blades may react with the ascorbic acid and inactivate it.

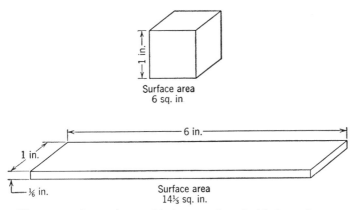

Surface area
6 sq. in.

1 in.

6 in.

⅙ in.

Surface area
14⅓ sq. in.

Fig. 80. The same volume of vegetable is more than double in surface area when 6 slices are cut from one cube.

Crisping. Chilling or crisping of salad greens and other leafy products will delay the loss of both ascorbic acid and flavor. The best results will be obtained if the food is placed in a storage container with high humidity and at a low temperature. The high humidity can be achieved by adding a few drops of cold water to the leaves and placing them in an air-tight plastic bag or other container before refrigerating.

Acidifying. Marinating or treating fruits and vegetables with an acid such as vinegar or lemon juice is a desirable procedure. This will enhance the flavor, and, as has been stated before, the acid protects the ascorbic acid and prevents browning of cut or torn edges. Oil dressings, however, tend to wilt the vegetable so that oil is added to crisp salads at the time they are to be served.

Cooking Fruits and Vegetables to Develop Flavor and Improve Eating Quality

The color, flavor, texture, and nutritive value that have been so carefully guarded during preparation may be changed, lost, or discarded unless fruits and vegetables are carefully cooked. However, no matter how good a food is nutritionally, unless it can be eaten it will do you little good. Individual likes and dislikes cannot be disregarded. Many of the revolutionary methods of cooking to preserve color, flavor, and nutritive value are eventually accepted by evolutionary methods. Perhaps the student who was chided about the large quantity of water on her potatoes had a point when she said, "But see how much less this is than the amount I used before."

Color and color changes in cooking. Colors in plant parts result from the presence of one or more of the four groups of substances termed *pigments*. These are the water-soluble *anthocyanins* and *flavones*, and the non-water-soluble (fat-soluble) *chlorophylls* and *carotenoids*. These pigments change in color under various preparation and cooking conditions.

The *anthocyanins* are responsible for the red, purple, blue, and violet shades in plants—including the flowers used for decoration instead of eating. The sequence of color change is red to purple, to blue or violet, to green, to yellow as the solution in which they are dissolved becomes progressively more alkaline. The blue, violet, and greens (but not yellow) can be changed to red upon the additions of acid. This can be illustrated in the cooking of red cabbage. The intact leaf appears to be a dark purple-red. If the juices are pressed out so that the juices from the interior of the leaf are mixed with the pigment from the leaf, a rich blue liquid is obtained. Cooking in neutral or alkaline water is equivalent to pressing out the juices, and a blue cabbage results. Addition of lemon or vinegar will restore the red color. Often the cabbage is cooked with sour apples so that the cooking water is acidified. The acid not only preserves the red color but also crisps the texture and adds flavor.

Anthocyanins are present in only a few so-called nonacid foods (cabbage, radish, and beets) but are found in many of the acid fruits (cherries, plums, concord grapes, etc.). Radishes are seldom cooked, and the pigments of beets are more stable to alkali than are the anthocyanins of other foods, so that color changes caused by changes in acidity are largely limited to the red cabbage.

The anthocyanins are extremely water-soluble. Even when beets are cooked intact with a part of the top and the entire tap root, the cooking water becomes red. If the beets are shredded or cubed before cooking the color may be leached until the vegetable is a pale red.

Contact of the foods containing anthocyanins with either iron or tin also affects their color, causing them to fade or discolor. Bing cherries, prune plums, and other fruits of similar color when canned in untreated metal containers may turn pink or lose their color entirely. Note the lacquered interior of tin cans used for the preservation of the red foods. Interesting color changes can be created in red fruit-juice punches by adding pineapple juice, which contains tin salts.

The *flavones* are present in many vegetables, but they may be seen in only a few. They are colorless in neutral or acid solutions and therefore are seen only in seemingly white vegetables when these are sufficiently alkaline to permit the light yellow color of these pigments to develop. Cauliflower, potatoes, and Spanish onions become yellow when cooked in alkaline or hard waters, but if a small amount of white vinegar, cream of tartar, or lemon juice is added to the water, these vegetables will be snowy white. The yellow color sometimes seen in white rice is a flavone. Acid causes a crisping of the texture and changes the flavor of plant foods. Thus it must always be considered if the bleaching effects of the acid are desirable.

The flavones are water-soluble, therefore the water in which the otherwise colorless plant is cooked may have a yellow or opalescent color. Flavones are present in other colored vegetables but cannot be seen because of the other strong-colored pigments. If the white vegetables containing flavones come in contact with iron, they become first green and then brown. Chipped enamel pans or iron kettles are not suitable cooking utensils for these vegetables as the iron is available for chemical reaction and causes discoloration. The discoloration is not harmful, only undesirable from an appearance point of view.

Chlorophyll is a green fluorescent pigment that is not soluble in water. It becomes olive-drab in the presence of an acid, and this accounts for the characteristic shades of cucumber pickles. Chlorophyll is also unstable to heat, and this explains in part the brownish hue of canned or overcooked green fruits and vegetables. This latter change is accelerated in acid, and a part of the reaction is no doubt caused by the release of acids normally present in the plant tissue. Broccoli, green beans, brussels sprouts, celery, and asparagus are often noticeably brown when cooked. Broccoli, particularly, needs to have the stalk split if it is to become tender before color changes occur and buds become mushy. The green Pippin apple will have a drab green skin when baked, and the green gooseberry and Thompson seedless grapes are blue-green when cooked. The brightening of the color that may be observed when the green vegetables are beginning to cook is the result of softening the chloroplasts that hold the color, and this softening permits diffusion throughout the plant.

Green vegetables cooked in alkaline water or water to which a small amount of baking soda has been added will have a bright green color; however, the soda softens plant tissues and hastens inactivation of ascorbic acid and generally is undesirable. Unlike the anthocyanins, any change in the original green color cannot be restored.

Carotenoid pigments cause the yellow-orange or yellow-red color in foods. Some forty of these pigments are known; at least four are precursors of vitamin A (see Chapter 13). All are fat-soluble. The yellow color in the oil portion of a tomato sauce or salad dressing and the yellow color imparted to the hands when one scrapes carrots are the result of the solution of carotenoids in oils.

The carotenoids do not change color appreciably when mild acids or alkalis are added. When exposed to air, these pigments oxidize, and this affects the vitamin A values but not the colors.

Carotenoids accompany any of the chlorophyll coloring in plants so that the vitamin A value of the green vegetables is caused by yellow pigments, not green. The deeper the chlorophyll coloring, the greater the amounts of carotenoid pigments also present. This can be seen only in maturing plants when the chlorophyll disappears, and the hidden yellows and reds are disclosed.

Other color changes in fruits and vegetables are caused by either oxidative enzymes or chemical changes in substances other than the pigments. The tannins, which give the astringent qualities to plants, may turn a purple-brown color in the presence of iron salts. This browning does not occur in an acid medium and can be prevented by the addition of lemon juice or white vinegar. The mechanism of browning caused by the *oxidative enzymes* is not fully understood. However, browning may be inhibited by the following means: (1) heating to destroy the enzymes; (2) freezing to delay the enzyme action; (3) adding an antioxidant such as sulfur dioxide during drying, or ascorbic acid during freezing; (4) removing the air by vacuum packing; (5) replacing the air with carbon dioxide or nitrogen; (6) preventing oxygen from coming in contact with the food by immersing it in water or other liquid; and (7) decreasing the enzyme action by adding an acid.

Flavor and odor. The flavor and odor of vegetables and fruits varies widely. Some are bland and without odor; others have a very distinctive flavor or odor. Some contain enough sugar to give a very definite sweet taste, others have a sour taste as a result of their acid content. Flavor constituents other than sugar and acid are aromatic compounds, volatile sulfur compounds, esters, and tannins. The aromatic compounds give the characteristic flavor to pineapple; the volatile sulfur compounds are responsible for the flavor of onions (Fig. 81); and tannins impart the astringent quality to persimmons.

Flavors may be changed considerably by cooking, and both the amount of heat and the length of time that heat is applied are factors in these changes. Those substances that decompose to volatile substances when heated account for the cooking odors. It is well to remember that odor and flavor given off to the atmosphere may be very pleasant to the olfactory senses but that they are lost forever from the food. Some of the flavor-giving compounds are soluble in water, and if the food is overcooked or cooked in a large amount of water, the flavor may be lost to the cooking water. Enough of the flavor and odor may be lost during storage and cooking that even food originally highly flavored will have a bland undesirable flavor when eaten. On the other hand, undesirably strong flavors may develop on long cooking. Onions, for example, become milder in flavor on long cooking; cabbage becomes stronger.

Texture and tenderness. Texture and tenderness of fruits and vegetables are elusive characteristics and are usually judged subjectively. They are dependent upon such conditions as: maturity or degree of ripeness; the cooking medium and the ingredients added to it; and the length of the cooking time. When changes are made in either the texture or tenderness of a plant many other changes also occur.

Maturity of plants affects texture and tenderness in different ways.

A

Fig. 81. Vegetables containing sulfur include the onion family (A) which becomes milder in flavor the longer the cooking, and the cabbage family (B) which develops strong flavors on long cooking.

B

Seed portions of the plant have a high sugar content and are tender when they are immature, but during the maturing process they become coarse, starchy, and have a bland flavor. When mature, seeds require long cooking periods, whereas very young seeds require short cooking periods. The stem, root, and leaf portions of plants develop in much the same manner as the seed and seedpod; the outside of the stem becomes stringy at first, and then finally the whole stalk will have a woody texture. When leaves become old, heavy coarse veins develop, and both color and flavor are poor. Flowers have the most preferred texture and tenderness when they are in the bud stage. Such flowers as cauliflower and broccoli are not usually eaten after they are in full bloom. Fruits progress slowly from the hard green immature stage to the ripe stage and then deteriorate very rapidly. Maturing of fruit is usually accompanied by changing the starch to sugar, a gradual decline in the amount of acids, and softening of the fleshy parts. Fruits, with few exceptions, have the most acceptable texture for eating when they are fully ripe but have not started to disintegrate. Tubers mature very like fruit but have a longer stable period at the peak of their maturity.

Changes that occur during maturing are important in preparation preliminary to cooking as well as to the time required for tenderizing and complete cooking. Mature vegetables usually have a greater waste and require a longer cooking time than the young and immature products. However, fruits and tomatoes require little preparation, have little waste, and cooking time is shortened when they are fully ripe.

Heating plant material in a moist atmosphere softens the tissues, and if heating is continued for a long enough time, the vegetable material actually falls apart. This tenderness is the result of (1) hydrolysis of protopectin to water-soluble pectins and pectic acid; and (2) an actual breakdown of some of the cellulose. Substances such as acid, sugar, salt, calcium chloride (used commercially for firming whole tomatoes in canning), and lime added to the cooking water increase the firmness of the structure and lengthen the cooking time. Sugar added to fruits during the cooking period prevents the softening of the tissues, and pieces hold their shape better than if the sugar is added at the end of the cooking period. Generally, if unbroken firm pieces of fruit are desired, the sugar is added at the beginning; if a sauce is needed, sugar is added after cooking.

The softening of the plant structure during cooking allows many of the nutrients to dissolve in the cooking water. Only the amount of water that can be consumed with the food should remain at the end of the cooking period. One-fourth to $\frac{1}{3}$ cup of water per pound of vegetable or fruit is usually adequate for long-cooking varieties; and enough of the washing water will generally cling to the leafy vegetables so that no cooking liquid needs to be added (kale may be an exception as it seems to absorb water). It is good practice to use a tight-fitting lid to prevent loss of water by way of escaping steam. Considerable emphasis is placed upon the *steaming method* of cooking plant foods because the resultant products are used extensively as the basis for many main dishes (Fig. 82). The following recommendations promote maximum retention of nutrients, color, flavor, and a firm but tender product:

(1) *Preparation*—prepare vegetable just before cooking, retaining as much of the plant as is practical.

(2) *Cooking pan*—use a pan with a flat bottom, a tight-fitting lid, a diameter suited to the size of the heat source, and a volume suited to the amount of food being prepared.

(3) *Cooking liquid*—use as small a quantity as is practical, leafy

Fig. 82. The authors place considerable emphasis on steaming method of vegetable cookery for retention of maximum nutrients and palatability characteristics. (Courtesy of National Association of Margarine Manufacturers, Lincoln, Nebraska.)

vegetables will generally have sufficient wash water clinging to them; roots, stems, flowers, and seeds need only ¼ to ⅓ cup of water per pound of food.

(4) *Developing steam*—place the vegetables and hot water in the pan, cover, bring rapidly to a boil, lower the heat to simmer.

(5) *Doneness*—steam until the vegetable reaches the "just-done" stage or until the starch is cooked.

(6) *Seasoning*—the seasonings, butter, or sauces are usually added at the end of the steaming period; salt may be added at the beginning if it is desirable to take advantage of the slight firming action.

(7) *Cooking time*—the steaming time varies from 5 to 25 minutes depending upon the part of the plant used, the size and shape of the pieces, the stage of maturation, or degree of ripeness.

(8) *Serving*—ascorbic acid is inactivated and flavors are lost on holding, therefore prompt serving is desirable.

The average times for steaming of the common vegetables are given in Table 29.

Variation in Preparation of Cooked Fruits and Vegetables

As in the cooking of meats there are two general methods of cooking fruits and vegetables: dry heat and moist heat.

Dry-heat cooking. Baking, in which the food is surrounded by heated air in an oven or top-of-the-range baker, is a method of cooking that employs dry heat. Potatoes are popularly prepared by baking in their skins, as are winter squash, peaches, pears, and apples. Onions, tomatoes, green peppers, and eggplant are frequently stuffed and baked. Oiling the skin of vegetables that are to be baked and wrapping in foil make soft skins; metal skewers or potato bakers hasten heat penetration.

Microwave cooking gives results similar to that produced by baking. The short cooking period permits retention of moisture without protective devices and aluminum foil cannot be used as it reflects the microwaves and prevents them from entering the food.

Deep-fat frying, a type of dry heat cooking is commonly used for potatoes and for many other vegetables and for some fruits after they are coated with a batter. The absorbed fat and the browning are additional flavoring media. Since cooking must be rapid to prevent undue drying of the food and breaking down of the fat many vegetables are precooked or cut in small pieces.

Frying or sautéing may also be used in cooking vegetables. Onions,

Table 29. APPROXIMATE TIME FOR THE STEAM COOKING OF COMMON FRESH VEGETABLES*

Vegetable	Method of Preparation	Steaming, Top Range, min.	Oven 350°F, min.	Baking 375°F–400°F, min.	Pressure 3–7 lb., min.
Artichoke (French)	Whole	35	60	...	30
Asparagus	Tender spears	12–20	30–50	...	10
Beans, lima, green	Immature seeds	20–35	40–55	...	15–25
Beans, snap	Cut 1" lengths	20–35	...	...	15–30
Beans, snap	French cut	15–25	25–45	...	10–20
Beets, new	Whole	40–60	60–80	40–60	30–40
Broccoli	Tender stalks and buds	15–20	...	...	12–18
Brussels sprouts	Whole	10–20	...	...	8–16
Cabbage (green)	1" wedges	15–20	...	...	12–18
Cabbage (green)	Shredded	8–15	...	...	6–13
Carrots	Diced ½"	15–20	25–40	...	13–18
Carrots (young)	Whole	20–30	40–50	...	18–25
Cauliflower	Flowerets	10–20	...	...	6–13
Corn	On cob	8–15	...	...	...
Kale	Whole leaves	8–20	...	...	...
Okra	½" slices	20	40	...	18
Onions, small white	Whole	25–35	...	...	20–30
Onions, large	Whole	35–40	...	50–60	30–35
Parsnips	Whole	30–45	...	...	...
Peas, green	Shelled	10–20	30–40	...	8–15
Potatoes, white	Whole	30–45	...	45–60	20–40

Potatoes, white	Quartered	20–30	...	...	18–25
Potatoes, white	Diced ½″	10–15	30–35	...	...
Spinach	Whole leaves	5–12	...	...	...
Squash (hubbard)	2″ squares	25–40	40–60	40–60	20–35
Squash (summer)	Small whole, or 1″ slices	10–20	30–40	...	8–15
Sweet potatoes	Whole	30–35	...	30–45	25–30
Sweet potatoes	Quartered	25–30	45–50	...	20–25
Tomatoes	Whole	5–10	15–30	15–25	...
Turnips	Whole	20–30	15–30	...	15–25
Turnips	Sliced	10–20	...	...	8–12

* Times cannot be given exactly because of the great variation in plant materials. Judgement must be exercised in determining doneness each time fresh vegetables are cooked.

potatoes, eggplant, apples, green tomatoes, summer squash, okra, and plantain and other bananas are frequently sautéed.

Broiling is a suitable method to use for plant foods which require very little cooking. Peaches, tomatoes, grapefruit, oranges, and the like are suitable for broiling. Shapes are well retained by this method, which permits sufficient cooking to change flavors.

Moist-heat cooking. This method includes steaming, pressure-cooking, simmering, braising, and scalloping. Steaming has already been discussed; pressure-cooking is also steaming but high temperatures for short periods of time are used. The total time for pressure-cooking of fruits and vegetables is only slightly less than when the ordinary covered pan is used and pressures above 5 to 7 pounds are not recommended. Simmering implies immersion in water, and the term might be used synonymously with stewing. Vegetables that are browned slightly in fat before steaming are said to be braised, and if milk or thin white sauce is the liquid media the vegetables are scalloped or creamed.

Seasoning vegetables. Many terms are used to designate the seasoning of vegetables. Some of the common terms are:

Au gratin, which implies the addition of cheese, generally the food is *en casserole* with a cream sauce.

Creamed indicates that a thin white sauce is poured over a steamed vegetable.

Creole sauce is tomato sauce with green pepper and other seasonings and may be added to the vegetable during cooking or immediately after.

Candied fruits and vegetables may be prepared by simmering the food in a thin syrup until the desired sweetness is obtained or precooked food such as carrots or sweet potatoes may be glazed by heating in a butter-sugar mixture.

Curried vegetables are prepared by adding a sauce seasoned with curry to steamed vegetables.

Dutchess potatoes are steamed, mashed potatoes seasoned and whipped with raw eggs, made into fancy shapes, and baked until firm. They are popularly served with planked meats.

Harvard or sweet-sour sauce is served with steamed beets, cabbage, string beans, and similar vegetables. Sugar and vinegar give the sweet-sour flavor and herbs such as celery seed, or butter may also be used.

Wilting of leaves is accomplished by pouring a hot dressing similar to a sweet-sour sauce over crisp leaves. Generally bacon is cooked, broken into bits, and some of the rendered fat is used. Sugar, vinegar, and salt are added to the bacon and fat, heated, and poured over the washed leaves of endive, spinach, lettuce, romaine, shredded cabbage, etc. This dressing may also be used over cooked potatoes to produce the hot German potato salad.

Scalloped or en casserole implies cooking in a milk or white sauce. Potatoes and carrots may be cooked in the casserole from the beginning or the vegetables may be precooked. Casserole dishes may contain many different kinds of vegetables.

Timbales and soufflés are vegetable custards. Generally, egg whites are beaten into a foam and the egg yolk, vegetable, and white sauce are folded into the foam. Timbales are individual servings, while soufflés generally are family-size dishes. They are baked as custard.

Variety in seasoning provides variety in vegetable dishes. Buttered vegetables may have flavorings of onions, herbs, nuts, or lemon. Browned butter makes an interesting change from the usual plain buttered vegetable. Crumbs browned in butter add considerable flavor and texture to steamed cauliflower or broccoli. Cream sauce, cheese sauce, tomato sauce, and other sauces are popular seasonings for vegetables. Mixtures of plant foods also increase variety in preparation. Apples "scalloped" with sweet potatoes, turnip mashed with potato, peas creamed with carrots or onions, and other combinations are common. Steamed vegetables may also be marinated in French Dressing and served as salad.

One-dish meals. These contain vegetables plus meats, cheese, milk, cereal, or other foods and represent a very common method of using vegetables. The one-dish meal may be a soup, stew, casserole, or salad. The finished product may contain all of the foods considered essential for the meal.

Vegetable or fruit soups made with vegetable or fruit stock with or without meat or milk make excellent lunch or supper dishes especially if served with toast, croutons, or crackers. The plant material may be fresh cooked, canned, dried, planned-overs, or accidental left-overs. Soups of this type have the best quality and flavor if the vegetable materials have a variety of textures and if they are cooked to the just-done stage. In order to accomplish this, the fresh vegetables can be added separately and in the order of their relative cooking time. Flavors may be changed and enhanced by the use of the seasonings and herbs. A famous chef once remarked that all soup recipes should start with the phrase, "Now take an onion. . . ."

Soups may be served hot or cold. The vegetable soups are perhaps best when hot, but fruit soups are delicious when chilled. Vegetable soups with added gelatine that are chilled until firm are good for hot weather lunches. The jellied vegetable soup is only carrying the idea of the tomato aspic one step further.

Casseroles are many in number and each person with a little imagination and a few vegetables could have a new and different one each week. One really nice thing about a casserole is that it can be an outlet for creativity. Preparing this type of a dish must be very dull for those individuals who must follow a cookbook slavishly. It might mean passing up some of the very interesting things in your own refrigerator or cupboard to go to the grocery store to buy the more prosaic foods mentioned in the recipe. Perhaps the two "casseroles" that typify the average thinking are tuna noodle and the proverbial spaghetti and meat balls with tomato sauce.

A casserole meal usually has a white sauce or a cereal base. The liquid for the white sauce could be milk, meat stock, vegetable or fruit juices, and the thickening for the white sauce might be flour, tapioca, cornstarch, cereal, or pastes. Concentrated soups or left-over gravies could be used in place of a white sauce. The mixture of foods is added to the sauce, and then it may be topped with a lid or a "crust." The crust may be made from many foods such as dough, crumbs, mashed potatoes, potato chips, and cornflakes. Even a fruit pie might be considered a casserole dish, and if only a small amount of sugar were used it could be a part of the main meal.

Fritters and croquettes may also be considered one-dish meals. The vegetables and meats are added to a stiff batter, shaped, and fried in deep-fat. The absorbed fat gives added energy value to the meal for those people who require it.

Desserts using cooked fruits. There are an endless number of these desserts, and they include crisps, cobblers, fritters, fruit pies, whips, soufflés, fruit creams, and frozen desserts.

Cooking frozen vegetables. Frozen vegetables are steamed in a manner similar to that used for the fresh vegetables. The cooking may be started while the vegetables are still frozen or they may be thawed. Any thawing prior to cooking should be done in the unopened package for best retention of flavor and nutritive value. For some packs, no water need be added because there will be a sufficient amount adhering to the vegetable. This vegetable, if cooked unthawed, should be placed in the pan ice-side down, otherwise the portion of the exposed vegetable will scorch before the steam can be developed from the ice. Other packs will require small quantities of water. The cooking time after thawing for frozen vegetables will be less than for comparable fresh products because the frozen vegetable is slightly precooked during a blanching process prior to freezing.

Frozen vegetables may be cooked by microwaves without removing them from the package. If they are transferred to a casserole for cooking, the ice-side should be upwards rather than down.

Cooking canned vegetables. Canned vegetables are already thoroughly cooked and need only to be heated or chilled to improve palatability. Vegetables are canned in water, so there is ample opportunity for nutrients to pass from the softened vegetable into the liquid during the processing and subsequent storage period. If the liquid is discarded, not only nutrients but also flavor will be lost. To offset these losses, it is recommended that the liquid be evaporated to the desired quantity by rapid boiling in an open kettle and the vegetables added to the concentrated liquid and heated. The canned vegetables are very well suited for products that require precooked vegetables.

Planned-Overs for Cooked Fruits and Vegetables

Considerable time and fuel can be saved if meals are planned in advance. Cooked fruits or vegetables which are suitable for soups, desserts, casseroles, or salads can be prepared at the same time as they are to be used alone as the main part of the meal. Foods cooked to be used later are referred to as planned-overs. The cooked supplies need to be wrapped to exclude air or to be placed in closed containers and stored in either the freezer or the refrigerator. Frozen products will keep for many weeks, but the products stored in the refrigerator have a storage life of approximately one week. An example of planned-overs is furnished by potatoes simmered in their skins. The freshly cooked potato may be served in the skin, peeled and seasoned, creamed, mashed, or served in some other way. The refrigerated planned-overs are ready for hash-browns, Lyonnaise, creaming, potato salad, casseroles, codfish balls, hash, and many other preparations.

FRUIT AND VEGETABLE SALADS FOR ANY PART OF THE MEAL

Salads not only contribute to the nutritional value of a meal but they also make excellent appetizers. They may be one-dish meals or one of the accompaniments in either the lunch or dinner. The salad can be used to fill in any nutritional gap which might occur in the meal because they need not be confined to fruits and vegetables, but they may also contain small amounts of cold meat, canned or fresh cooked fish, cheese, and even cereals or toast. Salad dressings make appreciable contributions to the over-all nutritional picture for they may contain fats or oils, eggs, milk, fruit juice, sour cream, cheese, herbs, crisp bacon, and almost any food that is available.

Preparation of Salad Ingredients

The desirable flavor, pleasing appearance, and the good texture of salad ingredients can be retained by careful preparation. The same precautions are used here that have been discussed under general preparation. Crispness and freshness are usually the most desirable characteristics of the salad ingredients, however, some wilted salads are used (lettuce and spinach). Lettuce and other leafy vegetables can be kept crisp in cold storage with a high humidity. If unusual crunchiness is desirable the greens may be wrapped in oiled paper, aluminum foil, or plastic bags and placed in the freezing compartment for 20 or 30 minutes just before adding the salad dressing. Care must be exercised to prevent freezing when this method of crisping is used.

The fresh appearance of the greens can be enhanced by tearing the leaf rather than cutting it, because the cut surface may be bruised and the metal of the knife may cause browning. The core of the leafy products can be broken loose by hitting the table top with the base of the core. Use a quick sharp blow and the core can then be lifted without further cutting, and the leaves will separate easily.

Tomatoes and other fruits that lose juice readily are best if cut just before they are added to the salad. Citrus fruit sections and small fruits may be left whole.

With few exceptions, salads have a better flavor, appearance, and eating quality if the ingredients are bite size. Two exceptions to this general rule are: cabbage, which seems to be better accepted if finely shredded; and the ingredients of a molded salad.

Many salad ingredients are improved if they are marinated. This is especially true of meats and succulent vegetables. Leafy vegetables wilt when marinated and unless this effect is desirable they should not be treated with the marinade.

Combining Salads

The arrangement of salads adds much to their aesthetic value. Grotesque, fixed, or still life arrangements should be avoided, as well as overdecoration, artificial colors, and inedible additions. Natural garnishes and pleasing color combinations arranged at random without design make pleasant pictures. However, slices of vegetables or fruit sections arranged in an orderly fashion are not unpleasant. If a fixed pattern is desired it may be accomplished easily by any one of the following methods: (1) the ingredients may be bound together with gelatine and allowed to set in molds; (2) fruits may be mixed with whipped cream or mayonnaise and frozen; or (3) halves of such fruits as peaches, pears, or avocados can be used.

Pineapple, grapefruit, or orange shells substituted for salad bowls and filled with mixed fruits make desirable arrangements. However, the traditional lettuce cup, which can be eaten, is always a pleasing garnish (see Fig. 83).

The acid of the salad dressing protects the ascorbic acid of the fruits and vegetables, and if the acid is in the form of fruit juices it will contribute additional vitamins and minerals. When milk, cheese,

Fig. 83. The lettuce cup is an attractive and popular background for serving salads of any type. (Courtesy of Western Growers Association, Los Angeles.)

FRUITS AND VEGETABLES FOR VITAMINS AND VARIETY · 329

and creams are used as part of the fat they not only add vitamins but will add to the calcium and protein supply. The eggs and oils of the dressings contribute essential fatty acids as well as act as carriers for the fat-soluble vitamins in which the salad greens and fruits are very rich.

The salad dressing adds not only to the nutritional value of salad but also to the appearance and flavor. The salad dressing may be mixed with the salad or it may be served separately. The latter procedure allows each person to use the amount he desires and those individuals who like untreated raw vegetables may have their salad *au naturel*.

For most occasions the salad dressings are served cold; however, hot dressings may be used for German potato salad or wilted greens.

Storage of Salads

The storage of salads is not a great problem because most salads are prepared just before serving; however, the flavor of some salads such as potato, or those that contain fish, chicken, and meat are improved if they are allowed to marinate for 1 or 2 hours. Storage of such a short duration is not a problem and a covered bowl or any type of refrigerator container can be used. The cover is necessary to prevent drying, absorbing odors, and giving off odors.

HEALTH ASPECT OF FRUITS AND VEGETABLES

The sanitation and wholesomeness of fresh, frozen, and canned fruits and vegetables has been thoroughly investigated. The microorganisms commonly found on the foods are soil forms and they are not pathogenic. Among the soil-borne microorganisms is *Clostridium botulinum*, which may be present occasionally. This bacterium forms toxins as it develops or grows. It thrives in the absence of air and acid, and the spores are not destroyed by boiling or freezing. No toxins form at freezing temperatures, however, and *commercially canned foods* are so carefully processed and inspected that outbreaks of botulism have not occurred from this source for more than thirty years.

Home canned nonacid foods should be heated for 10 minutes before they are tasted unless it is known that they have been properly processed. The heat treatment changes the toxic substance to one that is harmless. It is always wise not to eat any canned foods that contain gas bubbles, have a rancid or flat sour odor, or that are mushy and disintegrated.

Creamed vegetables should be stored under refrigeration. The same precautions should be used for these as is recommended for all creamed foods (see Chapter 5).

Insect sprays may be residual, therefore, all fruits and vegetables should be washed or have the outside leaves or peel removed before eating. Fruits and vegetables may be contaminated by food handlers or animals. Thyphoid, *Salmonellae*, and *Staphylococci* may be carried by these foods. Pathogenic bacteria are destroyed by freezing, canning, or cooking. Whenever the sanitation of the fresh vegetable supply is questioned it is a good precaution to cook the food.

For the most part the fruits and vegetables found in the American markets are sanitary and wholesome, and one may eat them without fear of contracting disease or poison.

SUMMARY

Fruits and vegetables make their greatest contribution to the food supply by furnishing vitamins, minerals, and bulk. The nutritive value of these plant materials depends upon the type and part of the plant used, the conditions under which it was grown, the marketing and storage conditions, and the methods of preparation or processing.

Intelligent and efficient buying of fruits and vegetables is aided by a knowledge of market conditions, and an understanding of the grading systems used. The grades of the perishable varieties that were established when harvested may not be meaningful by the time the foods reach the retail market. Therefore, the consumer must know the signs of freshness and good quality in fresh fruits and vegetables.

Plant foods may be prepared in many ways and used in any part of the meal. They can be served alone, added to other foods, cooked as main dishes, or used as desserts.

For the most part fruits and vegetables found in the American market are clean, wholesome, and nutritious.

Reading List

1. American Medical Association, Council on Foods and Nutrition, 1951, *Handbook of Nutrition*, The Blakiston Co., New York, Chapters XXV, XXVII.
2. Charles, V. R. and F. O. Van Duyne, 1954, "Palatability and retention of

ascorbic acid of vegetables cooked in tightly covered saucepan and in a waterless cooker," *J. Home Econ.*, **46**:659.

3. Garran, W. E., 1956, "Spinach, oxalic acid and calcium," *Food and Nutrition Notes and Revs.*, **13**:101.

4. Halliday, E. G. and I. T. Noble, 1946, *Hows and Whys of Cooking*, University of Chicago Press, Chicago, Chapter I.

5. Hansen, Harry (Editor), 1957, *World Almanac*, New York World-Telegram, New York.

6. Hotchkiss, A., M. Wood, and P. Findlen, 1940, "Cooking quality preferences for potatoes," *Am. Potato J.*, **17**:253.

7. Ives, M. G. and M. Dack, 1957, "Safety of inside enamel coatings used in food cans," *Food Research*, **22**:102.

8. Justin, M. M., L. O. Rust, and G. E. Vail, 1956, *Foods*, Houghton Mifflin Co., Boston, pp. 78–99; 144–185.

9. Lee, F. A., 1951, "Nutritional value of frozen foods," *Nutrition Revs.*, **9**:1.

10. Rouse, A. H., C. D. Atkins, and E. L. Moore, 1957, "Factors contributing to the storage life of frozen concentrated orange juice," *Food Technology*, **11**:218.

11. Sherman, H. C. and C. S. Lanford, 1957, *Essentials of Nutrition*, The Macmillan Co., New York, pp. 356–361.

12. Sweetman, M. D. and I. MacKellar, 1954, *Food Selection and Preparation*, John Wiley and Sons, Inc., New York, Chapter 9.

13. Taylor, C. M., G. MacLeod, and M. S. Rose, 1956, *Foundations of Nutrition*, The Macmillan Co., New York, Chapter 22.

14. Terminology Committee, Amer. Home Econ. Assoc., 1959, *Handbook of Food Preparation*, American Home Economics Association, Washington, D. C.

15. Van Duyne, F. O., R. F. Owen, J. C. Wolfe, and V. R. Charles, 1951, "Effect of cooking vegetables in tightly covered and pressure saucepans on reduced ascorbic acid and palatability," *J. Amer. Diet. Assoc.*, **27**:1059.

16. Ward, A., 1931, *The Encyclopedia of Food*, Peter Smith, New York.

CHAPTER **9**

Fig. 84. This model sugar crystal shows the form and shape taken by all sucrose crystals. (Courtesy of C & H Sugar Corporation, San Francisco.)

CHAPTER

9 . . . CARBOHYDRATES ADD PLEASURE TO MEAL PREPARATION

Starches and Sugars

THE ROLE OF STARCHES AND SUGARS IN THE DAILY MEAL PLAN

THE BUYING AND CARE OF STARCHES AND SUGARS

Starches
Sugars and Syrups
Jams and Jellies
Toppings

STORAGE OF STARCHES AND SUGARS

STARCH AND SUGAR COOKERY

Starch
Sugars and Syrups
Crystalline Confections
 Concentration of the Sugar
 Interfering Substances
 Rate of Crystallization
 Amount of Agitation during Crystallization
Amorphous Confections
 Brittles
 Toffees
 Divinities
 Caramels and Taffy

SUMMARY

READING LIST

STARCHES AND SUGARS ARE SO COMMONLY USED IN SMALL AMOUNTS in food preparation techniques that they are frequently overlooked both as to nutrient contribution and as to food constituents. It has been shown that carbohydrates play an important role in nutrition. It is true that most starches and sugars contribute little more than energy value. However, they are frequently used with milk and fruit and thus aid in increasing the quantity of these foods in the diet. Although it is possible to obtain an adequate amount of carbohydrates from cereals, vegetables, and fruits, the sugars especially have so many uses in food preparation and are so universally well-liked that it seems wise to make a discriminate use of these products rather than to attempt to eliminate them from family meal plans or to condemn the use of refined sugars and syrups. As is true of other foods, these must be used in moderation so that they remain simply a "cog in a wheel" rather than a "monkey wrench in the machinery" of the body functions.

Starches are used primarily as thickening agents in the making of soups, sauces, casseroles, puddings, and so on; and the uses for sugars, syrups, jams, and jellies as sweetening agents are many and often start with breakfast and continue through the evening dessert.

THE ROLE OF STARCHES AND SUGARS
IN THE DAILY MEAL PLAN

All starches are chemical unions of many glucose molecules and are changed during digestion to simple sugar (glucose). The common sugars—cane, beet, maple, milk,—are also complex molecules and are changed during digestion by hydrolysis to simple sugars before being absorbed. In this respect the refined starches and sugars are no different from the starches and sugars that occur naturally in foods. Glucose and other simple sugars are rapidly and readily absorbed from the intestinal tract.

It would be difficult to utilize an excessive amount of refined starch in ordinary meal planning. If both gravy and pudding were served in each of two meals of the day, it is unlikely that a person would obtain more than ¼ cupful of starch or approximately 120 Calories. Sugar, however, is very palatable, and the average consumption per person in 1957 [1] was reported to be 97.1 pounds per year or ap-

---

[1] World Almanac, 1959.

proximately ⅔ cupful per day. This would be equivalent to approximately 500 Calories per day. Should ⅔ cupful seem to be much more than one person might consume in one day, scrutiny of the two menus in Table 30 might reveal how easily it could be obtained. It

Table 30. A COMPARISON OF THE POSSIBLE SUGAR CONTENT OF TWO SIMPLE MENUS FOR A DAY'S INTAKE OF FOOD—⅔ CUP IS 32 TEASPOONFULS

	Menu I		Menu II	
Food		Possible Sugar, tsp.	Food	Possible Sugar, tsp.
Breakfast				
Grapefruit half, sugar		2	Tomato juice	0
Cereal, sugar, milk		3	Pancakes, ¼ C. syrup	7
Toast, butter, jelly		3	Bacon	0
Coffee, cream, sugar		2	Coffee, black	0
Lunch				
Grilled cheese sandwich		0	Chefs salad, dressing	½
Sweet pickle chips		1	Corn muffins (2)	1½
Chocolate ice cream (½ C.)		4	Jelly	3
Coffee, cream, sugar		2	Sherbet (½ C.)	5
			Small cookies (2)	3
			Milk	0
Dinner				
Roast lamb, mint sauce		3	Baked ham	0
Cream slaw		1	Glazed sweet potato	2
Buttered peas		0	Asparagus tips in cream	0
Celery and carrot curls		0	Sliced pineapple, cottage	
Cherry pie		10	cheese	2
Milk		0	Strawberry shortcake	8
Iced tea		3	Milk	0
Total sugar		34	Total sugar	32

should be apparent from these common menus, that the inactive person requiring only 2000 to 2500 Calories per day might need to consider his sugar intake carefully.

Sugars in moderation may be desirable in the family meal plan to satisfy the appetite for sweet and to make up some of the extra energy not supplied by the recommended servings of the foods in the Daily Food Guide. Jams, jellies, and fruit syrups are pleasant additions to breads and cereals. They are high in energy value, and they may contain small quantities of the vitamins and all of the minerals of the fruits from which they are made. Confections and synthetic flavored toppings are concentrated sugar products without the added vitamins and minerals. When these foods are eaten, it would seem desirable to have them only at the end of the meal. Sweets are known to depress the appetite, and if eaten before the regular meal, they may reduce the appetite so that the meal is not completed. High concentrations of sugar may be irritating to the digestive tract; if sweets are taken at the end of the meal the quantity of sugar will automatically be controlled because the sugar will not be used to satisfy the appetite.

The taking of confections, soda pop, and other sweets between meals is considered poor nutritional practice, and it is especially important to remember this when training children in good food habits. Dried fruits and fruit juices might serve as substitutes because they not only contain the sugar to satisfy the appetite for sweet but also other nutrients, including some thiamine necessary for the metabolism of sugars.

Small amounts of minerals and vitamins are present if the sugars are not completely refined. A comparison of the nutrients accompanying 100 Calories of the refined sugars and syrups with those accompanying 100 Calories of various jams and jellies and dried fruits are given in Table 31.

It can be seen in Table 31 that dark molasses contains appreciable amounts of calcium and iron, but this product is so bitter that it is used in dilute concentrations and in only a few dishes. Blackstrap molasses, used primarily for animal feed, contains a higher concentration of the various nutrients than do any of the other syrups because it is the remains of the sugar processing, but it is usually rejected for human food because of its intense bitter taste. This should not discourage the use of these products for those who like them. There is, however, no reason why one should attempt to use bitter foods when it is more pleasant to obtain the same nutrients from dried fruits or other equally palatable sources.

THE BUYING AND CARE OF STARCHES AND SUGARS

Starches

Cornstarch, tapioca, and arrowroot are the starches most commonly used as thickeners. Rice starch, potato starch, and wheat starch are

Table 31. MINERAL AND VITAMIN CONTENT OF 100 CALORIE-PORTIONS OF UNREFINED SUGARS AND SYRUPS, FRUIT JELLIES AND CERTAIN DRIED FRUITS[*]

Food	Size of 100-Calorie Portion Meas.	Wt., gm.	Cal-cium, mg.	Iron, mg.	Vita-min A, I.U.	Thia-mine, mg.	Ribo-flavin, mg.	Nia-cin, mg.	Ascorbic Acid, mg.
Sugar, brown	2 Tb.	28	20	0.8	...	...	...	...	...
Sugar, maple	2 Tb.	30	...	...	...	...	...	...	...
Honey	1¾ Tb.	36	2	0.3	...	...	...	...	...
Molasses, dark	2¼ Tb.	45	125	2.8	...	...	0.02	...	...
Jam, strawberry	2 Tb.	40	4	0.2	...	...	...	...	2
Jelly	2 Tb.	40	4	0.2	...	...	...	...	2
Apricots, dried	6–8 halves	38	32	2.0	3000	...	0.06	1.2	2
Figs, dried	2 medium	38	70	1.1	30	0.06	0.04	0.6	5
Raisins, dark	4 Tb.	40	32	1.2	20	0.08	0.04	0.2	...

* Nutritive values, U.S.D.A. Agriculture Handbook No. 8.

A

B

Fig. 85. The processing of starch and corn syrup from grains entails many steps. The grain flows through a grating (A) and is cleaned and then stored in elevators. One of the first steps is to steep the grain (B); rotex shakers separate fiber from the starch and gluten slurry (C), and centrifugals separate starch from the gluten (D). The starch is then spray-dried in huge spray-driers (E) and sold as starch or made into syrups such as Karo (F). (Courtesy of Corn Products Refining Company, Chicago.)

C

D

E

F

available in some markets. A waxy cornstarch, which does not separate from the liquid during frozen storage of gravies and sauces, is used commercially but is generally not available on the retail market. Flours are often used as thickeners, but because they are not pure starch they will not be included here.

The common cornstarch may be purchased under different brand names, but these brands do not differ appreciably (see Fig. 85 for general manufacturing process). Tapioca may be obtained in different size particles; in order of decreasing size they are Large Pearl, Medium Pearl, and Minute or Quick-cooking. Any of the sizes of tapioca may be used for thickening fruit soups, fruit pies, and puddings. Arrowroot is not so commonly found in the food markets but is used extensively in the commercial pudding mixes.

The cost of starches varies with the types. Cornstarch usually costs slightly less per pound than tapioca but both of these products are generally less expensive than the starches made from potato or rice. All starches "go a long way," and therefore price is relatively unimportant.

Sugars and Syrups

Sugars may be purchased either in crystalline form (see Fig. 84) or in solution as syrups. Crystalline sugars vary in kind of sugar, crystal size, and amount of impurities left for flavoring. Syrups vary in concentration of sugar, types of sugars, and in degree of refinement. Only four of the many sugars known to exist in nature are of importance in food preparation. *Sucrose* is the most common of these, and when the term "sugar" is used in culinary terminology, refined sucrose as granulated sugar is to be understood. *Dextrose (glucose), levulose (fructose)*, and *maltose* are present in various of the common sweetening agents.

The fully refined crystalline sugar products are composed of only one sugar (see Fig. 86). The syrups and the incompletely refined products of the double sugars, sucrose and maltose, contain small amounts of simple sugars—the result of hydrolysis. For food preparation purposes, the market sugars and syrups may be classed according to the predominating sugar. Such a classification is shown in the following outline along with the common names under each class or category:

A. Sugars and syrups predominately sucrose
  1. Fully refined sucrose from either sugar beet or sugar cane
    a. Granulated

b. Superfine—granulated

c. Dessert or Berry sugar—finer than the above

d. Powdered or Pulverized—ground but containing no drying agent

e. Confectioners sugars—powdered to various degrees of fineness as indicated by the number of X's on the label; contains 3 per cent cornstarch as a drying agent

f. Cube or Loaf sugars: plain or decorated

2. Sucrose containing impurities for flavor and small amounts of invert sugar[2]

a. Maple sugar: plain or molded in fancy shapes

b. Brown sugars: light, medium, and dark

c. Raw sugar: not considered high quality because of the extraneous substances present and the high acid content

3. Sucrose syrups—often containing impurities for flavor and small amounts of invert sugar

a. Maple syrup—concentrated sap of the sugar maple tree

b. Sorghum—concentrated juice of the sorghum cane, which is similar to sugar cane

c. Sugar syrups: golden syrup or cane syrup

d. Molasses: light, medium, blackstrap, and Barbados

B. Sugars and syrups predominately glucose

1. Crystalline products sold as Cerelose, corn sugar, glucose, or dextrose

2. Syrups derived from cornstarch and containing varying amounts of maltose and dextrins.[3]

a. Karo: light and dark—obtained by acid hydrolysis of cornstarch and containing approximately 40 per cent glucose

b. Sweetose—obtained by the enzyme hydrolysis of cornstarch and containing approximately 55 per cent glucose.

c. Dried syrups—used in commercial processing

C. Syrups containing mixtures of sugars

1. Honey, which is primarily levulose and dextrose with small amounts of sucrose

a. Comb honey—the bees wax is retained

b. Liquid honey—no part of the comb retained

c. Whipped honey—a portion of the levulose is removed so that the dextrose will crystallize and produce a thick spread

---

[2] Invert sugar is a hydrolysis product of sucrose composed of equal amounts of the simple sugars, dextrose, and levulose.

[3] Dextrins are complex molecules from first stages of starch hydrolysis without either good thickening properties or sweet taste.

Fig. 86. The fully refined crystalline sugar products are composed of only one sugar. In the refining of sucrose from sugar cane, clamshell buckets transfer the raw sugar from storage bins (A) to the refinery where the raw sugar is made into a syrup and clari-

C

D

fied through black bone char filters (B); large vacuum pans are
then used to convert the clarified and decolorized syrup into the
form of crystalline sugar (C) which is packaged into sift-proof
bags for retailing (D). (Courtesy of C. and H. Sugar Corporation, San Francisco.)

d. Honey butter—whipped honey is mixed with butter

2. Waffle syrups—contains varying proportions of cane syrup, corn syrup, and flavors.

The prices of sugars and syrups vary with the kind, the processing, and the size of the market unit. Granulated sugar is generally the least expensive and has cost approximately 10 cents a pound for several years. Brown, confectioners, and cube sugars are slightly higher in price than plain granulated sugar. Sugar in the form of molasses is generally double the cost of refined sugar.

Maple syrup and maple sugar, made by evaporating the sap from sugar maple trees, is often ten times the cost of granulated sugar. Syrups flavored with either maple syrup or synthetic maple flavor are sold at considerably lower price than pure maple syrup.

Corn sugars and syrups are generally higher in price but are used less widely in home food preparation than are granulated sugar and sugar syrups. Corn sugars and syrups are common, however, in baby formulas.

Large amounts of these corn products are used by food industries for many purposes, especially for sweetening agents when it is desired to obtain a definite body in a beverage or syrup without producing an overly sweet product. These sugars are less sweet than levulose and sucrose.

Honey varies in price with form and flavor as well as the size of the market unit. It generally is one of the more expensive forms of sweetening ranking next to maple sugar in cost. Honey is sweeter than other syrups as a result of the high levulose[4] content, therefore less honey should be used to obtain the same degree of sweetness provided by other syrups. Honey is prized for its special and delicate flavor rather than its sweetening power.

Molasses is approximately 60 per cent sugar, however, since syrups may occupy less space than their equivalent in crystalline sugar, one pint (2 cups) of molasses contains just slightly less than one pound of sugar (2¼ cups). Less sweetness may be apparent in molasses than in an equivalent amount of sugar because molasses contains acids.

Crystalline lactose (milk sugar) may also be purchased at drug stores and some grocery stores. Milk sugar is used in compounding some baby formulas rather than in general food preparation.

---

[4] Levulose is the sweetest of the sugars.

Jams and Jellies

Jams and jellies are often as high in sugar content as the sugar syrups—50 to 65 per cent—but because of their fruit content, they are considered in a class by themselves. The terms given to these jellied products signify the type and portion of fruit used in their preparation and are as follows:

Fruit Jellies are made from fruit juice only, and they must retain their shape when unmolded.

Jams are made from crushed fruits.

Butters are made from puréed fruits.

Marmalades are made from the various citrus fruits and will contain slices of rinds in pieces large enough to be easily recognized.

Preserves are similar to jams except the fruit is retained whole instead of crushed.

Conserves contain crushed fruits and nutmeats.

Commercial jellies are usually somewhat stiffer than jellies prepared at home because the commercial varieties must remain firm throughout the cycle of shipping, shelving, purchasing, storing, and serving. Jellied products are made especially for use as spreads on breads. They may also be used in making tarts, sweet rolls, and jelly rolls; or they may be spread thinly on a cake and used instead of frosting, thinned for topping on desserts or waffles, or used as flavoring ingredients in the preparation of puddings and ice creams. Cranberry, currant, or other tart jelly is often served as an accompaniment for roast fowl or pork, and mint jelly is traditional with lamb. Danish cooks add currant jelly to cooked red cabbage. This not only gives a delectable flavor but also restores the red color (see Chapter 8).

Jellied products can be made at home, often with considerable saving in cost when fruits are plentiful. Pectins, one of the constituents of fruits essential for gel formation, are marketed in easily used powders or liquids. These commercial pectins can be added to fruits that do not contain a sufficient amount of natural pectin to give the desired stiffness.

Toppings

Toppings are another class of foods containing large amounts of sugar. They are used with puddings, cakes, and similar foods and are usually shelved near the ice cream as a suggestion that they may be used with that product. Toppings made in the home may be less costly than the commercial products.

CARE AND STORAGE OF STARCHES AND SUGARS

Starches require no special care in storage. Sugars need protection from moisture and insects—especially ants. Granulated sugar takes up moisture readily from the atmosphere and forms annoying hard lumps. Covered canisters are generally satisfactory for sugar storage. Brown sugar contains some water but may either lose or take up moisture during storage. Evaporation of water causes lumping and too much moisture makes the product syrupy. Hardening of brown sugar may be prevented by storing it in an airtight container, in an ordinary container with an apple as a humidifier, or in the crisper of the refrigerator. If lumps develop in brown sugar they may be loosened by a few minutes of heating in the oven at a low temperature.

Syrups, jams, and jellies, generally contain a sufficiently high concentration of sugar to act as a preservative against fermentation. However, molds may eventually appear if an unsealed container is left at room temperature. These molds do not render the product inedible but may give it an off-flavor. Generally toppings do not contain sufficient sugar for protection against either mold or fermentation at room temperature.

STARCH AND SUGAR COOKERY

Starch

Starches have little use in food preparation other than as thickeners. In this respect they act by taking up moisture and swelling (hydration). Except in the instant puddings, which contain specially treated starches, the swelling takes place only during cooking. When swelling has reached a maximum, the starch is said to be gelatinized or cooked. Pure starch will be transparent at this stage whereas flour will remain cloudy because of the protein content. Starch may not become fully swollen if there is insufficient liquid present, and occasionally a sauce will be observed to thicken with the addition of liquid when it was expected to thin because of the dilution. Cooking serves to thicken the completely hydrated starch by evaporating the excess liquid.

Methods of mixing used in starch cookery are designed to disperse the starch granules evenly throughout the product. Starch will clump when added to hot liquid if some interfering agent is not present. This interfering agent may be sugar, fat, or a small amount of cold liquid. Sugar, if it is to be used in the preparation, serves to divide the starch particles when the starch-sugar mix is added to the hot liquid, for example, in making cocoa. Fat is as effective as sugar, for example, as it is used in gravy and white sauce. A small amount of cold liquid may be added to the thickening agent to make a paste. This paste is then added to the heated liquid with stirring.

Flour is the common thickener used for gravy and white sauces. Flour may be treated in the same manner as the pure starch thickeners, but the cold water paste will be thicker than starch paste because of the presence of the water-loving gluten.

Tapioca is generally not in powder form and therefore it can be added to hot liquids in dry form in a manner similar to that used for cooking cereals (see p. 209). Large pearl tapioca should be soaked before cooking, and it will take considerably longer cooking time than the smaller tapiocas require.

Heat, acid, sugar, certain other products, stirring, and in some instances egg cause starch gels to thin. Partial breakdown of the starch molecule to a simple nonsugar particle termed *dextrin* occurs in the heating of starch, either in the dry state or in the presence of moisture. Dextrins have less thickening power than the original starch molecule does, so that if a sufficient amount of *dextrinization* takes place during food preparation, thinning may be observed. Dextrinization may occur when dry heat is used, as in the browning of flour for gravy. Then the gravy will not thicken even when the cooking time is extended, although extra cooking is expected to thicken the gravy by evaporating the liquid.

Increased thickness is generally observed in most starch products with increased cooking, but arrowroot and potato starches lose their capacity to hold water when heated. This may account for lack of demand for these particular starches.

Acid hastens the break down of starches in direct relation to the amount of acid present. Juices used for tartness in orange and lemon sauces are acid, therefore, it is wise in the making of these sauces to allow ample time for the starch thickener to swell and cook before the fruit juice is added in order to have a minimum of acid hydrolysis of the starch. There will be some thinning of the sauce when the juice is added, as a result of the dilution effect, therefore, gel that is thicker than that desired in the finished product is needed for the base. The rinds of citrus fruit are added only for flavor and have no effect on the thickening process.

Lemon and orange sauces are used for many purposes, for example: a thin sauce is used over steamed puddings, cakes, and dessert soufflés; medium thick sauces are used for lemon and orange puddings; and pie fillings are thick sauces that will hold their shape when the pie is cut.

Sugar, as has been noted in Chapter 4, decreases stiffness of puddings and sauces in direct proportion to the amount used. This accounts for the greater stiffness of a thick white sauce in comparison to a corn starch pudding with the same type and amount of starch thickener.

Butterscotch puddings in which the flavor is derived from brown sugar or a caramel syrup, may thin after the *addition of egg*. Egg normally gives additional thickness, as well as desirable flavor, to starch puddings but may be adversely affected by substances in butterscotch products. This phenomenon is not yet well understood.

Excessively browned meat drippings that are used for gravy may hasten the breakdown of starch. Extra cooking used to evaporate moisture will thin rather than thicken the gravy because the meat drippings will continue their breakdown action. The exact cause of this thinning action is not known.

The amount of *stirring* during cooking and cooling will also affect the thickness of starch-thickened products; the starch granules may be physically altered by the agitation. Stirring is generally unnecessary after the particles have been evenly distributed, but cooking should be continued until the starch is fully swollen and transparent.

Some of the starch thickeners may be used interchangeably. Flour is generally used in gravy, but cornstarch would be equally as effective. Conversely, cornstarch pudding recipes can be made with flour. Cornstarch, rice starch, arrowroot, and potato starch are approximately equivalent in thickening power. However twice as much flour as cornstarch or 1½ times as much tapioca as cornstarch must be used for equivalent thickening. Proportions commonly used in making puddings and sauces that involve the use of starch are given in Table 32. The nutritive contributions of these products are shown in Table 34.

Sugars and Syrups

Sugars and syrups have many uses in food preparation other than as sweetening agents. These uses include:

(1) Tenderizing action in starch puddings, custards, and all flour mixtures.

Table 32. BASIC INFORMATION FOR THE PREPARATION OF STARCH-THICKENED PUDDINGS AND SAUCES

Product	Starch		Sugar	Salt	Liquid		Fat*	Other Ingredients	Yield
	Type	Meas.			Type	Meas.	Meas.		
Pie filling, lemon	Cornstarch	¼ C.	1 C.	½ tsp.	Water	1 C.	1 Tb.	Grated rind 1 lemon; ¼ C. lemon juice; 2 egg yolks†	Filling for 1 6-inch pie or 3 servings
Pudding, cherry tapioca	Tapioca, quick-cooking	1 Tb.	¼ C.	⅛ tsp.	Cherry juice, sour	¾ C.	…	½ C. pitted sour cherries	½ C. or 2 servings
Sauce, vanilla	Cornstarch	1 Tb.	⅓ C.	⅛ tsp.	Water	1 C.	1 Tb.	1 tsp. vanilla	¾ C. or 3 servings
Syrup, orange‡	Cornstarch	1 Tb.	½ C.	¼ tsp.	Orange juice	¾ C.	1 Tb.	Grated rind 1 orange; 2 Tb. lemon juice; nutmeg, if desired	¾ C. or 3 servings

Product	Method of Preparation	Cooking	
		Approximate Time	Doneness Test
Pie filling, lemon	Mix starch with half of sugar; add to hot water; stir until thick; cook until transparent. Mix yolk with remainder of sugar; add starch paste; return to pan and continue cooking. Add fat, juice, and rind; mix thoroughly.	15 min. (over hot water) 2 min. to cook yolk	Transparent and thick
Pudding, cherry tapioca	Mix tapioca and sugar and salt; add to hot cherry juice; cook to transparent. Add cherries.	15 min. (over hot water)	Transparent medium thick
Sauce, vanilla	Mix starch with sugar and salt; add to hot water; boil until transparent; add fat and vanilla.	5 min. at boiling	Transparent
Syrup, orange‡	Mix starch with sugar and salt; add to hot orange juice; boil until transparent; add fat, rind, and lemon juice.	5 min. at boiling	Transparent

* Use butter or margarine for flavor.
† Reserve whites for soft meringue topping.
‡ Fruit syrups of this type may be used for pancakes, ham, or puddings. Tart fruit juices other than orange may be used.

Table 33. BASIC INFORMATION FOR THE PREPARATION OF CONFECTIONARY

Product	Sugar	Salt	Liquid Type	Meas.	Fat*	Other Ingredients
Brittle, peanut	1 C.	½ tsp.	Water	¼ C.	1 Tb.	1 C. peanuts (5 oz.); ½ tsp. soda, if desired; ½ C. corn syrup
Caramels	1½ C.	¼ tsp.	Light cream	1 C.	1 Tb.	½ C. corn syrup; 1 tsp. vanilla
Divinity	1 C.	⅛ tsp.	Water	¼ C.	...	1 egg white, stiffly beaten; ½ tsp. vanilla; ¼ C. corn syrup
Fondant	1 C.	...	Water	½ C.	...	⅛ tsp. cream tartar; flavorings and colorings as desired
Fudge, chocolate	1 C.	¼ tsp.	Milk	½ C.	1 Tb.	1 oz. bitter chocolate; 1 Tb. corn syrup; ½ tsp. vanilla
Taffy, molasses	1 C.	...	Water	⅓ C.	2 Tb.	⅓ C. molasses; ⅛ tsp. cream tartar
Toffee, almond	1½ C.	...	Water	2 Tb.	½ C.	1 C. almonds (6 oz.); chocolate and pecans for coating (4 oz. chocolate bits and ½ C. shaved pecans)

Product	Method of Preparation	Cooking Approximate Boiling Time	Doneness Test	Yield
Brittle, peanut	Combine all ingredients except peanuts and soda; cook to 88° F above the temperature of boiling water; add nuts and soda and pour quickly onto oiled pan; pull to thin	15 min.	300° F at sea level; syrup should be a tan color	1 lb.
Caramels	Combine all ingredients except vanilla; stir frequently during cooking; cook to 63° F above the temperature of boiling water; add vanilla; pour into pan to cool	30 min.	275° F at sea level	¾ lb.
Divinity	Combine sugar, salt, syrup, and water; cook to 56° F above the temperature of boiling water; cool slightly then beat gradually into egg foam; add vanilla (nuts if desired)	10 min.	268° F at sea level	½ lb.

Fondant	Combine cream of tartar, sugar, and water; cook without stirring to 26° F above the temperature of boiling water; cool to approximately 140° F; beat until stiff then knead; add flavorings and color when candy is to be finished.†	15 min.	238° F at sea level	½ lb.
Fudge, Chocolate	Combine all ingredients except fat and vanilla; cook with frequent stirring to 24° F above the temperature of boiling water; cool to approximately 140° F; beat until stiff then knead; fat and flavor may be added before beating	15 min.	236° F at sea level or soft ball in cold water	½ lb.
Taffy, Molasses	Combine all ingredients; cook to 63° F above the temperature of boiling water; cool to approximately 140° F; pull	15 min.	275° F at sea level	½ lb.
Toffee, Almond	Soften fat; add sugar and water and cook with constant stirring to hard crack stage or 98° F above the temperature of boiling water; add nuts and brown; pour onto unoiled pan; coat with chocolate if desired.‡	10 min.	310° F at sea level Syrup should be a tan color	1 lb. uncoated 1¼ lb. coated

* Use butter or margarine for flavor.

† Nuts and candied fruits may be worked into fondant which is then shaped and coated with chocolate or bon-bon coating. Fondant may also be softened over water, flavored and colored, and dropped onto waxed paper for mint patties. Nuts may also be stirred into softened flavored fondant for minted nuts.

‡ Melt chocolate over hot water; cool, beat, and spread on one side; sprinkle with nuts while chocolate is soft. Chocolate requires several hours to solidify; it may be desirable to permit one side of chocolate coating to harden before turning to coat other side.

(2) Serving as a readily available food for yeast and thereby increasing the rate of fermentation in yeast-leavened products.

(3) Increasing the browning of baked goods.

(4) Glazing of products such as baked goods, vegetables, doughnuts, and nuts.

(5) Firming of cooked fruits and pickles.

(6) Aiding in the retention of ascorbic acid in fruits by decreasing contact with air.

(7) Raising the osmotic pressure of solutions so that microbial spoilage is inhibited in jellies, jams, and other products with a high sugar content—large proportions of sugar are needed for this effect.

(8) Adding body to beverages and sauces.

(9) Acting as an interfering agent in the crystallization of another type of sugar.

In these functions sugar acts as an accessory, and most of the uses have been discussed in other chapters. The preparation of frostings and candies entails the use of sugar as the main ingredient and therefore properly occupies one of the most prominent parts of "sugar cookery."

The preparation of candies and frostings is concerned mainly with the formation of sugar crystals or the prevention of the development of crystals. Generally these products are made of sucrose with other sugars acting as interfering substances. Confections in which sugar crystals are discernible are termed *crystalline*. When no crystals are apparent they are termed *amorphous*.

Crystalline Confections

Fudges, fondants, and pralines are examples of crystalline candies. Except for the old-fashioned rock candy of unusually large crystals, the crystalline candies are considered most desirable when their crystals are small enough to feel velvety to the tongue.

In the preparation of crystalline candies and frostings, several factors should be considered: (1) concentration of the sugar solution; (2) interfering substances; (3) rate of crystallization; (4) amount of agitation during crystallization; and (5) ripening of the confection. The same factors affect crystal size in candies as were discussed under frozen desserts where crystals were of ice rather than sugar (see Chapter 5).

Concentration of the sugar solution. The concentration of sugar in solution may be determined by the boiling temperature of the solution since the raising of the boiling temperature is in direct proportion to the number of particles in solution. Candy making is therefore facilitated by the proper use of a thermometer. When milk is one of the ingredients, as in fudge and caramels, a film of milk solids may form on the thermometer bulb thus giving an erroneous reading. In such cases the cold water or the "soft ball" test may be used as a check for the temperature test. To make the soft ball test, approximately ¼ teaspoonful of candy should be dropped into a bowl containing at least 1 cup of cold water, and allowed to cool about 30 seconds. The sugar has reached the desired concentration when the sample can be gathered together into a ball with a somewhat softer consistency than that desired in the candy. Evaluation by this type of test requires experience, and care must be taken to be certain that the water is cold.

Frostings are made slightly softer than candies because they must be spread while still pliable. The same ingredients and methods may be used for both products, but the cooking time is decreased for the frosting in order that more liquid will be retained to give a softer quality.

On rainy days or in an atmosphere of high relative humidity sugar products become sticky as a result of taking up moisture from the air. This may be partially offset by cooking to a somewhat more concentrated solution or to a temperature approximately 2° F higher than would be used normally.

Interfering substances. Substances other than the predominant sugar, even another sugar, may effectively prevent sugar molecules from joining to form large enough particles to be seen or felt as a definite crystalline structure. These substances are referred to as interfering substances. Several interfering agents may be present at one time, but their effectiveness is determined by the total numbers. Corn syrup, cocoa, butter, egg, gelatine, pectin, and milk all help to produce fine crystals in candy. Nuts and fruits have no appreciable effect because their particles are large and the total number of particles that can be used is insignificantly small.

Hydrolysis of sucrose during cooking gives invert or simple sugars, which act as the interfering substance. Cream of tartar or other acid is often used to increase the rate of inversion so that a sufficient amount of invert sugar will be formed during the cooking. Therefore the length of the cooking process must be carefully controlled in order that the desired amount of inversion takes place. Too much inversion results in a sirupy product, which would be as undesirable as too little inversion. At least 10 minutes should be allowed for the boiling of candy that contains an acid, for example, fondants. If the desired concentration of sugar, as indicated by temperature, is reached rapidly, it may be necessary to add water in order that the heating can be continued. If the time required to concentrate the sugar becomes prolonged the rate of boiling should be increased.

The rapidity of boiling a syrup for a fondant or other crystalline confection made with corn syrup or nonacid material as the interfering agent, has no appreciable bearing on the texture of the candy because the interfering agent does not need to be formed since it was added directly to the product.

Rate of crystallization. This is the most difficult to control of the five factors. In a syrup that will crystallize, a very abnormal state develops during cooling. The syrup is said to be supersaturated with regard to sugar concentration; this means that more crystals are dissolved than the solvent normally can hold in solution at that temperature. Such a system is very unstable, so that dust, a rough surface, or slight agitation can instigate the formation of crystals. The lower the temperature of the syrup before any crystallization takes place, the more supersaturated it becomes and therefore the more rapidly crystals will form when once they are started. After crystallization is started, the more rapidly it is completed the smaller the crystals will be because they will not have an opportunity to join together.

Candies allowed to cool to room temperature are usually so viscous that they are difficult to beat, therefore beating is started when they are slightly warmer than body temperature (about 125° F). This relatively high temperature at which beating is started tends to decrease the rate of crystallization. Large crystals are prevented from forming by continuing the beating during the remainder of the cooling period.

Amount of agitation during crystallization. This factor influences crystal size. Crystallization is induced in the cooled supersaturated syrup by beating, and the greater the amount of agitation during crystallization the smaller the crystal size will be. Beating should be very rapid in order that many nuclei (cores or crystal seeds) form simultaneously rather than a few that gather larger amounts to them. When the candy becomes too stiff for beating, further agitation can be carried on by kneading. The entire mass should be gathered up quickly before it becomes crumbly. A spatula is more effective than a spoon for scraping the candy quickly off the platter or out of the pan. The *heat of crystallization* causes a slight softening to occur during kneading when the candy is completely crystallized. This is not easily perceived, and it may require some experience to recognize this phenomenon.

Ripening. Ripening confections for a few days improves the eating quality of kneaded candies. They should be stored in an airtight container during the ripening period. Fudges are ready to eat at the end of the ripening period, however, fondants are generally flavored, colored, and shaped after this period. If very soft candies are desired, enzymes that break down the sucrose to simple sugars may be added. This latter is done in commercially processed chocolate-covered cherries or other very soft-centered candies.

Amorphous Confections

The making of amorphous candies such as brittles, caramels, and taffies entails the prevention of the formation of any discernible crystals. This may be accomplished by melting the sugar or by the use of a sufficient amount of interfering substances.

Brittles. These candies are made by melting dry sugar and permitting some of it to decompose, that is, caramelize, to prevent crystallization and to obtain browning and flavors. Alkalis increase caramelization of sugar, and a small amount of soda may be added to the melted sugar. This not only increases rate of caramelization without producing bitterness but also gives porosity to the brittle through the production of carbon dioxide gas. If nuts are used, they can be added at the same time as the soda. The melted sugar must be spread immediately because it hardens quickly.

Toffees. Toffees are brittles with a high proportion of butter or margarine. Some recipes call for a small amount of liquid (cream), whereas others depend upon the small amount of liquid present in fat. Toffees must be stirred constantly during the melting of the sugar so that the fat does not separate from the sugar. A folding motion seems more effective for this purpose than a round-the-pan stirring motion. Toffees are caramelized to a golden tan color at which stage they will form a "hard crack" with the cold water test; that is, the ¼ teaspoon dropped into a cupful of cold water will harden almost immediately into a "hard crack" or brittle particle.

Almonds are the usual nuts used for toffee. Peanuts, cashews, sliced Brazil nuts, pinenuts, or sesame seeds make equally delicious toffees. Untoasted nuts or seeds may be added during the last few minutes of cooking in order to toast them in hot sugar. Toffees must be poured immediately onto a cookie sheet where they are generally spread to ¼ inch in thickness. The high fat content of the candy makes oiling of the pan unnecessary. Toffees may be coated with chocolate and nutmeats after they have hardened. If cleavage lines are made in the candy during cooling, shape of pieces may be controlled when the candy is broken for serving.

Divinities. Divinities, which contain a very high proportion of egg white, are amorphous. A sugar syrup is cooked to the desired concentration, cooled slightly, and beaten into an egg white foam. Additions of nuts and fruits may be made when the candy is stiff and ready to be shaped.

Caramels and taffy. These are chewy candies. Crystallization of sugar is prevented by a high proportion of corn syrup. In addition, caramels contain milk solids, which also inhibit crystallization. Caramels are cooked, with occasional stirring, to the desired sugar concentration and allowed to cool without agitation. The stirring during cooking is necessary because of the milk solids which are easily scorched. Taffy is cooked to the desired sugar concentration without stirring and is cooled until it can be handled ($125°$ F approximately). The agitation is accomplished by pulling.

Proportions for the making of certain candies are given in Table 33. The nutritive values of these products are shown in Table 34.

SUMMARY

Starches and sugars are carbohydrates and as such play an important role in nutrition. They are both readily digested and assimilated. Starches particularly are very inexpensive items as they are used primarily for thickeners and a small quantity goes a long way. Sugars and syrups are used extensively as sweeteners and have many other uses in food preparation. Refined granulated sugar is inexpensive, but the sugars and syrups prized for their delicate natural flavors may be relatively expensive. Both starches and sugar items are easy to keep without spoilage.

Starches are used for thickening liquids. This function may be affected by heat, acid, sugar, and agitation. Sugar cookery entails primarily the making of frostings and candies. Cooking principles in sugar cookery are concerned with the control of crystal size after dissolving and concentrating the sugar. The size of crystals in crystalline products is affected by the amount of agitation during crystallization. Amorphous products such as brittles, toffees, caramels, and taffy have no discernible crystals.

Table 34. NUTRITIVE VALUES OF ONE SERVING OF STARCH AND SUGAR PRODUCTS ACCORDING TO THE PROPORTION OF INGREDIENTS IN TABLES 32 AND 33*

Product	Size of Serving	Energy Value, Cal.	Protein, gm.	Calcium, mg.	Iron, mg.	Vitamin A,† I.U.	Thiamine, mg.	Riboflavin, mg.	Niacin, mg.	Ascorbic Acid, mg.
Starch Products										
Pie, lemon	⅓ 6-inch pie	425	4	70	0.9	330	0.04	0.09	trace	9
Pudding, cherry tapioca	½ C.	150	...	7	0.2	460	0.02	0.01	0.10	3
Sauce, vanilla	¼ C.	150	...	...	...	150	...	...	...	...
Syrup, orange	¼ C.	175	1	12	0.1	260	0.05	0.02	0.20	30
Confectionary										
Brittle, peanut	1 oz.	140	1	8	0.5	30	0.01	0.01	0.80	...
Caramels	1 oz.	175	...	20	0.6	140	0.01	0.02	0.20	...
Divinity	1 oz.	130	...	5	0.4	...	...	0.01	...	...
Fondant	1 oz.	100	...	...	...	...	...	...	...	...
Fudge, chocolate	1 oz.	140	...	20	0.3	80	0.01	0.05	0.05	...
Taffy, molasses	1 oz.	130	...	22	0.6	115	0.01	0.01	0.02	...
Toffee, almond (coated)	1 oz.	170	2	23	0.6	120	0.50	0.60	0.30	...

* Nutritive values calculated from U.S.D.A. Agriculture Handbook No. 8.
† Vitamin A values based on butter or margarine.

Reading List

1. Bogert, L. J., 1960, *Nutrition and Physical Fitness*, W. B. Saunders Co., Philadelphia, pp. 16–20; 322.

2. Hansen, Harry (Editor), 1959, *World Almanac*, New York World-Telegram, New York.

3. Hughes, O., 1955, *Introductory Foods*, The Macmillan Co., New York, Chapter 8.

4. Nelson, T. J., 1949, "Hygroscopicity of sugar and other factors affecting retention of quality," *Food Technology*, 3:347.

5. McCann, M. B., M. F. Trulson, and S. C. Stulb, 1956, "Noncaloric sweeteners and weight reduction," *J. Amer. Diet. Assoc.*, 32:327.

6. Meeker, E. W., 1950, "Confectionary sweeteners," *Food Technology*, 4:361.

7. Radusch, D. F., 1953, "Diet and dental health," *J. Amer. Diet. Assoc.*, 29:555.

8. Sherman, H. C. and C. S. Lanford, 1957, *Essentials of Nutrition*, The Macmillan Co., New York, pp. 15–19; 372–373.

9. Sweetman, M. D., and I. MacKellar, 1954, *Food Selection and Preparation*, John Wiley and Sons, Inc., New York, Chapter 14.

CHAPTER **10**

Fig. 87. Spices for the United States are carried by caravan to Alexandria, Egypt for shipment. (Courtesy of American Spice Trade Association, New York.)

10 . . FOOD ADJUNCTS PROVIDE ZEST FOR MANY MEALS

BEVERAGES, CONDIMENTS, AND APPETIZERS QUANTITATIVELY ARE A small part of the diet. Since moderate amounts may add much to the enjoyment of meals, the adjuncts contribute indirectly to the overall nutrition. Certain income groups may appear to spend an undue percentage of the budget for food adjuncts, but if the principal foods of the diet consist of cereals and legumes, food adjuncts may permit a desirable variety in the preparation of these basic foods. The increased variety will contribute much to the psychological acceptance of the food if not to the physiological needs of the body.

With a wealth of seasonings, both domestic and imported, available to the consumer, "arm chair travel" through foods can be as varied and as frequent as one wishes (Fig. 87). Soysauce, kelp salts, and soy bean curd are commonly used in the Orient; oregano is a favorite herb for Italian and Greek dishes; curry and chutney bring India to the table; and sharp chili peppers accent the Mexican-style foods.

BEVERAGES

Coffee, tea, and chocolate products, all of which are imported, make up the bulk of materials used for beverages in the United States. They owe their popularity to their flavoring and stimulating substances.

Coffee

Coffee is the berry of the coffee tree, which is grown in tropic and subtropic regions. The fruit is similar to a cherry, having a pulpy mass surrounding the seed. This pulpy material is removed during the curing processes leaving a silvery skin encasing the seed, which is the so-called "coffee bean." When the skin is removed, the bean divides into two hemispheres.

Divided beans are roasted to develop the typical coffee flavors and aromas. As the amount of roasting is increased, the beans become progressively darker and of a more intense flavor. In the trade, the degree of roasting is indicated by the terms light, cinnamon, medium, high, city, full city, French, and Italian.

The characteristic flavor and aroma of coffee are provided by volatile essential oils that are collectively termed *caffeol*. *Organic acids* and *caramel* which are present in the bean, also contribute flavor as well as color to coffee beverages. The stimulating substance is *caffeine*. Caffeine can be removed during processing without seriously altering either flavor, aroma, or color to make *decaffeinized coffees*. An increased bitterness, which is liked by many, is obtained by adding a small amount of roast chicory root to some coffees. Whenever the chicory is added, it is so stated on the container.

More than a hundred different kinds of coffee are brought into the United States, and most of the market coffees are blends of several varieties. The well-known Java and Mocha are Arabian varieties of coffee, which are preferred by many individuals. Small amounts of one or both of these varieties are included in most blends.

Coffee beans are available on the market, but most consumers prefer to buy coffee already ground. The National Coffee Association recognizes three basic grinds of coffee: regular for percolators, drip for dripolators, and fine for a vacuum coffee maker. Pulverized coffee is also available in some markets for special beverages such as the Turkish coffee.

Instant or soluble coffees are produced by extracting the caffeol, organic acids, caramel, etc., from either coffee or decaffeinized coffee and then evaporating the liquid. Soluble coffees make good brews but, to the connoisseur, they never seem to reach the perfect flavor of freshly brewed coffee.

Liquid coffee concentrates both canned and frozen may be found in some markets.

Buying and care of coffee. The expected number of servings obtained from a pound of ground coffee is approximately 45 cups when the usual 2 level tablespoons are used for each cup of coffee. The price per cup of coffee beverages varies with grade, blend (usually indicated by the brand), form, and size of the market unit. Soluble coffee generally is a slightly cheaper form than either the whole or ground coffee bean. In any type of coffee the price per unit of weight will decrease with an increase in the size of the market unit.

Grinding the coffee beans increases surface area and thereby accelerates oxidation of essential oils, which results in staleness and loss of flavor. Much of the market coffee is packed under vacuum or with an inert gas so as to retain flavors over long periods. The care of coffee in the home entails only the retention of flavor. Since flavoring compounds of coffee are volatile, it is reasonable to expect that loss will occur if the container is opened and that the rate of loss will increase with increase in the storage temperature. It would seem a desirable practice to use coffee directly from the original container rather than aerating it by transferring it to a special canister. Rate of flavor loss will be slower in the refrigerator than at room temperature. However, there is no microbial spoilage or food loss problem in coffee as there is in many foods when kept at room temperature.

The brewing of coffee. Coffee beverages are prepared by extracting water-soluble substances from the ground coffee beans or dissolving a powder or liquid concentrate in water. The extractives do not go into solution readily in the cold, and consequently hot water is used for making the various coffee beverages. Variation in the coffee purchased affects the palatability of the finished brew but is only one of the many factors responsible for the body, color, aroma, and flavor of the beverage. Other factors include:

(1) Amount of coffee used per cup of water.

(2) Length of the brewing period.

(3) Freshness of the coffee.

(4) Flavor of the water-dissolved gases and minerals contribute to flavor of water and will carry over into beverages.

(5) Temperature of the water—tannins and bitter substances are more soluble in boiling water than in water at lower temperatures. Therefore, simmering temperatures permit the extraction of flavor with a minimum of undesirable substances.

(6) Material of which the pot is made—glass, enamel, and stainless steel do not impart flavors to the beverage, whereas aluminum and pewter may react with the coffee and cause off-flavors.

(7) Residues in the pot or cup—if utensils used for beverages are not free of former coffee residues and washing powders that will dissolve in the fresh brew, they will impart a stale or soapy taste to the coffee.

(8) Freshness of the brew—flavor decreases as the beverage stands, however, flavor is better retained if the coffee is kept warm rather than being reheated.

(9) Method of brewing—this may affect clarity and sparkle but probably has less effect on flavor than any of the other factors listed above.

The method of brewing coffee depends upon the type of coffee maker used. These may be classified into four types:

(1) Percolator—water is forced by steam pressure in small quantities over the ground coffee.

(2) Dripolator—water is placed in a container above the ground coffee and allowed to drip slowly through it.

(3) Vacuum pot—water is forced by pressure from a lower cham-

ber into an upper chamber that contains the ground coffee. The water then remains in the upper chamber until heating of the lower chamber is stopped and the pressure decreased.

(4) "Coffee pot"—ground coffee is placed directly into the hot water and allowed to steep until the desired concentration is developed.

In all types of containers the temperature of the water can be kept below the boiling point, and this facilitates the extraction of a maximum of flavor with a minimum of bitter substances.

Tea

Tea is made from the young leaves of an evergreen shrub that is grown in the Orient. Tea leaves have been used to make infusions for beverages since about 350 A.D. Market teas are generally divided into three classes: fermented, or black; unfermented, or green; and semi-fermented, or Oolong. Differences within each class are the result of methods of processing, age of leaves, and local growing conditions. All teas are made from leaves that are withered, dried, rolled, and fired. Green tea is steamed to inactivate enzymes, whereas black tea is allowed to oxidize and ferment before being fired. Infusions of black tea are less astringent than similar infusions of the green because tannins are rendered somewhat less soluble by the fermentation process. Oolong tea has some of the characteristics of both black and green teas.

Principal components of the tea beverages are caffeine, tannin, and the essential oils. Caffeine gives the stimulant quality, tannin the astringent characteristic and most of the color, and the essential oils give flavor and aroma.

Buying and care of tea. It is estimated that 1 pound of tea leaves will make 300 cupfuls of infusion when 1 level teaspoonful tea per cup of water is used. Tea is sold in several forms and in packages of varying amounts. Tea leaves may be loose or in individual portions packaged in porous bags. The size of market units generally are ⅛ pound to 1 pound. Concentrates of tea infusion are *instant* or *soluble tea* and *liquid concentrates.*

The unit price of any style of tea decreases with increase in the size of the market unit, and marketing single servings of tea in packages approximately triples the cost. There are on the market many different blends of tea leaves and many specially flavored teas such as spiced, flower-scented, and smoked. These special teas are considerably higher in cost than unflavored teas. Spices, sweetening, and flavorings as desired can be added to teas when they are prepared if one wishes to have inexpensive but refreshing variety in tea flavors.

Tea is generally considered to have a longer shelf life than coffee and thus perhaps need not be kept in the refrigerator. Tea should, however, be stored in an air tight container and kept in a relatively cool place.

The steeping of tea. Tea beverages are commonly made by adding boiling water to the leaves and allowing them to steep 3 to 5 minutes to extract a maximum amount of stimulant and flavor with a minimum of tannin. Cloudiness in tea is caused by a reaction of tannin with minerals in the water; this often forms a film on the tea and much of it remains in the cup after the tea is consumed. Lemon or other acid bleaches some of the tannins and lightens the color of the tea. The factors affecting flavors in teas are essentially the same as those discussed for coffee.

Iced Coffee and Tea

The full flavor and sparkle of either iced tea or coffee are best obtained when the beverage is freshly brewed. The beverage is made double strength and is poured while hot into glasses filled with chipped ice, thus becoming diluted to normal strength from melted ice (Fig. 88). Sugar dissolves in iced beverages with difficulty so that it is desirable to offer sweetening as a sugar syrup rather than as crystalline sugar, or the hot beverage can be sweetened before it is poured onto the ice.

The Physiological Effect of Coffee and Tea

Effects of the stimulants in these beverages on the body have been widely discussed and are still debatable. Both beverages have a diuretic effect, which is not considered harmful for adults unless the beverages are consumed in excessive amounts. Excesses of coffee or tea may also irritate the digestive tract and overstimulate the nervous system. Moderate stimulating effects may be desirable for adults, however, the stimulus varies among individuals and with the tolerance they have acquired. Many people like a warm beverage with their meals, thus coffee and tea are popular and provide a pleasant way of obtaining a portion of the fluid intake for the day.

Fig. 88. The full flavor of beverages is retained during the meal by chilling freshly made brew (A). Iced tea is often served with a sirup sweetener since granulated sugar dissolves with difficulty in cold liquid (B). (Courtesy of General Foods Kitchen, White Plains, N. Y.)

Chocolate and Cocoa

Chocolate and cocoa are commercial names given to products manufactured from the beans of the cacao tree. The beans are fermented, sun dried, shelled, roasted, and broken into "cocoa nibs." Chocolate is made by grinding cocoa nibs. The heat resulting from grinding liquefies the fat contained in the bean and produces a fluid mass, which is molded into slabs or bars. Milk solids, sugar, and flavoring if desired may be mixed with the fluid mass before molding. Cocoa is partially defatted chocolate in powder form.

In addition to essential oils, chocolate and cocoa contain *starch*, *cocoa butter, theobromine,* and *cocoa-red pigment;* these substances add thickening, enriching, stimulating, and coloring properties respectively. Small amounts of protein, tannins, and caffeine are also present.

Chocolate and cocoa may be *Dutch-processed* for which the cocoa nibs are treated with alkali. This darkens the color, reduces the chocolate flavor, and renders the product somewhat more soluble.

Chocolates available on the market may be bitter, semi-sweet, sweet, and milk chocolate. Ground chocolate and chocolate syrups are produced, and they are convenient forms for the preparation of beverages, sauces, and puddings.

Breakfast cocoas contain 22 per cent fat whereas other cocoas may have a fat variation from 6 to 35 per cent. Instant cocoas have been treated to render them readily soluble, and they may contain sweeteners and milk solids.

Buying and care of chocolate and cocoa. Products termed bitter or cooking chocolate usually are packaged with 8 one-ounce squares individually wrapped in each package. Semi-sweet or dot chocolates are similarly packaged, and semi-sweet chocolate bits are in 4½-, 6-, or 12-ounce packages. Bitter chocolate is somewhat less expensive than sweetened chocolate but does not lend itself to the uses made of other types. Dot chocolate is sweetened and contains substances that make it a better coating material than the other types.

Market cocoas are commonly packaged in ½-pound, 1-pound, or 2-pound containers. Prices among cocoas will vary with the type, amount of fat, brand, and size of the market unit. Cocoas cost slightly less than chocolates, and both products are more economical in a larger container than in small containers.

Chocolate and cocoa stored in a warm atmosphere may become gray as the result of the separation of fat from other constituents. When this occurs a stale flavor usually results. These undesirable reactions may be prevented by storage at temperatures no higher than 70° F.

Chocolate and cocoa in food preparation. Bitter chocolate and cocoa can be used interchangeably in most food preparation, but cocoa is stronger in flavor and contains a higher percentage of starch and a lower percentage of fat than chocolate does. One ounce of chocolate is approximately equivalent to 3 tablespoons of cocoa plus 1 tablespoon of fat.

Chocolate is melted when it is to be blended with other ingredients. To prevent scorching and excessive evaporation, chocolate should be covered and melted over hot water (Fig. 89). The squares can be conveniently melted in their own wrappers and if the wrapper opening is uppermost, they are easy to handle after the chocolate has melted.

In preparation of baked products, it should be remembered that both chocolate and cocoa are slightly acid, and therefore it will be necessary to increase the sugar in the standard recipe to give sweetness as well as tenderness. Because chocolate and cocoa contain starch they will add to the thickness of batters. If an alkaline reaction is produced in batters containing chocolate, as in a devil's-food cake to which soda

Fig. 89. Chocolate is made pliable by melting over hot water; it may then be used as a coating or easily blended with other ingredients. (Courtesy of American Institute of Baking, Chicago.)

Fig. 90. Seven-minute frosting flavored with soluble coffee granules blends well with red devil's-food cake. (Courtesy of Instant Maxwell House Coffee.)

has been added, the characteristic mahogany red color is produced, but chocolate flavor is decreased (Fig. 90).

Preparation of milk beverages flavored with chocolate is discussed in Chapter 5.

Other Beverages

Various coffee and tea substitutes and cocoa-containing beverages are on the market. One of the best-known and oldest of these is Postum, a roasted cereal. It is marketed in a ground or soluble form similar to the coffee products.

A wide assortment of ready-to-use beverages may be purchased from the grocer. Most of these are bottled in single portion sizes and many are carbonated. These bottled beverages may contain caramel (for color) and caffeine in addition to organic acids, sweeteners, and the flavoring substances that characterize each. As compared to the cost of an equivalent quantity of coffee or tea the ready-to-use beverages are considerably higher in price. Unless the sweetener is a sugar product or the flavor is a fruit juice, these beverages have little or no nutritive value. Powders containing acids and synthetic fruit flavors are marketed and these generally are to be sweetened as desired when prepared.

CONDIMENTS

Substances of pronounced or spicy flavors are termed condiments. These include herbs and spices, vinegars and spicy sauces, and products

372 · INTRODUCTION TO FOODS AND NUTRITION

Fig. 91. Spices are imported from almost every country in the world. (Courtesy of American Spice Trade Association, New York.)

seasoned with them such as olives, pickles, chutney, and relishes. Markets maintain as wide choices in condiments as in other items, and the families who enjoy adventuring in foods will keep a wide assortment on hand (Fig. 91).

Herbs, Spices, Flavorings

The people of the United States are alert to the flavor delights possible with the wise use of herbs and spices. The variety of these products in markets confirms this belief because grocers do not stock items for which there is no demand.

Herbs. The common herbs listed in Table 35 give an indication of the types available and common uses to which they are put in food preparation in this country.

Spices. These may be purchased either whole or ground. Whole spices are used with herbs to produce a combination of flavors suitable for pickles or stews. Spices commonly used include allspice, cayenne (red pepper), chili powder, cinnamon, cloves, ginger (dried or candied roots), mace (the outer portion of nutmeg), nutmeg, paprika,

Table 35. COMMON HERBS AND SUGGESTIONS FOR THEIR USES IN FOOD PRODUCTS

Herbs	Parts of Plants Used	Common Uses
Anise	Seed, whole or ground	Cakes, cookies, applesauce, and beet or cabbage salad
Balm, lemon	Leaves	Tea and punch
Basil	Leaves	Tomato sauces, soups, stews, salads, vinegars, and fish
Bay	Leaves	Soups, sauces, and stews
Caraway	Seeds	Cakes, cookies, cheese, rye bread, salt sticks, salads, and salad dressing
Cardamon	Seeds, ground	Cookies, breads, pastries, and ingredient of curry powder
Celery	Seed	Soups, salads, and sauces
Chives	Leaves similar to onion tops	Salads, omelets, baked potatoes, and other dishes where a delicate onion flavor is desired
Coriander	Seeds	Cookies, candies, pickles, and gingerbread
Cress, Water	Leaves	Salads, soups, and stews
Cumin	Seed	Sugar cookies and enchilada sauce
Dill	Seed	Pickles, cheese, potato salad, and fish sauces
Fennel	Seed	Fish, sauces, soup, omelet, and specialty breads
Fenugreek	Seed	Soups and stews
Garlic	Bulb, divided into cloves or toes	Salads, meats, soups, sauces, and butter
Geraniums (rose, peppermint, lemon)	Leaves	Jellies and punches
Marjoram, Sweet	Leaves	Zucchini, salads, cream soups, chops, stews, and stuffings
Mints (many different flavors)	Leaves	Sauces, jellies, tea, and candy
Oregano	Leaves	Salads, tomato dishes, and meats

Herbs	Parts of Plants Used	Common Uses
Parsley (many varieties)	Leaves, fresh or dried	Soup, stew, salad, sauces, etc˙ (garnish or flavor)
Poppyseed	Seed	Rolls, cakes, and cookies
Rosemary	Leaves (needles)	Roast lamb and veal, meat stews, herb soup, and salad
Saffron	Stigmas of flowers	Rice dishes, bouillabaisse, and other fish dishes (color and flavor)
Sage	Leaves	Stuffing, cheese, roast pork, and fish chowder
Savory (winter and summer)	Leaves	Meats, meat sauces, beans and split pea soup (winter savory is stronger than summer savory)
Sesame	Seeds, whole, meal, or as a paste	Cookies, cakes, rolls, candy, muffins, and salads
Tarragon	Leaves	Salads, vinegar, and sauces for meats
Thyme	Leaves	Stews, soups, and sauces

pepper, and turmeric (see Fig. 92). Mixtures of spices are ground together to make pleasing combinations. Curry powder is a mixture of ground spices and owes its yellow color to turmeric. Curry powder is used with rice, creamed eggs, or creamed meat dishes. Poultry seasonings and pumpkin pie spices are also examples of spice combinations.

Special preparations of spices or herbs may be mixed with table salt to facilitate the mixing of a small amount of flavoring material with salad, stew, or other dishes. Onion, garlic, and celery salts are in this category. Smoke salt is a recent addition and monosodium glutamate may be mixed with salt and sold under the various trade names. This last is widely used to emphasize the meat flavor of chicken, rabbit, and other mild flavored meats. Mixtures of seasoning salts are available.

Extracts and other flavorings. Extracts are solutions of natural essential oils or synthetic substitutes. Such flavorings may be sold as concentrates or they may be dissolved in alcohol or oils for ease of dispersing when used in various preparations. Vanilla, lemon, orange, almond, rum, garlic, onion, and many others are available. Synthetic flavorings are less expensive than extracts of essential oils but may not give the same satisfaction in food preparation.

A

Fig. 92. Spices are obtained from bark, roots, seeds, and berries. Cinnamon comes from the bark which is carefully slit and peeled from the tree in long strips (A); during curing it curls into tight sticks termed quills which are cut into uniform lengths and tied into bundles for shipping (B). Ginger is a tuberous root which is dried and often peeled before shipping (C). Mace and nutmeg come from the seed of the fruit of a tropical evergreen tree. The seeds are harvested by use of long poles (D). The lacy flesh-like material which surrounds the nutmeg is the mace; here West Indian women carefully sort the mace into grades (E).

B

C

D

E

F

(E). After the mace has
dried, the blades resem-
ble types of coral and
the nutmeg resembles
walnuts (F). Pepper, the
most popular of spices
comes from the fruit of a
climbing vine (G) which
is trained onto tall poles
like grapes and is har-
vested from ladders (H).
Harvested peppers are
spread onto large mats to
dry in the sun during
which time they become
black and shrivelled (I).
(Courtesy of American
Spice Trade Associa-
tion.)

H

G

I

Wine, brandy, and other fermented beverages are also used as flavoring materials in food preparation and the French chefs are particularly noted for their judicious use of wine in the production of savory meat dishes. During the cooking process the alcohol evaporates as it does in the baking of bread or other products containing alcoholic solutions of essential oils. But, as with essential oils, subtle flavors are imparted to the food.

Coffee concentrates and the grated rinds of citrus fruits are other commonly used flavoring materials.

Vinegars and Spicy Sauces

Vinegars. Vinegars are usually fermented from apples (cider vinegar), grapes (wine vinegar), other fruits, and grains; however, white distilled vinegars may be made from pure chemicals. Specially flavored vinegars such as tarragon are made by adding the herb or spice to the fermenting materials. Herb-flavored and wine vinegars are generally strong-flavored and may be slightly more acid than cider vinegar. They are also decidedly more expensive than cider or distilled vinegars.

Spicy sauces. *Prepared mustards* contain powdered mustard seed mixed with turmeric, vinegar, and other seasonings. The bright yellow mustard is a mild type, whereas the brown-colored variety contains horse-radish.

Horse-radish is also processed for use as a condiment. It is made from the ground root of the horseradish plant and is processed in vinegar. It may be used alone with meats or mixed with other spices for sauces or salad dressings. A popular sauce for serving with baked ham is compounded by folding 1 to 2 teaspoonfuls of prepared horse-radish into 1 cupful of whipped cream.

Soy Sauce and *Worcestershire Sauce* are both commonly used condiments. Soy sauce is made by fermenting soybeans and roasted wheat with a small amount of salt. It is used for soups, stews, salads, or for coloring gravy. Worcestershire sauce contains soy sauce as one ingredient but it also contains many other seasonings. It may be regarded as a flavor concentrate and as such, when used in moderate amounts, adds zest to prepared dishes such as salad dressings, meat loaves, stews, etc.

Tabasco sauce is made from the hot tabasco pepper and may be used in any dish where its bitiness is desired—soups, oysters, cocktail sauce, and salad dressings—a few drops go a long way.

Vinegars and the sauces are not expensive items and are ordinarily used in such small amounts that an insignificant percentage of the food budget would be spent for them. All of these items contain acids and/or spices and salt, which act as preservatives, and these products need not be refrigerated.

Olives, Pickles, Chutney, Relishes, Tomato Catsup, and Chili Sauce

Olives. These may be picked and processed when immature or when mature and ripe. Freshly picked olives contain bitter and astringent materials, which are removed during processing. Processing may include either fermentation or brining, and the products may be sold as whole olives, pieces, pitted, or stuffed. The processed fruits are covered with water, brine, or oil, and sold in bulk or in small sealed containers. They are usually graded for size before curing, and the terms used to designate size are, in order of increasing size by increments of $\frac{1}{16}$ inch: Small, Medium, Large, Extra Large, Mammoth, Giant, Jumbo, and Colossal.

Pickles. Cucumbers of different varieties and maturity comprise the bulk of the pickle products. A few other vegetables are used, as well as fruits and rinds of certain melons. Cucumber pickles vary in size from the tiny one-inch gherkin to the mammoth six-inch dills. Pickles may be sliced in chips, wedges, or left whole. Sugar, salt, and vinegar are used in varying proportions to give different flavors, and spices, mustard seed, dill, or celery seed provide further variety. Many of the cucumbers are brined or fermented before processing into pickles in order to obtain flavors from these treatments.

Mixtures of vegetables are used for pickles. One such mix contains cauliflower, onion, and cucumber seasoned with a mustard sauce and is termed *mustard pickles*. Some of the mixtures of vegetables are in the specialty food section of the grocery store and are arranged in glass containers in elaborate designs.

Crab apples, apricots, peaches, pears, and kumquats are the commonly pickled fruits. Capers are pickled buds of the caperbush grown along the Mediterranean. They are used in tartar sauce and similar dishes.

Chutneys and relishes. Types of sweet pickles in which the foods are in small particles are usually referred to as chutneys or relishes. Chutneys generally contain raisins to give sweetness, acid fruits to add tartness, and chilies for flavoring (Fig. 93). Relishes are made of vegetables such as corn and pimiento, cucumbers and chili, and other combinations.

Catsup and chili sauce. These are products containing a large proportion of concentrated tomato. Catsup is a puréed material, whereas

Fig. 93. Chili peppers are the fruit of a small shrub. (*Courtesy of American Spice Trade Association, New York.*)

chili sauce contains some materials large enough to be identified. Both products contain vinegar, sugar, spices, and possibly small amounts of chemical preservative so that they may be left at room temperature for relatively long periods of time. As concentrates of tomato, these products contain much of the nutritive value of the tomato. However, most of the ascorbic acid is lost in the long boiling periods necessary to concentrate the tomato. Nutritive loss is not important since generally these products are consumed in small quantities.

APPETIZERS AND SNACKS

Appetizers and snacks make up another category of food adjuncts that the consumer may choose to consider in the food budget. These include anchovies, anchovy paste, caviar, pickled and smoked herrings, sardines, and many other similar items as well as the foods which may be eaten out-of-hand such as potato chips, corn curls, crisp bacon rinds, salted and roasted seeds and nuts, parched corn, cocoanut chips, seasoned prepared cereals, and the many "dips."

The nutritive value of the appetizers and snack foods should not be overlooked in the daily diet, however, many of the snack foods contribute little besides fats and carbohydrates. Any of the products that are French-fried will contain large amounts of fat. For example, 1 ounce of boiled potatoes will contribute 25 Calories to the diet, but 1 ounce eaten as potato chips provides 150 Calories. The cheese, meat, and avocado "dips" contain the same nutrients as similar products used as a part of any meal and may be considered in their respective food groups in the Daily Food Guide.

Appetizers and snack foods are relatively expensive when compared to other food items, but if used only occasionally and considered as part of the entertainment, the total cost to serve six people would probably be no more than the cost of two theater tickets. The possible cost of some accessory food items is given in Table 36.

SUMMARY

A brief discussion of commodities making up a category of items termed food adjuncts is presented. Included are beverages, condiments, appetizers, and so-called snack foods. It is recognized that adjuncts as a whole contribute few if any nutrients to the diet but that they may have value in promoting other nutrient-bearing foods to acceptance and thereby become valuable constituents of everyday foods.

The stimulating and diuretic effects of beverage materials are noted and it is recognized that individuals differ in their tolerances to these substances. Factors affecting flavors of beverages are presented and principles involving their preparation are explained.

Prepared foods that have their flavors subtly accentuated through the judicious use of herbs and spices are summarized; and the foods comprising the appetizer and snack groups are briefly discussed.

Reading List

1. Blair, S., 1956, "Spice adds new appeal to salads and desserts," *Institutional Feeding and Housing*, **7**:52.

2. French, C., 1950, *A Manual of Spices and Herbs*, The R. T. French Co., Rochester, New York.

3. Hughes, O., 1955, *Introductory Foods*, The Macmillan Co., New York.

4. Jacobs, M. V. (Editor), 1951, *The Chemistry and Technology of Foods and Food Products*, Vol. II, Interscience Publishers Inc., New York.

Table 36. COST OF FOOD ADJUNCTS AND SNACKS*

Commodity	Cost of Market Unit	Size of Market Unit	Cost of One Serving
Beverages†			
Coffee, regular grind	$0.75	1 lb.	$0.017/cup
Coffee, instant	0.99	6 oz.	0.010/cup
Tea, black, loose	0.43	4 oz.	0.005/cup
Tea, black, bags	0.65	3.84 oz.	0.015/cup
Cocoa, breakfast	0.64	1 lb.	0.006/cup
Chocolate, bitter	0.45	½ lb.	0.015/cup
Cocoa, instant	0.29	½ lb.	0.029/cup
Condiments			
Olives, mammoth, ripe	0.27	4½ oz.	0.030/½ oz.
Olives, med., green, stuffed	0.31	1¾ oz.	0.045/¼ oz.
Olives, chopped, ripe	0.13	2¼ oz.	0.015/¼ oz.
Gherkins	0.39	12 oz.	0.034/oz.
Pickle chips	0.23	15 oz.	0.017/oz.
Mustard Pickle	0.39	11 oz.	0.035/oz.
Dill Pickle	0.10	4 oz.	0.050/2 oz.
Watermelon Rind	0.31	10 oz.	0.031/oz.
Relish	0.28	12 oz.	0.023/oz.
Capers	0.21	2¼ oz.	0.023/¼ oz.
Snacks			
Chee-tos (corn and cheese)	0.25	4 oz.	0.062/oz.
Fritos	0.29	6½ oz.	0.048/oz.
Bacon Rinds	0.23	2 oz.	0.115/oz.
Potato Chips	0.39	4½ oz.	0.090/oz.
Pretzels	0.29	8 oz.	0.036/oz.
Peanuts, salted	0.39	7½ oz.	0.050/oz.
Cashews, salted and smoked	0.59	6 oz.	0.100/oz.
Pepitas (pumpkin seed)	0.41	4 oz.	0.101/oz.
Soft Drinks	0.10	6 oz.	0.100/6 oz.

* Prices in Los Angeles in December 1958.
† Prices are those without sugar or milk unless so stated.

5. Kaufman, C. W., 1951, "Recent advances in coffee technology," *Food Technology*, **5**:154.

6. Lane, B., 1950, *The ABC of Spice Cookery*, American Spice Trade Association, New York.

7. *The Encyclopedia Americana*, 1957, Vol. 3, "Beverages," p. 598, Americana Corp., New York.

8. Ward, A., 1931, *The Encyclopedia of Food*, Peter Smith, New York.

9. Wright, K. G., G. J. Everson, and D. Johnson, 1957, "Do spices increase acceptability of therapeutic diets?" *J. Amer. Diet. Assoc.*, **33**:895.

CHAPTER **11**

Fig. 94. Supermarkets are purveyors of food, kitchen gadgetry, cosmetics, and magazines. (Courtesy of All American Market, Downey, Calif.)

11 . . MARKETING AND MEAL MANAGEMENT

MEAL MANAGEMENT BEGINS WITH THE
MARKET

**Selection of Market to Suit the Family Standards and
Pocketbook**
Types of Markets
Choosing a Market

PLANNED FOOD BUYING

Budget Making
Division of the Food Dollar
Shopping Lists
Large Quantity Buying
Price Comparisons
Home Food Production
Balancing the Budget

EQUIPMENT AND LONG-RANGE BUYING OF FOOD

MEAL MANAGEMENT IN THE HOME

Equipment
Menu Making for Good Nutrition
Complete Home Preparation
Partially Prepared Foods
Completely Prepared Foods

CHANGES TO MEET SPECIAL CONDITIONS

Overweight
Underweight
Pregnancy

EFFECT OF CULTURAL BACKGROUND ON
MEAL PLANS

THE MECHANICS OF MEAL PREPARATION

FOOD PRESENTATION

Table Setting
General Serving Methods
Country-Style Service
Family-Style or English Service
Russian or Continental Service
Apartment Service
Compromise Service
Buffet and Tea Service
General Serving Procedures

SUMMARY

READING LIST

T

HE AVERAGE AMERICAN FAMILY HAS THREE MEALS A DAY STARTING with a good breakfast after a relatively long period without food. The various items from the Daily Food Guide to be included in specific meals, along with the method of preparation, comprise the menus for the day.

In most situations weekly or longer time planning of menus is more efficient than planning for short periods. Marketing should also be arranged to be done as infrequently as practical for each family. Large quantity buying of some items can result in conservation of time as well as money. Menus can be planned to fit the food budget before marketing is begun by using newspaper advertising, radio reports, consumer guides, and records and experiences of previous purchases.

Many factors will influence the plans and practices of meal management. Among these factors will be the offerings of the markets, the tastes and preferences of individual members of the family, the interest in food preparation, and the money and time available for marketing and preparation.

Finally, meal management includes the serving practices, and these would normally be included in menu plans.

MEAL MANAGEMENT BEGINS WITH THE MARKET

Americans are so accustomed to the conveniences of the present day markets that only a few people have any idea of what life and the obtaining of nutritious foods was like before such markets existed. Many of the supermarkets are bewildering mazes of food, kitchen gadgetry, pet supplies, garden supplies, cosmetics, and magazines (see Fig. 94). Some of these vast markets require 30 to 40 minutes just to stroll through the aisles and a matter of hours to make price comparisons and evaluate the products. This great assortment of supplies has advantages; however, unless values are considered carefully not only are time and energy wasted but also money will be spent for unnecessary items. One should approach such markets armed with a complete grocery list and clearly thought through alternates because it is easy to overspend the budget or have a poor diet.

Selection of the Market to Suit the Family Standards and Pocketbook

The food markets of today are innumerable, varying in size and variety from the supermarket or the deluxe restaurant to the banana stand and the hot dog counter. Because of this wide buying field, education for buying is required, and consideration of the selection of the market or marketing system to fit each family condition is important.

All people do not demand the same services from a market. Thus, different types of stores and marketing services have developed to meet these individual needs and wishes. Some families are willing to pay for charges necessary for extra labor and capital needed by the market for accepting telephone orders, keeping records of individual sales, financing a month's supply of groceries, and delivering food. Other families prefer to save money by going to the store, making their own selections, and paying cash at the time of purchase. Three general types of marketing services have evolved to meet these demands: the call and delivery; the cash and carry; and a combination of these two.

Types of markets. The method of marketing and the marketing services that one selects will be determined by his time, money, means of transportation, and standards. Advantages and disadvantages of the more common methods of retail marketing of foods that comprise the three general types of marketing services are discussed in the following material.

House-to-house selling of foods is common, and the whistle of the "ice cream man" is familiar to all. The types of door-to-door selling of food are of three classes:

(1) The peddler who comes only occasionally; his product may be superior or inferior.

(2) The rolling store. This is a moving corner-grocery store, that, if well managed, can be a great convenience.

(3) The salesman with a clientele; the dairyman, the vegetable man, the egg salesman, and the baker. Of the three, the salesman with a clientele is perhaps the most welcome, and his services can be used to best advantage.

Door-to-door selling is costly and adds a small amount to the price of each item; however, this extra cost may not amount to as much as a trip to the market in the family automobile. Those items that are needed in relatively small quantities and that are perishable may be purchased advantageously from this source. For example, if one needs 6 quarts of milk and the delivery charge is 2 cents per quart the extra 12 cents would not be as great as the cost of a 4-mile round trip to the market in the family car. However, if on the way home from work one passes a "dairy-to-you" market, and thereby can take advantage of the low cost of such marketing without extra driving cost, then home-delivery of milk may become a luxury.

Street selling may be of two types, the push-cart peddler and the curb market. Push-cart peddlers are much more common on the East Coast than in other parts of the United States. They are being discouraged or even prohibited because of unsanitary methods of handling goods, traffic congestion, street nuisances (especially of fish), and possible weight and measure shortages.

Curb markets are found in large cities. Some of these are permanent, others are temporary. The Long Beach (California) Morning Market, the Knoxville (Tennessee) Farmers Market, and the Central Market in Baltimore (Maryland) are examples. These markets are really a series of stalls each owned and operated by one person or a family. The products may be excellent or they may be poor. Careful selection is necessary. Usually when these markets are of the direct producer-to-consumer type the products are exceptionally good. If price evaluations and comparisons are made within the market and care is taken not to buy unwanted items, then these markets have real advantages.

Public retail markets are often known as farmers' markets, and their primary purpose is to serve as a direct outlet for farm produce (see Fig. 95). In these markets consumers are likely to find fresh fruits and vegetables at their best as well as rare or unusual varieties of food. They are not unlike the curb markets except that they are usually better supervised. For example, the Farmers' Market in Los Angeles has a strict price control, and the competition is in quality only. This particular market is glamorous, and one can easily be lured away from the budget and the grocery list.

Road-side markets are increasing in direct proportion to the increase in the number of automobiles. Buying from this source is a hazardous undertaking unless one is familiar with the market and personally knows that the food is of high quality. Road-side markets may offer for sale the best products that are raised by the farmers or the food sold by the farmers may be only those products that are not suitable for marketing through wholesale channels and may be so-called "culls." On the other hand, a road-side market may not be a farmers' outlet at all but a huckster may have purchased the food from the farmer or from a wholesaler and beguiles the passerby into thinking that he is an authentic farmer with fresh produce for sale.

The corner grocery is a small market, usually privately owned and catering to the people living nearby. Selection is limited. However, this type of store can be as great a convenience as the rolling-store or

Fig. 95. Farmers markets serve as a direct outlet for farm products. (Courtesy of Farmers Market, Los Angeles.)

the door-to-door salesman with a clientele. Because of the small stock, the owner cannot take advantage of large quantity buying and as a result prices may be slightly higher than in large stores. This high cost may be offset by convenience.

Mail-order-buying in the past was commonly used for the purchase of food, but today such buying is confined to specialized products and luxury items. Household magazines carry advertisements for such foods as smoked turkey, special pickles, maple syrup, and many others. These items may be no better than those that can be bought in nearby markets for one-half the price of the mail-order variety. On the other hand, they may be choice and foods that cannot be obtained from any other source.

Supermarkets (see Fig. 94) have great appeal for the masses, especially for those consumers with a moderate or lower than moderate income, and for those who are willing to do without services. The supermarket managers have made thorough studies to determine the best selling lines of goods in each community. They then limit their stock to these items and adjust regularly to new items (new items may total as much as 40 per month). They have a rapid stock turnover, thus the cost of financing and storage is lowered.

Since, in general, a price rather than a quality appeal has been emphasized, many people have erroneously concluded that products sold by the supermarket may be of poor quality. A study of their goods revealed that the products were of the same quality as those sold in other markets. Also, when private brands were stocked products were graded according to standards of the United States Department of Agriculture.

General stores, the old-fashioned type, are returning minus the "pot-bellied" stove and the gossip. It is really an outgrowth of the super-market and may be called a *shopping-center*. Some large general stores will cover several acres and they will sell all of the products needed for survival plus pet supplies, potted plants, fabrics, and sports equipment. They may even have a post office, employment service, and a swap center. Such markets may present a real adventure in buying but in order not to be enticed into acquiring things one neither wants nor needs, the store should be thought of as a small city. Therefore, if all one needs is food, then he may do well to go only to that section.

Vending machines are used extensively in marketing foods. In fact, of all items obtainable from vending machines, food has the largest volume, and there are plans for increasing this method of food marketing. Foods commonly sold by means of automatic vending are milk, coffee, apples, baked products, sandwiches, soft drinks, candy, nuts, popcorn, ice cream, and in some cities whole meals. Vending machines are a great convenience and make accessible certain food items that would otherwise not be available for rest periods in industries and other similar conditions. When milk is available by this method the consumption increases and even surpasses that of soft drinks. It is encouraging to contemplate that when foods of high nutritive value are automatically vended for snacks, diets may be greatly improved.

Restaurants are innumerable and range from the small, untidy street stand to the deluxe upholstered varieties. The price range in food is as great as the range in standards. However, the great majority of restaurants are moderately priced, and whole families may enjoy the luxury of "eating-out" (Fig. 96).

Choosing a market. The selection of markets is a matter of individual preference, however, quality of food and accessibility may be major factors in the decision. The ultimate cost of food can be greatly increased by driving many miles to secure it. If one is going to drive the long distance he should have some assurance that the quality of the food is better than that of the nearby market. A man in one of the large metropolitan areas drove 30 miles each Saturday to buy "fresh" eggs from a road-side stand. One morning he arrived at the stand early and saw the same man who delivered eggs to the market three blocks from his home deliver a large supply of eggs to the stand.

Marketing guides might well include:

(1) Know your market and whenever possible know the market manager.

(2) Know how the food is cared for.

(3) Know how the food is stocked and how often the market restocks perishable foods.

(4) Have good plans and shop carefully.

Regardless of the type of marketing services demanded of the market chosen, there are several characteristics that are common to all good food markets:

(1) They provide the commodities and services that the consumer wants.

Fig. 96. Restaurants provide total food preparation with service in pleasant surroundings. (Courtesy of Stouffer Corporation, Cleveland, Ohio.)

(2) They have a wide variety of specific items from which to choose.

(3) They are sanitary and foods are protected from contaminants.

(4) They provide information concerning products offered for sale so that price and quality comparisons are possible.

(5) They do not use "pressure" selling methods.

(6) They are managed efficiently and costs of all goods and services are kept to a minimum.

The person who eats all of his meals in a restaurant has problems in food buying which are very different from those just discussed. This person will profit by making a careful study of meal patterns and methods of preparation in the various restaurants he frequents. Unless the food is varied and cooking methods are used that conserve nutritive value the habitual restaurant eater will find himself undernourished even though he has eaten a large quantity. Flavor may be used as a partial guide to nutritional value of food served. The fresh, sweet flavor of a cooked vegetable is usually indicative of retained nutritive value, and crispness may be a measure of the ascorbic acid content of a leafy salad.

If no one restaurant provides the variety necessary for an adequate diet it would be advisable to eat "around." If this precaution does not seem to provide enough of all nutrients a habit of having fresh fruit in his room for desserts or snacks could be developed. For the person who eats out occasionally, nutritional value is usually secondary to atmosphere and gastronomical satisfaction.

PLANNED FOOD BUYING

Long range planning is an important step for the attainment of good nutrition and economical buying. Advance planning for food expenditures is really providing an intelligent control over one's money, and this should result in the greatest satisfaction from his expenditures. A well-prepared food budget should help people to eat economically, to buy intelligently, and to live comfortably. No hard and fast rules can be given for preparing a food budget because they are a combination of individual preferences, income, season, and geographic location. However, certain generalizations may facilitate the preparation of a budget.

Budget Making

Food budgets include not only groceries, meat, milk, and vegetables but also the cost of all foods eaten in restaurants. It does not include such items as brooms, washing detergents, pet food, etc., even though they are purchased at the food market. These items appear in other parts of the total family budget.

The accounting necessary for the budget is no more difficult than that used in keeping an accurate record of the bank account and it is equally important. Usually one member of the family is more adept at this type of work than are others, and details may be delegated to that person. After the method of accounting and planning has been worked out and details assigned, the amount of time needed to keep a budget will not be great. A carefully prepared budget may save many hours of labor and much money, as well as prevent many disappointments.

Division of the food dollar. The percentage of the income spent for food varies from family to family and depends not only upon individual tastes and preferences but also on the amount of family entertainment that requires food. The family who prefers hamburgers, oatmeal, beans, cabbage, and evaporated milk to sirloin steak, ready-to-eat oats, cashews, artichokes, and extra-rich milk will have a much less costly diet, yet one that is equally as nutritious, as the family who prefers the latter. If food preparation is used as a hobby for the family it might spend as much on food as another family would spend for its food plus the cost of a hobby.

The problem of predicting cost of food in terms of percentages of income has always been a difficult one. No one can go without food and the family with a low income must provide the same edible quantity per person as the family with a high income. Among the low income groups as much as 75 per cent of the family budget may be used for food, while for other families, less than 5 per cent is used. Unlike other consumer goods, there is a definite upper limit to the quantity of food that any person can consume, and there is also an upper limit to the amount of money an individual may pay for food. The average family spends between 15 and 40 per cent of its total income for food.

It is necessary for each family to determine the amount of money that will be available or that must be provided for food for the year or the budget period. This will vary a great deal, even among families of the same income and size, because of differences in food habit, spending choices, time available for preparation, number, age, and occupation of the family members, location of the home, standard of living, and home food production.

A simple food budget apparently based upon a recommendation originally made by Lucy Gillett [1] has been useful for quick budget checking. It calls for a division of the food dollar into five approximately equal parts:

(1) One-fifth or less for meat, fish, poultry, and eggs.
(2) One-fifth more or less for breads and cereals.
(3) One-fifth or more for milk and milk products.
(4) One-fifth more or less for fruits and vegetables.
(5) One-fifth or less for fats, sugars, food adjuncts, and other groceries.

High income families may spend more than one-fifth for meat and those with a low income may spend more than one-fifth for cereals (see Table 37).

Whether or not this formula will yield an adequate diet depends upon the selection made within each group. The Daily Food Guide (see Chapter 1) will be of considerable help in making wise selections.

Shopping lists. After the money is divided into five parts, then detailed weekly menus can be made and from these menus complete shopping lists can be compiled. This will mean sitting down with a work sheet and writing out not only the plans but suitable alternates for meats, vegetables, and other seasonal foods. The alternates prevent hurried decisions, which may upset the adequacy of the original plan or overspending of money allocated to food.

When the shopping list has been compiled it should be thoroughly checked to be certain that for every day there is at least the recommended number of servings from each of the food groups and that within a week the individual food items from most of the groups are varied. Family diet patterns may vary considerably in composition and cost and yet be nutritionally adequate. A good diet depends more on the food selected than on the amount of money spent for food. The exact measurement or weight of food to be used by any family is difficult to estimate.

Large quantity buying. Detailed budget plans may be filed and at intervals (at least once every six months) they may be analyzed. The total amount in both cost and quantity of the five food groupings should be determined. Also, the entire amount of individual food

---

[1] Gillett, L. H., 1936, "Basis for estimating budgets with a human quality," *J. Home Econ.*, **28**, 585–591.

Table 37. A MARKET ORDER FOR FOUR PEOPLE FOR ONE WEEK PERIOD ILLUSTRATING THE DIVISION OF THE FOOD DOLLAR INTO FIVE APPROXIMATELY EQUAL PARTS

Food Division	Selections	Amount	Cost of Items*	Total for Group
Meat, fish, poultry, eggs	Beef, chuck roast	3 lb.	$ 1.50	
	Beef, hamburger	1½ lb.	.60	
	Chicken, stewing hen	4 lb.	1.55	
	Eggs, medium	2½ doz.	1.50	
	Fish	1¼ lb.	.85	$ 5.80
Bread, cereals	Bread, whole wheat	4 loaves	1.16	
	Cake	1	1.00	
	Cookies	2 doz.	.50	
	Cornflakes	½ box	.14	
	English muffins	1 doz.	.57	
	Flour	8 C.	.20	
	Macaroni	½ lb.	.12	
	Oatmeal	2 C.	.05	
	Rice	2 C.	.09	
	Wheat, quick cooking	2 C.	.10	$ 4.60
Milk and milk products	Cheese, cheddar	1 lb.	.66	
	Cream, whipping	½ pt.	.34	
	Ice cream	1 qt.	.43	
	Milk, evaporated	1 can (tall)	.11	
	Milk and cream, half and half	3 pt.	.60	
	Milk, solids, non-fat	2 C.	.22	
	Milk, whole fluid	20 qt.	4.40	$ 6.76
Fruits and vegetables	Apples, dried	1 lb.	.45	
	Grapes	1 lb.	.15	
	Melon, New York	1	.20	
	Oranges	4	.15	
	Orange juice, frozen	2 cans	.44	
	Peaches	4	.21	
	Plums, prunes	2 lb.	.25	
	Strawberries, fresh	2 boxes	.50	

Beans, green	1 lb.	.25
Broccoli	1 lb.	.19
Cabbage	2 lb.	.12
Carrots	6	.09
Celery	1 bu.	.10
Cucumber	1	.07
Eggplant	1	.28
Lettuce, iceberg	1 head	.15
Peas, frozen	10 oz.	.21
Pepper, bell	1	.05
Potato	5 lb.	.79
Romaine	1 head	.12
Squash, summer	1 lb.	.19
Tomatoes	4	.25
Tomato juice	1 qt.	.31
		$ 6.00

Fats, sugars, and food adjuncts

Bacon	2 lb.	1.26
Beans, Navy	2 C.	.17
Butter or margarine	2 lb.	1.20 or .58
Coffee	1 lb.	.75
Condiments		.15
Fat, cooking	1 lb.	.33
Mayonnaise	1 C.	.15
Oil, salad	1 pt.	.15
Peanut butter	1 C.	.21
Pickles	1 pt.	.25
Salad dressing	1 C.	.22
Sugar, brown	½ lb.	.07
Sugar, granulated	2 lb.	.20
Vinegar	1 C.	.10
Walnuts	½ lb.	.57
		$ 5.92

* Based on prices in Los Angeles, January 1959.

items should be totaled so that estimates of the total amount of staple items needed for each budget period can be made. Wise large quantity buying can be predicted and practiced only if such cost records as well as quantity records of foods are known.

When detailed long-range plans are made cost comparisons are possible, and the consumer can take advantage of sale items and caselot or other quantity buying. When food is purchased in quantity much of the hand-to-mouth buying is prevented. If all consumers would co-operate in such a plan, the cost of selling food could be lowered, which in turn would lower the cost of food. The consumer who goes to the market three times each day is taking much of the store employee's time and thereby raising the overall cost of food. The average home-maker feels, if she has a total food supply for 2 days and staples for 2 weeks, that she has an unduly large investment in food. The best man-ager is the consumer who buys staples for 1 to 6 months and perish-able items for 3 days or a week.

If young people start this long-range buying when they first establish a home, no great original burden is placed upon the family finances. A $150 capital investment would start a family of two on such a plan and from that point, financially, it is just like buying on any other basis. As the case of peas is used, a new one is purchased, and seldom do more than one or two large quantity items need to be replaced at one time. The overall budget will provide for these large items, and the balance in the budget at the end of each month should be carried forward to next month's food account.

Price comparisons. The actual marketing or selecting of individual items is important to getting the most for the food dollar. One or 2 cents difference between food items may mean as much as a 10 per cent saving or a 10 per cent added cost. The 1 or 2 cents may seem unimportant for one item but for $100 worth of food it could mean $10—seldom does one make 10 per cent on any other investment.

Do not hesitate to ask prices! Many people state that they are embarrassed to make close cost comparisons because they fear that others will think they do not have enough money. These same people should know that the buyer for the market makes very close cost evaluations when he purchases the market supply and thinks even 1 per cent is worth considering.

Home food production. The entire budget plan should be adjusted if any foods are available without purchase. For example, the family that finds it economical or desirable as a hobby to have a garden or to keep a cow or a flock of chickens need not spend as much money for food as the family without these food sources. The importance to food budgets of home food production cannot be overemphasized. The home garden can supply, at low cost, quantities of food needed in a good diet. A well-designed home food-production plan can release money for the purchase of other goods.

Balancing the food budget. The family food budget should balance at the end of specified periods just like the budget of any good business organization. The homemaker who can buy an Easter hat or a fur coat with money saved from the food budget is either cheating the family on food or has too much money set aside for this item. In either event a revision of the budget is in order.

EQUIPMENT AND LONG-RANGE BUYING OF FOOD

Long-range planning and buying require some special equipment. Adequate storage space is essential, and this may mean rearranging or even adding equipment. Extra cupboards, a cooler, and a freezer are helpful items, but not absolutely essential.

Storage space for canned foods, cereals, coffee, etc., should be dry and in most instances cool to prevent deterioration. Therefore, high kitchen cupboards and damp basements should be avoided. If the home has a cool dry basement or pantry, these are excellent places to store canned foods and root vegetables.

The rising cost of home construction and the more universal use of gas, electricity, fuel oil, or a bottled fuel have eliminated large basements in newer houses; however, many have retained or even added the pantry. When an adequate basement is missing, the pantry or other basement substitute such as a service porch, a large closet, the garage, or special outdoor cupboards may be used. Whatever storage space is designed, it should be considered in relation to climate. Outdoor storage is not possible in either hot or cold climates.

Coolers are useful in the absence of basements. They make it possible to store large supplies of root vegetables. A cooler can easily be made from a closet, a tall cupboard, or installed in the service porch if it was not included in the original house plan. The principal prerequisites are an opening to the ventilated space below the house or to the basement, a vent from the top, and wire shelves. This makes, in effect, a wind tunnel with cool air coming from under the house. This air should be filtered to keep out dust, and also, for warm climates or areas that have warm summers a small exhaust fan for the vent could be installed and thus increase the rate of air flow.

Freezers or frozen food locker space will enable one to buy frozen foods and meat in quantity. Such perishable items as soup stocks, baked beans, and certain casseroles can be packaged in meal-size quantities and then frozen. Extras, as from home gardens, other home-produced food or left-overs can also be preserved by freezing.

With a well stocked larder the emergency three-day food supply suggested by the Civil Defense Authority should not be a problem. In fact, it might, with careful planning, be possible to live comfortably for several weeks without going to the market.

MEAL MANAGEMENT IN THE HOME

The kitchen is probably the most changeable room in the house. In great-grandmother's day it was a large spacious room and many family activities were carried on here. It was the warmest and most pleasant room in the house during the cold winter months. Cooking was done on a coal or wood range, and all day long breads, pies, soups, stews, and coffee were produced.

As the nation changed from a predominantly agricultural economy to an industrial one the kitchen changed accordingly. It became an aseptic, compact, efficient laboratory. However, again the trend is back to the spacious work center with many activities centered there. The kitchen may even open to the living-dining room area for hospitality and informality when the hostess does her own cooking (see Fig. 97).

Equipment

Equipment in today's spacious kitchen is designed and arranged for efficient working. Step-saving arrangements, stools, labor-saving devices and pre-prepared foods have replaced the rocker and the dish-pan of peas for shelling. Much of the "folksiness" of the kitchen work has gone with these changes, however, today the art of food preparation is being considered as a hobby by many women, and they speak proudly of their "scratch" cakes and other creations.

The arrangement and equipment of the kitchen are important to good meal management. Supplies that are used most often should be near the place of use and within easy reach. Adequate small equipment increases work efficiency—two measuring cups may save time in making baked products. However, preplanning may compensate for lack of equipment, for example, if dry ingredients are measured before

Fig. 97. The kitchen may open into the living area for hospitality and informality.

liquid ingredients, one spoon can be used for both types of measuring without washing.

One of the first precautions that should be noted is not to over-gadgetize. Hand tools cannot be completely replaced by power tools. The hand beater in many cases is more efficient and time-saving than the electric beater—not because there is less work for the actual beating but because there is less work involved in washing the beater. Household work could still be one of the homemaker's best forms of mild exercise, yet the kitchens are arranged so that she never bends, reaches, or walks, and then she pays to go to gymnasiums to take bending, stretching, and bicycling exercises. There could of course be a compromise between the inefficient kitchen of the colonial days and the sterile laboratory of a few years ago.

Actual pieces of equipment necessary for efficient kitchen management vary greatly. Pans, bowls, and tools should be selected with great care. Pans are most satisfactory if they are used for the particular job for which they were designed—a heavy pan for long, slow, and even cooking; a thin pan for fast heating or for even browning. Bowls should be of a shape and size to give efficient stirring and the shape is far more important than the color. The capacity of pans and bowls should be compatible with the amount of food to be prepared. The knife style should suit the food it is to cut, and the metal used in the knife should hold a cutting edge and not change the color of the food.

The amount of equipment needed depends upon the ability of the individual to visualize the possibilities of each item. For example, the Dutch-oven, which to many is for pot roasts only, can function as frying pan, potato baker, stewing pan, casserole, or even a baking oven. It is interesting to analyze each piece of equipment and evaluate its versatility. Such an analysis also helps to determine whether or not the best use is being made of each item. This is not to be interpreted to mean that one should not accept new things. Do not, however, accept all new things blindly or be pressured into buying equipment at high prices that is not as efficient or useful as those at lower prices or as the equipment that one already owns.

Buying of large items such as ranges, refrigerators, and freezers, which mean an appreciable outlay of capital, deserves careful consideration. These items should be selected to fit the particular needs of the specific family concerned. Is a clock-controlled oven needed or merely a kitchen clock? Is the speed of microwave cooking (electronic) needed or will a slower device be adequate? These and many other questions should be answered before equipment is purchased.

For the homemaker who has two full-time jobs, a wife and mother and a career, the microwave oven may be a great help. Meals can be cooked in a short time with this device and even the baby's bottle can be warmed in seconds without fuss or a water bath (see Fig. 98). Clock-controlled ovens and other clock-controlled equipment can also be used to save time as food will cook while one is at work.

Menu Making for Good Nutrition

Deciding what to eat for all the days of all the weeks of all the years takes thought and good planning and is a rewarding experience. The destiny of the family health and well-being is in the hands of the person who plans the meals (see Fig. 99).

Meal planning and preparation can be a family affair and not the responsibility of any one member. Meal plans, family budget, and methods of preparation could be discusssed in the family council. If this procedure is followed each member of the group should accept the meals that are served.

Fig. 98. The micro-wave oven will heat foods in a matter of seconds. (Courtesy of Gaffer and Sattler, Los Angeles.)

The first prerequisite to good menu planning is meeting the nutritional needs of the entire family. The Daily Food Guide and similar devices are designed for easy planning of well-balanced meals. The food selected by means of such guides will meet only the basic needs for protein, vitamins, and minerals. The quantity of food necessary to satisfy the appetite and meet the energy demands of each member of the family may be greater than the amounts suggested from each group. The variety chosen within each group must meet the taste preferences of the individual family.

There is no reason why one meal could not be planned and prepared so that foods are suitable for the entire family. All nutrients are needed by all age groups. What more logical conclusion than that they be obtained from the same foods.

Foods high in sugar or fats are generally well-liked but too often have an unduly high caloric value in proportion to their mineral and vitamin content. In a well-balanced menu plan, the amounts of these foods might need to be adjusted. There is no reason why they should not be eaten frequently but in small amounts and at the end of the meal. Children who have had sweets between meals usually come to the table with finicky appetites.

Fig. 99. Breakfast, the first meal of the day, is quite logically considered to be a very important one. (Courtesy of Southern Counties Gas Co., Los Angeles.)

Fat leaves the stomach more slowly than carbohydrates and proteins. Some fat with meals is desirable because of this slow digestion, which delays the onset of hunger. Moderation in fat intake at all ages should be practiced. When both metabolic rate and activities are slowed as one starts his second forty years, fat intake may need to be even further curtailed. Individuals have no appetite for their next meal if the previous one contained too much fat. However, a poor appetite is not always caused by a high fat diet, but may be a lack of other essential nutrients.

Second, the person who plans menus must take care of psychological needs as well as physiological needs. This should not be too difficult because in this country countless kinds of food are available the year round, cooking fuel is plentiful, and there is practically no limit to the special purpose pots and pans available.

Food acceptance may be a psychological factor. To be able to eat and enjoy a variety of foods makes it possible to gain the social advantages of eating with others. Not many people have eating problems but perhaps all have one or more foods that they do not like. It is wise and often fun to learn to accept these disliked foods. Many times less preferred foods are perfectly acceptable when mixed with a more popular food. Turnips and rutabagas become much milder in flavor when mashed with potato as is done in certain European countries. Casseroles are excellent dishes in which to introduce small amounts of a new or less preferred food or hide foods entirely which some members of the family refuse to eat.

Appearance of food is an influential factor in food acceptance. Serving of unappetizing though nourishing food may cause nutritional deficiencies if the food is not eaten. Selection and preparation for nutrition and sensory satisfaction must go hand in hand (see Fig. 100).

Meals become interesting and homemakers will find ready acceptance of foods if there are:

(1) Contrasts in crispness of foods—raw vegetable salad served with cooked food.

(2) Contrasts in methods of preparation—boiled potato instead of French-fried with fried chicken.

(3) Contrasts in flavors—perhaps just avoiding the serving of two strong-flavored foods (cabbage salad and cooked broccoli) at the same meal will accomplish this.

(4) Contrasts in colors—potato and cauliflower give contrasts in flavor but the combination loses savor because of the sameness of color. Yams with cauliflower will brighten the plate and increase the enjoyment of the food.

(5) Contrasts in shapes of food—interesting touches can be given by using different shapes, for example, slices, shreds, cubes, balls, patties, wedges, or waffle cut.

(6) Contrasts in types of foods—if tomato juice appetizer is used, other than tomato salad should be planned not only for interest but also to give wider horizons in nutrients.

(7) Contrasts in types of seasonings—with green beans one may think only of melted butter, but browned butter, nutmeg, bacon bits, onions, mushrooms, cream sauce, sour cream, lemon, herbs, or others give changes in taste for the same steamed vegetable.

The third consideration to good menu planning is selecting food to fit the budget. The same meal can be purchased at various cost levels, as has been made evident in preceding discussions.

The fourth prerequisite to good menu planning is selecting methods of preparation that will fit the time and energy available as well as the taste demands of the family. There are many ways of preparing an individual food, which gives considerable latitude for choices. Thus family preferences can be considered. If a food is served but not

Fig. 100. Meals become more interesting if there are contrasts in textures, shapes, temperatures, and flavors. (Courtesy of American Institute of Baking, Chicago, and the National Association of Margarine Manufacturers, Lincoln, Nebraska.)

eaten, the well-planned meal becomes unbalanced and food groups will be missing from the diets of those members of the family who leave their food. Also, those who leave food are wasting food.

Each homemaker must decide how much time and energy she wishes to devote to food preparation and then govern her work accordingly.

As the number of women working outside of the home has increased and as food production has become industrialized food preparation has been simplified. Elaborate home meals with many courses have been replaced by simple food served from the kitchen or family style. Not only the type of meal but the amount of home preparation is changing. Much of the measuring and combining and even cooking is done outside the home.

The decision as to how much preparation is to be done in the home is an individual problem. Food that requires complete preparation, partial preparation, and no preparation is considered in the following sections.

Complete home preparation. This is perhaps used by few people except for those who use food as a hobby. Some individual foods are more commonly prepared from "scratch" in the home than others. These include fruits and vegetables, many meats, some milk products, most egg products, and some cereals.

Potatoes represent one of the commonly cooked vegetables that has not had wide acceptance either canned or cooked and then frozen. Also, fresh fruits and vegetables used in salads are not satisfactory if purchased ready to eat or even partially prepared.

Meat has had very poor acceptance when canned, and frozen pre-cooked meat has not replaced the just-cooked rare steak or roast in the average diet. Some companies are marketing heat-and-eat roasts and steaks which are rare, medium, or well-done. They are cooked to the proper stage of doneness and then frozen. These are only in the experimental stage.

Milk products such as puddings, pie fillings, many soups, custards, and similar products are made in many homes. Cheese dishes are usually more acceptable if freshly prepared than canned or frozen products, but "home-made" ice cream is generally a special occasion food.

Eggs, because of their good keeping quality, have not generally been pre-prepared. Frozen cooked eggs are considered unsatisfactory because the white becomes tough and rubbery, and to date canned eggs have not appeared in the markets.

Flour is still sold in considerable quantity, which would indicate that many people prepare baked products. Some long-cooking cereals—rice, oatmeal, etc.—are sold in considerable quantities.

Partially prepared foods. These foods are becoming very common, and have wide acceptance. Included in this group are quick-cooking foods, partially mixed foods, instant foods, and the so-called heat-and-eat foods. The quick-cooking and the partially mixed foods could be considered as quick preparation foods. They include quick-cooking cereals, minute rice, cake mixes, pancake mixes, condensed soups, canned fruits and vegetables—to name but a few. These have had wide acceptance and some are no more costly than food completely prepared in the home.

The quality of these foods depends upon ingredients in the product as purchased, ability to follow preparation directions, and type of flavorings or supplements added. These partially prepared foods can all be used in creative cooking, and several cook books that use such foods as the basis for all dishes have been written.

Instant foods might be included in this group. They require the addition of only one substance, usually a liquid, and then just stirring. Instant tea, instant coffee, instant pudding, instant cereal, and instant powdered milk are common items on the grocery shelf.

Heat-and-eat foods, which require very little work other than removing the wrapping and placing in the oven, are the most simplified of this group. Brown-and-serve rolls, "T.V. dinners," frozen waffles, frozen baked potatoes, some canned soups, and canned vegetables are examples of this category. The many canned items in this group are not new and have been time tested. The frozen foods are relatively new and are still in the developmental stage.

Completely prepared foods. These foods have been increasing in number and evidently in popularity. Bread is perhaps one of the oldest and most highly accepted foods in this list. Ice cream, sherbet, and ices are also old favorites in this group. Cakes, pies, cookies, other baked products, crackers, lunch meats, cheese, candies, potato chips, other snack foods, jams, jellies, canned fruits, milk, cereals, fruit juices, pickles, and many others are so common that we may not even class them with the convenience foods, but rather with the staple groceries. Few of these are new, and the fact that they have remained on the market for many years indicates their wide acceptance.

Partially and completely prepared foods are the ones which are classed as *convenience foods.* They are an outgrowth of the industrialization of food production. They are accepted because they fit into mechanized living situations, they save time and give many choices of preparation and are thereby a boon to women working outside the home as well as providing the stay-at-homes with alternatives. There are very few items of food that are not available as convenience foods, and competitive firms are daily increasing the number of items and choices.

Industry has found that the consumer is interested in palatability, convenience, and economy in that order and along with these, the retention of nutritive values. Convenience foods should therefore be purchased with care, as only through discriminate buying will the improvement of qualities be forced. Also, it should be recognized that service is purchased along with the food and the success of a convenience item may be determined by how much the consumer is willing to pay for the particular service which is rendered.

CHANGES IN MEAL PLANS TO MEET SPECIAL CONDITIONS

The person who plans menus for the family may have the added responsibility of providing an adequate diet for some members of the family who require special foods or special diets. The most common situations encountered in the home are overweight, underweight, and pregnancy.

Overweight

Overweight, one of the harassments of today, may be real or imagined, therefore, before any program of reduction is undertaken one should have a physical examination by a competent physician. If one is really overweight then a sane and sensible program of losing weight should be inaugurated. This usually means a long program because a change of eating habits as well as weight reduction may be indicated. It may not be possible or advisable to lose weight rapidly.

The condition may be of two types, mild (*overweight*) or gross (*obese*). If one is 25 per cent over the estimated recommended weight for his height and body type he is considered obese. Obesity could possibly involve a disturbance in the hormone balance, but this condition is rather rare even though one may like to blame his obesity on his glands rather than overindulgence in food.

The amount of extra weight that one may have and still be in fashion follows cycles. Currently the thin feminine figure for girls is the style, whereas thirty years ago the thin boyish figure was fashionable. This does not mean that thinness is always the fashion, and in some cultures obesity may be considered as truly beautiful.

It is not within the scope of this text to consider the physiology or the medical implications of overweight. It is important for anyone who is planning to reduce his weight to know that it is not a simple process. He should not borrow a reducing diet from his neighbor as he would a cup of sugar, nor should he follow a diet from a newspaper or magazine. But rather a diet should be designed to fit his particular needs and at the same time make those changes in his eating habits that will enable him to retain his new weight without undue hardship.

Physicians who have made thorough studies of metabolism in overweight believe that slow reduction (1 or 2 pounds per week) is the only safe method. This may seem to take forever, especially if next week one wishes to wear a size 12 party dress and now requires a size 14. But thinking carefully about this it will be noted that a pound per week for 1 year, produces 52 pounds of weight loss. Or, at 2 pounds 104 pounds can be lost. Few people need to lose even 52 pounds and a year in one's expected lifetime (68 to 72) is not a great percentage of time, especially if the reduction is permanent.

Before the reducing diet is planned a complete food and diet history should be obtained. It is not enough to mentally recall the foods eaten; they should be written down and carefully studied. People who overindulge in food tend to forget their snacks and writing them down makes a firm impression. This history will reveal the number of Calories commonly eaten and the adequacy of the daily diet for other nutrients. It will also indicate the type of food liked. Any diet must be approached realistically. If a person has been eating candy, excessive desserts, or large quantities of butter it is safe to suspect that he will not stop suddenly, thus they should be included in small amounts in the reducing diet.

If the minimum number of servings from each of the food groups in the Daily Food Guide is incorporated into a day's menu, the diet will be adequate in protein, vitamins, and minerals but the Calories will not total more than 1000 to 1500. The variation depends upon the selections within the groups. If the person reducing requires for his size, activity, and metabolism 2200 Calories daily, this will decrease his intake below his need approximately 950 Calories. In one week he would have used 6650 Calories more than he ate and this could mean a weight reduction of 1½ pounds (1 pound of body fat is equivalent to approximately 4000 Calories). Using this plan the person reducing can eat with the family and not appear to be eating differently.

Lowered Calorie intake may cause one to feel hungry before the next meal. If this occurs, milk may be saved for between meal snacks, or celery, lettuce, nonfat bouillon, or lemon juice in water can be taken. If one is a member of a group who habitually snacks in the evening, fruit or milk may be saved for this occasion.

People who have told their friends about their reducing program say that one of their greatest problems is the advice they receive from people who have no special training in diet therapy. Therefore, if the reducing diet does not look different from the diets of others there will be little temptation on the part of friends to make well-meaning but often unkind remarks about the diet.

During weight reduction regimes there will be periods of a week or ten days when no weight loss occurs, then suddenly 3 or 4 pounds will be lost and the new weight maintained. This does not mean that fat is not being lost before the weight reduction is noticed, but the failure to lose weight is the result of water taking the place of fat. Since water is heavier than fat, one might even gain in weight. This does not mean a gain in fat or a permanent gain in weight.

About the only advice that can be given the overweight person is to have patience and "make haste slowly."

Underweight

The underweight person has the reverse problem of the overweight, and likewise he should consult a physician. Before starting a program to gain weight it is necessary to determine the cause of excessive thinness. Probably the most common cause of underweight is an inadequate total food intake. If this is the cause and food is not consciously omitted, the person may have trouble eating a larger amount. It is often more difficult for an underweight person to gain weight than it is for an obese person to lose weight.

The dietary history should be taken and analyzed as for reducing. The amount of food necessary to gain weight must be added. The gain should be slow in order that the eating pattern can be changed. Since the appetite of underweight persons is usually poor the food must have eye and odor appeal.

The normal basic diet including suggested food from the Daily Food Guide is the foundation for a gaining diet. The amounts from each group are increased and desserts, candy, and special rich dishes can be included. Snacks should be encouraged and a bedtime snack that is almost a meal can be added. Thus a high Calorie diet is only a normal diet with increased energy foods.

Pregnancy

Pregnancy puts an added strain on the body that must be met by additional nutrients. Through improved nutrition of mothers the babies born today have a better chance of survival and good health than ever before, and mothers are generally spared the complications and difficulties that formerly accompanied both pregnancy and child-birth. The body should be well-nourished long before pregnancy occurs, but much can be done by good nutrition practices during the period of pregnancy.

Diet needs during pregnancy are not unlike the adequate diet of the nonpregnant state except that the expectant mother should consume the amount of milk recommended for growing children or increase her intake of foods high in calcium, and be careful that she has consumed her share of proteins and vitamins. A serving of liver each week and one extra serving of meat may compensate for the lack of niacin in extra vegetables needed to furnish added vitamins. If these foods are increased, they should replace some foods that have a high energy value, otherwise the diet will become too high in energy foods and the mother will put on excess weight.

The quantity of food may be increased during the last three months of pregnancy to take care of the rapid growth of the fetus; before this time there is not a great increase in weight. During the early stages of pregnancy the mother may be eating for two, but one of them is *very* small.

THE EFFECT OF CULTURAL BACKGROUND ON MEAL PLANS

Everyone has the basic drive of obtaining nourishment for the body, but nothing seems quite so individualistic as preferences in palatability characteristics of food—appearance, texture, moistness, and flavor. Many of these preferences are conditioned by availability—past as well as present—so that cultural groups or members of a family tend to have similar preferences. It can definitely be said that the cultural background of each individual affects his eating habits. When a person has lived in any one country all or the greater part of his life, he will take to a new homeland his eating patterns and his recipes (Fig. 101).

In the new country the immigrant may be able to find all of the food he was accustomed to having in his native land, or he may have

Fig. 101. A combination tortilla press and baker is used to make tortillas at a Mexican national labor camp. The average Mexican laborer will consume 18 to 20 tortillas each day. (Courtesy of Sunkist Growers, Los Angeles.)

to adapt some of his recipes to new foods. Plants and animals used for food are very similar throughout the world, and most of the so-called "foreign foods" are actually only unfamiliar combinations, methods of preparation, and flavoring ingredients.

In the United States perhaps more than any other nation the average diet represents a melting pot of all of the eating patterns of the world. Many immigrants eat by this composite pattern except for festive occasions at which time they will revert to the typical foods of their native country. Others who are still lonely for their birthplace cling to their native foods for many years or they may never part with them.

Because the American eating pattern is a composite of many countries, because members of your family or your neighbor may be foreign born, or because traveling to many lands is becoming common, a study of food preparation of other countries should be a part of a broad education. It seems important that people condition their palate to accept the unfamiliar in foods which they might meet in their travels or their neighbor's kitchen.

Arm chair travel with adventures in foods can be really exciting. It would be impossible to give a comprehensive discussion of all foreign foods here. Also, this would take much of the adventure away from reading and talking about them. Lasting friendships can be formed in an exchange of recipes among cultural groups. It has been truly stated that you never know a person well until you have eaten with him.

A study of the food of any country is not a study of recipes but includes people, climate, economy, fuels available, standard of living, agriculture, and religions (Fig. 102). In general books are not written on the subject of these foods—recipe books, yes, but not complete analyses. The information must be collected from many sources. The validity of sources of information should be tested by consulting with a person who has recently lived in the country. This will take a long time because each country will have variations of a basic diet pattern or even many diet patterns, just as in the United States,

Fig. 102. The study of the food of any country is not the study of recipes but includes the people, fuels available, and standard of living. Sofia Tongouri bakes bread in an outdoor oven in Greece.

regional patterns of eating will be found. Consulting with people may, at first, seem like the "blind men who went to see the elephant"; each person will see the country's eating habits as his family ate or as the people of his town ate. Therefore, many people should be consulted and many sources should be read. This is a rewarding experience and one meets many interesting people.

Individuals are inclined to give their favorite recipes or tell about their favorite holidays. But a food study needs to include the foods of rural, urban, and city dwellers; laborer, banker, and educator; and daily diet, Sabbath diet, and holiday diet.

One of the things to look for might be the similarity of the breads in various countries. For example, almost every country has a pancake. They vary in thickness, flavor, ingredients, and time of day eaten, but they are all first cousins to the Western "Flapjack." There are many puffed sweet breads that are used for desserts—they include Chinese bean cake, French puff paste, Turkish Baklava, American cream puff, and Danish pastry. Beverages also are similar. Coffees are served in all countries and vary primarily in degree of roast, type and method of grinding, or materials used with them.

Basically the foods of the Daily Food Guide are included in the daily diet of all countries. Although their meal patterns differ from those of the United States, those countries that have survived and thrived have eaten a nutritious diet. Foods may look different but an egg in any country is still an egg and has the same nutritive value, whether it is soft-cooked or fried, in Egg Foo Yung, in Brioche, or in Crème Caramel.

THE MECHANICS OF MEAL PREPARATION

Timing and preparing of individual dishes in each meal so that all of the foods are hot or cold at the right time seems to be the greatest problem for the beginner. To the person who has never prepared more than one dish at a time the construction of several all at once seems a confusing task. Therefore, a work plan is necessary. At first this should be written out, later, after one has had much experience, the plan can be carried in the mind. However, few people can make the timing for all dishes of a meal come out right without some type of plan.

Work schedules may take some training and practice, if planning does not seem to come naturally. Before one starts the plan he must

Table 38. SUGGESTED PLAN FOR MEAL

Menu	Activities Involved	Early Pre-preparation
Roast Beef	Set oven, select pan and rack, wipe roast, insert thermometer, place roast in oven. Remove from oven and serve.	2:55–3:00 Prepare roast and place in oven 3:00–6:00 Cook roast
Gravy	Measure flour, liquid, and salt and add to drippings, mix thoroughly and stir while cooking. Place in serving dish.	
Baked Potato	Wash potatoes, dry, oil skins, puncture, and put in oven. Remove from oven, slit, and top with butter.	
Buttered Broccoli	Wash, trim, cut, and cook broccoli. Butter and place in serving dish.	
Tossed Salad and Dressing	Wash, cut, and tear vegetables, measure oil, vinegar, and seasoning. Mix and serve.	9:30–9:35 A.M. Prepare dressing
Bread and Butter	Place bread and butter on plates.	
Apple Cobbler	Set oven, pare and slice apples; measure flour, salt, fat, and water for crust; mix crust, top apples with crust, place in oven, cut and serve.	9:00–9:20 Prepare apples and crust for cobbler 9:20–9:50 Bake cobbler
Coffee and Milk	Measure water and coffee into percolator and plug into electric outlet. Pour milk.	
Others	Setting table, etc. Count out dishes, prepare centerpiece, and arrange table.	2:45–2:55 Cut and arrange flowers for centerpiece

* 1) Cook; 2) Assistant Cook.

5:30–5:45	5:45–6:00	6:00–6:15	6:15–6:30
		2) 6:00—Remove roast from oven and place on platter	
			2) 6:15—Make gravy and place in serving dish
1) 5:40—Prepare potatoes	1) 5:45—Place potatoes in oven		1) 6:25—Slit and butter potatoes, place around roast
	1) 5:55—Prepare broccoli	1) 6:05—Put broccoli on to cook	1) 6:30—Butter broccoli and place in serving dish
	2) 5:45—Prepare vegetables for salad	2) 6:05—Mix salad and place in salad bowl	
1) 5:30—Place butter on plate and set out serving dishes			1) 6:20—Place bread on plates
		1) 6:05—Serve cobbler into dishes	
			1) 6:15–Plug in percolator 6:30–Pour milk
2) 5:30—Count out dishes and set table			Dinner complete 6:30

arrive at the answers to these and other questions: How far ahead of cooking or serving time can each item be prepared? Which foods take the longest to prepare and cook? Which if any of the foods will be injured or enhanced by holding after cooking? At which point in the preparation could completion be postponed? The following procedure has been found satisfactory for making work plans for laboratory meal preparation:

(1) The items of the meal are listed.

(2) The preparation time, cooking time, cooling time (if necessary), and serving time are calculated.

(3) The total time for the four activities is estimated and the beginning clock time determined.

(4) The possible pre-preparation is carefully considered and this clock time adjusted.

Table 38 illustrates a laboratory work schedule for meal preparation.

Work efficiency takes some experience, and unless work methods are analyzed each time one practices meal preparation, progress will not be made. In fact one may acquire "sloppy" work habits that will be very difficult to change. The following suggestions are made to help promote efficient work:

(1) Keep working surfaces clean, put supplies away when they are no longer needed, and use the same equipment for as many processes as practicable.

(2) Do like tasks consecutively and in the same working area.

(3) Arrange work so that it progresses smoothly toward the point of ultimate use.

(4) Have few tasks in progress at one time, and complete as much of any one as is possible before starting a second.

(5) Use equipment for cooking that requires the least attention, oven, double boilers, heavy pans, controlled heating devices, and the like.

(6) Use equipment suited to the job being done.

(7) Prepare foods as far ahead of time as is compatible with the retention of nutrients and efficient work management.

(8) Prepare the food first that keeps the best if the last-minute work necessary for serving the meal includes several foods.

(9) Use trays or a cart for transporting table setting equipment. Complete as much of the actual table setting as possible before the meal is ready to serve.

(10) Wash, soak, or rinse preparation dishes as soon as possible after they have been used.

FOOD PRESENTATION

An intangible factor in nutrition is the psychological value of food, which may be enhanced by a pleasant setting and relaxed atmosphere attendant with its presentation. An orderly and attractively set table, conversation that is limited to pleasurable subjects and includes everyone in the group, and gracious table service all contribute to a desirable mealtime atmosphere and are not limited by income.

Convention continues to govern many practices in table setting and table service, but most of the so-called "rules" are based on good reasoning and consideration of the comfort and enjoyment of the person being served. These rules should therefore be considered as recommendations designed to promote gracious living.

Table Setting

Table settings can be attractive and still provide for comfort in eating (Fig. 103). The table arrangement should be neat and the color

Fig. 103. The table setting can be as elaborate as one wishes and still provide for comfort in eating. (Courtesy of Towle Silver Company, New York.)

combination appealing. A low centerpiece adds to the ease of conversation across the table. Flowers with excessive pollen and odor are to be discouraged as they detract from the food and may even cause discomfort for some individuals. In the past only cut flowers were used for centerpieces; however, today more permanent arrangements are used and they may include potted plants, ceramic figures, dried plant materials, artificial fruits and flowers, and many other things. Candles are appropriate only when light is needed, and if they are used, the height should be such that light does not shine directly into the eyes of people as they look across the table. Also, a large enough number of candles should be lighted so that one can see both what he is eating and the facial expressions of companions.

The table should be large enough for each person to have at least 24 inches along the edge. Place settings or covers should contain only the china, silver, and crystal necessary for the specific meal. This eliminates the effect of a pagan display of the family wealth. Flatware and plates will not be bumped or disarranged if they are placed about one inch from the edge of the table. There are many possible arrangements for the flatware, dishes, and "tumblers" as shown in Fig. 104.

Placemats are becoming popular and in many cases replace table cloths; however, any linen used should be clean and well ironed. When table cloths are used, a single fold down the center will prevent the cluttered appearance of a much folded cloth. Silence pads are suggested for either linen placemats or table cloths. Lace cloths are beautiful only because of their pattern and this will be hidden if a silence pad is used under them. This, then, automatically limits the use of the lace cloth. The suggested length of the overhang for all sides of the table cloth is 9 to 12 inches. A longer overhang might catch on the person being seated and could cause considerable embarrassment. The linen and method of service should be suited to the china and other accessories available. The napkin is usually folded and placed with the open edges toward the plate and the edge of the table (see Fig. 103). This placement facilitates transferring of the napkin from the table to the lap into a position where the top half can be used to wipe the fingers, thus protecting the clothing with the bottom half.

Chairs are placed for easy access and also in such a position that the table cloth will not be disarranged when people are being seated. If the front edge of the chair seat is parallel to and directly below the edge of the table, the chair need not be moved for one to sit on it.

A

B

Fig. 104. Flatware, china, and glassware may be arranged in a number of convenient ways and the place settings will still be balanced and attractive.

C

Also, if everyone follows the rule of approaching his chair from the left, much confusion and bumping can be avoided.

General Serving Methods

Details of all methods of service will not be attempted in this book. However, there are some fundamental practices common to all methods of service. These should be sufficient to give the student a sense of security in any eating situation. For more detailed information he may consult books dealing solely with this topic (see the Reading List).

The serving of food is a part of meal management and the method one chooses for serving will depend upon equipment, time, help available, customs, and cultural background. Gracious living can be created under either informal or formal situations. It is more the attitude of the hostess and the apparent ease with which she does things than the actual method of serving that leaves the impression of graciousness. Nourishing the body is only one function of the family meals. They may be means of entertaining friends or they may be occasions where business transactions are consummated and even where work promotions are determined. Since one is often a guest as well as a hostess one should learn to be at ease at meals in either situation.

Country-style service. This is a common method of food service. Food is placed in serving dishes, set on the table and then passed to the right from person to person, thus allowing each individual to choose the amount he wishes (Fig. 105). This is a good method of serving because it allows for individual variations in the amounts of food consumed. However, if the food intake of some members of the family is unbalanced by their taking unduly large amounts of one food and not enough of the others, one might choose a method whereby a more equitable distribution is automatic.

Family-style or English service. This is another popular method of food service that can be used for family as well as for entertaining (Fig. 105). All of the courses are placed on the table in serving dishes and father or some other family member serves the plates and they are passed to each individual in turn. The food is served with regard to quantity needed by individuals and also with regard to their food preferences. More parental control over children's selections may be maintained in this type of service than in country-style.

Russian or Continental service. This is a formal type of service. It is dignified and elaborate and can be used only with the aid of well-

Fig. 105. Country or English service can be used for the family as well as for entertaining.

trained servants (Fig. 104). The food is served in either of two ways: it may be placed on the plates and then set in front of the guests by a servant; or empty plates may be placed on the table in front of the guests who either serve themselves from serving dishes held by a servant or are served by the servant.

No food other than preserves, nuts, and/or bonbons appears on the dining table. A service plate, which is large and beautifully decorated, is in front of the guest when he is seated. This plate remains in place until the meat course is served. Appetizers, soups, salads, etc. are served on small plates which are placed on the service plate. As each course is finished the small plate is removed and replaced by one containing the next course. Thus, plate replaces plate until after the salad course is served. At this time the service plate is removed and the dinner plate is placed in front of the guest.

Russian service not only requires well-trained servants but also a large supply of china, glassware, and flatware. This type of service is limited in the average American home but is usually seen in public dining rooms and for banquets.

Apartment service. This is a modification of the Russian service (Fig. 104) but is informal. The plates are served in the kitchen and placed on the table immediately before the guests are seated. This has the advantage of partial control over the food consumed by each individual. The strictly formal or continental service is almost an historical procedure and has been replaced in homes by the modified style. Industrialization of our country has created a situation where few people have servants, and those who do have them do not have enough to serve a meal with truly old-world atmosphere. Also the trend toward informality and outdoor living makes even a meal served by the apartment service seem almost formal.

Compromise service. A compromise service (Fig. 103) that is a combination of English and Russian service can be used. In this instance only the salad and dessert courses are served from the kitchen and the remainder of the food is placed in serving dishes and either passed or served by the host or hostess.

Buffet and tea service. Tables for buffet and tea service should be carefully arranged so that a person may select food easily without being encumbered by knives, spoons, napkins, etc. This type of service is a glorified cafeteria, therefore, when one is setting such a table he should imagine himself at a cafeteria without a tray or a rail upon which to slide the plate or people to serve the food. This may help in arranging the table more pleasantly for the guest. Plates, of course, must be picked up first, then foods, then beverage, and last tray (if used), napkins, and silver. For a tea the beverage may be served before the food is selected. The plate with the cup of tea or coffee will usually be handed to guests by the hostess or an honored guest (Fig. 106). For teas this is satisfactory because only a small amount of food is to be taken.

The dishes containing foods that are hard to handle may be near the edge when the buffet or tea table is arranged. Less cumbersome food such as nuts, carrot sticks, and the like, can be farthest from the edge but in no case should a person have to reach across the center line of the table to pick up food. Foods that require cutting should be avoided unless tables or trays are provided for eating. Figure 107 shows a conveniently arranged buffet table.

Fig. 106. Informal tea or after dinner coffee may be served in the living room. (A—Courtesy of Towle Silver Company, New York.)

The buffet service is much more convenient if tables or trays are provided for eating. These tables can be set up ahead of time and the silver, water-glass, and napkin placed at the individual place-settings. This simplifies the arrangement of the buffet.

General Serving Procedures

Whatever method of serving is selected, certain procedures should be used. When food is offered by a server, the dish containing the food should be held in the left hand and offered to the left of the person being served. This prevents spills, elbows in the way, or other awkward situations and permits a guest to comfortably serve his plate with his right hand. If a guest is known to be left-handed an exception may be made, but generally the only deference made to one's left-

Fig. 107. A conveniently arranged buffet table permits the guest to serve himself easily and without being encumbered with napkin and silver.

handedness is to seat him on a corner where no one is seated at his left—many left-handed people are partially right-handed.

If plates or other dishes are to be placed on the table in front of the guests or removed from this position they may be placed and removed from either side. If they are to be placed from the left, the person serving should use the left hand, and if they are placed from the right, the right hand should be used; again this prevents awkwardness. Even in left-hand service, the beverage is normally placed on the right with the right hand. A decision might well be made as to which method is best for the situation, and this method should be used throughout the entire meal, however, the person serving should not reach across the place setting or cover. If the meal is to be served in several courses, the food, silver, and china for the finished course is removed before the next course is served.

No matter what type of service is used, sanitary handling of the china, flatware, and glassware as well as the food should be practiced. For example, one should avoid placing his hands on the eating surface of utensils or touching food that is to be eaten by another person.

SUMMARY

Meal management entails the planning of menus, the purchasing of foods, the preparing of the various dishes in the menu, and the serving of the meals. The amount of money available for food, the family tastes and preferences, and the extent to which the members of the family participate in work are recognized as factors influencing choices in the meal-management program.

Included in the food-purchasing activity are the choice of food markets, the opportunities for savings promulgated by purchase of staple items in large quantity, and the wide choices available in the types of any single item of food and the amount of service that may be purchased with it. A "convenience food" is defined as any item in which all or a major portion of the work of preparation has been done. This may be only the slicing of cheese or may include the entire bread-baking process or the cooking of a barbecued chicken that can be purchased hot and ready-to-serve.

Recommendations for ease in making interesting menu plans are given and suggestions made for changes of family meal plans to meet special conditions such as weight-losing, weight-gaining, and pregnancy.

Some of the similarities of plant and animal foods comprising the different eating patterns of various cultural groups are pointed out. The reader is challenged to accept the real opportunity for promoting international understanding by familiarizing himself with the factors influencing the food choices and preparation common in other lands and by widening his acceptance of unusual flavors in food.

Stressed in the meal preparation activity are the need for knowledge and skill in preparing of individual dishes and for thorough planning and repetitive experiences in interweaving of the time-work schedules for the individual dishes of a meal.

Methods of table setting and serving and the logic supporting their practice are discussed only briefly. Comfortable and pleasant surroundings with gracious manners are suggested as the only prerequisites of social hospitality.

Reading List

1. Beyer, G. H. (Editor), 1952, *The Cornell Kitchen*, New York State College of Home Economics at Cornell University, Ithaca.

2. Bogert, L. J., 1954, *Nutrition and Physical Fitness*, Saunders Co., Philadelphia.

3. Coleman, M. C., W. W. Tuttle, and K. Daum, 1953, "Effect of protein source on maintaining blood sugar levels after breakfast," *J. Amer. Diet. Assoc.*, **29**:239.

4. Coles, J. V., 1949, *Standards and Labels for Consumers' Goods*, Ronald Press Co., New York.

5. Cooper, L., E. Barber, and H. Mitchell, 1947, *Nutrition in Health and Disease*, J. B. Lippincott Co., Philadelphia.

6. Countess Morphy, 1935, *Recipes of All Nations*, Wm. H. Wise and Co., New York.

7. Encyclopaedia Britannica, 1958, Encyclopaedia Britannica Inc., Chicago, S. V. Diet.

8. *Essentials of an Adequate Diet*, U.S.D.A. Agr. Inf. Bull. 160, 1956.

9. Fitzsimmons, C., 1950, *The Management of Family Resources*, W. H. Freeman and Co., San Francisco.

10. Floore, F. B., 1959. "Silver tableware through the ages," *J. Amer. Diet. Assoc.*, **35**:582.

11. Gilbreth, L. M., O. M. Thomas, and E. Olymor, 1955, *Management in the Home*, Dodd, Mead, and Co., New York.

12. Goldmann, M. E., 1950, *Planning and Serving Your Meals*, McGraw-Hill Book Co., New York.

13. Gross, I. H. and E. W. Crandall, 1954, *Home Management in Theory and Practice*, F. S. Crofts Co., New York.

14. Handbook of Kitchen Design, Small Homes Council, Uni. of Illinois, Urbana.

15. Household Storage Units, Cir. 05.1 Small Homes Council, Uni. of Illinois, Urbana.

16. Household Finance Corporation, 1951, *Money Management, Your Budget*, 1950; *Money Management, Your Food Dollar*, Chicago.

17. Howard, M. S., L. S. Thye, and G. K. Taylor, 1958, "The Beltsville Kitchen-Workroom," U.S.D.A. Home and Garden Bul. No. 60.

18. Justin, M. M., L. O. Rust, and G. E. Vail, 1956, *Foods*, Houghton Mifflin Co., Boston.

19. Kinder, F., 1956, *Meal Management*, The Macmillan Co., New York.

20. McLean, B. B., 1949, *Meal Planning and Table Service*, Chas. A. Bennett Co., Peoria, Ill.

21. Monroe, D., H. Kyrk, and U. S. Stone, 1938, *Food Buying and Our Markets,* M. Barrows and Co., New York.

22. Niles, K. B., 1955, *Family Table Service,* Burgess Publishing Co., Minneapolis.

23. Proudfit, F. T. and C. H. Robinson, 1953, *Nutrition and Diet Therapy,* The Macmillan Co., New York.

24. Sherman, H. C. and C. S. Lanford, 1957, *Essentials of Nutrition,* The Macmillan Co., New York.

25. Starr, M. C., 1956, *Management for Better Living,* D. C. Heath and Co., Boston.

26. Trollstrup, A. W., 1952, *Consumer Problems,* McGraw-Hill Book Co., New York.

27. Tuttle, W. W., K. Daum, R. Larsen, J. Salzano, and L. Roloff, 1954, "Effect on school boys of omitting breakfast; physiologic responses, attitudes, and scholastic attainments," *J. Amer. Diet. Assoc.,* **30**:674.

28. U. S. Department of Agriculture, *More and Better Foods from Today's Pay Check,* U.S.D.A. Agr. Inf. Bull. p. 138, Mar. 1955.

29. U. S. Department of Agriculture, *Suggestions for Keeping Food Costs Low,* U.S.D.A. Misc. Pub. 662, August 1955.

30. Watt, B. K. and L. M. Annabel, 1950, *Composition of Foods—Raw, Processed, Prepared,* U.S.D.A. Agr. Handbook No. 8.

31. Wohl, M. G. and R. S. Goodhart, 1955, *Modern Nutrition in Health and Disease,* Lea and Ferbiger, Philadelphia, Chapter 36, "Food and Nutrition Relating to Work and Environmental Stress."

12 . . CONSUMER PROTECTION

TYPES AND SOURCES OF PROTECTION

Federal Agencies
    The United States Public Health Service
    The United States Food and Drug Administration
    The United States Department of Agriculture
    Other Federal Agencies
State and Local Agencies
Semi-official Agencies
Nongovernmental Agencies
Protection against Fraud and Fads
Quality Standards of Food Grading
Labeling of Foods
Weights and Measures

AVAILABILITY AND DISSEMINATION OF AUTHENTIC INFORMATION

Agricultural Extension Service
Colleges and Universities
Adult Schools
Forums
Workshops

SUMMARY

READING LIST

◀ **Fig. 108.** The fiftieth anniversary of Pure Food and Drug Laws was commemorated in 1956 by issuance of a 3-cent stamp carrying a photograph of the late Dr. Harvey Wiley, pioneer in legislation for safe foods. Here Dr. Wiley weighs food for his "Poison Squad"—a group of human volunteers who made history in the world's "most famous boarding house." The Poison Squad experiments went on for approximately five years beginning in 1903. (Courtesy of Food and Drug Administration, Washington, D. C.)

FOODS FOR HUMAN CONSUMPTION ARE PROBABLY MORE CONTROLLED, more regulated, and more inspected than any other of our consumer goods. The public demands protection of its health and its purse; therefore, laws and recommendations are necessary to secure this protection. There are approximately 170 million people in this country who must have their "three meals" every day. Millions of individuals are involved in the producing, processing, distributing, marketing, and retailing of the vast assortment of foods that are at the fingertips of the consumer.

The exercise of controls to assure safe foods, high in quality, aesthetically acceptable, properly labeled, in specified fill of the container, and within a reasonable price range requires a confusing network of supervisory functionaries. These range from the governmental agencies at federal (Fig. 108), state, and local levels through semi-official and unofficial groups to trade organizations. Semi-official groups are composed of people with special training who act in an advisory capacity to governmental agencies. The unofficial groups and trade organizations promote the improvement of both food quality and the conditions under which food is prepared and marketed.

Each of these agencies or groups has its own particular functions and objectives. These groups are concerned not only with supervision of foods from producer to consumer but also with the collection and dissemination of information.

TYPES AND SOURCES OF PROTECTION

The governmental controls and the agencies supervising them were established for the following reasons:

(1) To protect the public health by improving the sanitary quality, by preventing the use of toxic materials, and by preventing the addition of adulterants or inferior products.

(2) To promote new products and industries.

(3) To prevent fraud and unfair trade practices.

(4) To promote higher production and better distribution than existed previously.

Agencies that are nongovernmental usually deal with a specific commodity, and their activities are confined to helping only those groups requesting aid. These nonofficial agencies may be supported by the industry concerned or by groups of civic-minded citizens.

Federal supervision of food is limited to the food that crosses state borders or enters into interstate commerce. State supervision applies to food manufactured and sold within the state or food that is brought from neighboring states to be processed or used within the state. Local authorities may go into the nearby communities to inspect food that is to be consumed in their locality; this is particularly true of milk and dairy products. This complex system of supervision may result in a duplication of inspections but it also takes into consideration any irregularities or conditions peculiar to the specific community.

The *health of consumers* is protected by laws that prohibit the sale of harmful or toxic foods. This means that sanitary conditions under which food is produced, processing procedures, as well as additions made to the food, must be controlled. There should be no compromise in this control, and regardless of the final selling price, factors affecting the health of the consumer should all receive the same rigid scrutiny.

Protection of the *purse* requires an entirely different type of control. It includes such things as eliminating misrepresentation and fraud, providing facts necessary to making wise selections, and guarding against short weights and measures. Since these are not vital to life, many infringements may occur because the supervision is not as complete or regular as the supervision for health aspects.

Closely associated with both the health and economic aspects are standards of *aesthetic* acceptability. These standards vary and are for the most part psychological. There are certain conditions that may be revolting to everyone. For example, the idea of insects and rodents in food is not acceptable even though the evidence has been removed and the food washed or pasteurized. Laws have been made to prevent the sale of food not generally aesthetically acceptable. There has been, however, some question as to how far controls for the aesthetic standard should be extended.

Laws governing food inspection and food constituents, whether state or local, are constantly changing because of changes in processing methods, pest control, and other conditions. For example, many of the newer chemicals used in pest control may not be toxic unless used over a long period of time, thus toxicity becomes a matter of tolerance. The laws must be amended to include this and similar situations.

Methods of food inspection, food analysis, and food grading have been greatly improved within the last two decades. As a result the supervision of food production has been improved. The detection of toxic materials, adulterants, and other foreign matter has been aided by new and improved chemical, photometric, and spectrophotometric methods. Pressure gauges are used to determine maturity of fruits, and other instruments are used to determine sugar concentration, fat content, etc. Many of the grades are still evaluated by subjective means, but with the increase in research more objective methods are being developed. Electronic devices for detection of color, tissue damage, and even protein and moisture content are in the experimental stages.

Federal Agencies

Groups comprising the federal agencies setting standards and exercising supervision over food are in general located either in the divisions of the United States Department of Health, Education, and Welfare or in the United States Department of Agriculture. The facilities of these agencies do not permit a complete coverage of all food, therefore, selective enforcement is necessary. The enforcements may be informal with warnings or the industries may be given information designed to help improve conditions; or the enforcements may be more formal, and products may be seized and producers and sellers criminally prosecuted.

The United States Public Health Service. This is a part of the Department of Health, Education, and Welfare and has the direct supervision of milk and water supplies consumed on interstate carriers (trains, airlines, etc.). It also has established codes and ordinances for many foods. These ordinances concern such things as milk, water, shellfish, frozen desserts, restaurants, food-borne diseases, and trichinosis. The agency issues manuals of recommendation for the production, processing, and care of certain foods, as well as for the sanitary protection of food in restaurants and markets. It is to be remembered that these codes and ordinances are only recommendations and are not in force in all situations. However, many states, counties, and cities have established them as laws, and the consumer will need to inquire concerning the regulations governing local situations.

The United States Food and Drug Administration. This also is under the Department of Health, Education, and Welfare, and has jurisdiction within the limits of its authority, as defined by the Federal Food, Drug, and Cosmetic Act of 1939, over all foods moving in interstate commerce except meat and meat products. Meat and meat products are under the jurisdiction of the United States Department of Agriculture. Also, under normal conditions the Food and Drug Administration does not supervise the production or supply of fluid milk or fresh shellfish. It does, however, supervise the processing and sale of many milk products and investigates adulteration of processed shellfish. Its activities are mainly checking purity, standard potency, and truthful and informative labeling of the commodities covered by the various Acts over which it has jurisdiction.

The United States Food and Drug Administration has a *Food Standards Committee* composed of six members—four representing the states and two the federal government. This committee has adopted approximately 150 food definitions and standards that will promote honesty and fair dealing in the interest of the consumer. Once such standards are officially established, they have the force of law. Abstracted versions of these standards and definitions are printed, and anyone who wishes this information may secure copies from the Federal Food and Drug Administration. Either the Food and Drug Administration or interested parties may initiate the establishment of standards for any food.

The United States Department of Agriculture. This agency exercises a great variety of controls and supervision over the production or processing of foods, especially meat and meat products. One of its principal functions is to direct research or otherwise acquire information concerning food, and through publications make this information available to the people of the nation. It also makes results of its research available for practical use through the *United States Office of Experiment Stations* and *Federal Extension Services*. These agencies, in cooperation with their counterparts within the states, conduct classes, have radio and television programs, and issue news reports.

As a taxpayer and consumer one should know about the vast research program that is conducted at the 12,000-acre *Agricultural Research Center* at Beltsville, Maryland, and also at the four *Utilization Research Branches* (Fig. 109). The research activities are extended beyond the confines of these laboratories by means of contracts with various public and private agencies and institutions.

The Institute of Home Economics of the Agricultural Research Service of the United States Department of Agriculture analyzes consumption and nutritive values of food, investigates human nutritional requirements, and appraises the nutritive adequacy of national and regional food supplies and diets. This Institute also makes suggestions for obtaining the greatest satisfaction and nutritional value from the food money. Methods of conserving nutritive value during cooking are investigated, and new and improved methods of home canning, freezing, and dehydrating are recommended. Recipes are developed that

Fig. 109. Research facilities of the federal government include four utilization research laboratories such as this one at Albany, California. (Courtesy of Western Utilization Research Branch, United States Department of Agriculture, Albany, Calif.)

will make use of our changing food supplies, new products, or surplus commodities—for example, recipes using surplus commodities for the school lunch program.

The *Meat Inspection* agency of the United States Department of Agriculture conducts numerous types of inspection to insure wholesome domestic and imported meat and meat products. This inspection applies not only to cattle, sheep, and swine, but also to goats and horses. The services of this branch are available to processors upon request.

The *Marketing Program* is a part of the *United States Agricultural Marketing Service*. This program includes the market news service; inspection, classing, grading, and standardizing services; freight-rate service; and administration of the national school lunch program as well as the special milk program. The market news service provides timely and reliable market reports on all major agricultural products. This information is supplied to newspapers and radio and television commentators. The grading service is being demanded by the consumer for more and more products. It is currently in general use for eggs, fresh meat, and canned foods. A discussion of the grading of each of these products has been given in the specific chapter devoted to the products.

Other federal agencies. Other federal agencies that help to control our food supplies are the *United States Fish and Wildlife Service*, *United States Interstate Commerce Commission*, and the *Federal Trade Commission*. The Fish and Wildlife Service protects all game animals and fish. It conducts studies not only on protection and on conservation of fish and game but also on the use of these in the diet and methods of preparation. The Interstate Commerce Commission regulates common carriers for the transport of commodities across state borders. The Federal Trade Commission is authorized to prevent false or deceptive advertising practices for any food. The powers given this body indicate that subtle misrepresentation as well as blaring untruths could be eliminated. This has not yet been realized. In the future it may also be possible to require that certain facts be stated rather than just omitted.

State and Local Agencies

Many of the states have counterparts of the federal agencies that control and regulate food grown, manufactured, or processed and sold *within* the state. Many states have adopted legislation similar to the Federal Food, Drug, and Cosmetic Act of 1939. This makes greater uniformity in food control and simplifies the supervision of food production. The agency or agencies enforcing the laws may vary from state to state. The authority is usually vested in the State Health Department or the State Agriculture Department or both. Regulations and enforcements vary slightly from state to state, and each person should become familiar with his own state and local food laws.

Some states have developed trade barriers in order to protect either crops or industries of their state. These include inspection at state borders of fresh fruits and vegetables to prevent pests from entering the state and quarantines of diseased plants and animals to prevent the spread of disease.

Semi-official Agencies

The National Research Council of the National Academy of Science is a semi-official organization composed of scientific authorities. This body acts as advisor to governmental agencies. Its outstanding contribution to foods and nutrition was the formulation of the Recommended Daily Allowances by its Food and Nutrition Board (see Chapter 1). Through other groups they have also made studies of the adequacy of diets under various conditions.

There are other agencies of this type such as the *American Red Cross* and the *Food and Agriculture Organization of the United Nations*.

Nongovernmental Agencies

The unofficial agencies that help to protect the consumer are many and include such national professional organizations as the *Institute of Nutrition*, the *American Dietetic Association*, the *American Home Economics Association*, the *American Medical Association*, and many others. Also active are the industry supported organizations such as the *American Meat Institute*, the *National Dairy Council*, the *Cereal Institute*, the *National Canners Association*, the *Evaporated Milk Association*, and the *Western Growers Association*—to name but a few. State and local organizations such as the nutrition councils have also been set up to promote the welfare of specific groups.

All unofficial groups either conduct and report research or report the results of research conducted by other agencies. They may define and set up standards for food or they may do only promotional work by bringing the qualities and advantages of various foods to the attention of the consumer. For example the Greater Los Angeles Nutrition Council, Incorporated, is a local unofficial organization and has as its major purposes:

(1) The promoting of good nutrition by serving as a source of factual information about food.

(2) The promoting of good nutrition by conducting a program for the improvement of food habits, of diets, and methods of achieving nutritional well-being.

(3) The acceptance and advocation of standards of nutrition established by carefully controlled scientific investigations by qualified investigators.

(4) Sponsoring and supporting research in nutrition or health or any subject related thereto.

Organizations such as this are composed of informed people who are either working in research or in advisory capacities where health and welfare are concerned.

Protection against Fraud and Fads

Protection against fraud is a difficult strategy. Fraud is a willful deception that will probably always be practiced because many people exhibit an inherent lack of responsibility for the social welfare of their fellowmen and because of the gullibility and greed of others.

Probably the most common and least harmful of all economic frauds is the addition of water, artificial color, and artificial flavors to food and beverages. Addition of water results in diluting the nutritive value of the food, and addition of color and flavor gives the appearance of a superior or more valuable product than the ingredients warrant. In neither of these cases is the food toxic nor will one immediately suffer physically. Other nontoxic adulterants that may be used are saccharine in place of sugar, chicory or cereals in place of coffee, or spice substitutes in place of true spice. The economic fraud is not always a matter of substitutions or additions; certain substances may be subtracted, for example, fat from milk or oil from chocolate. Substitution, addition, or subtraction of food materials from one single food is perhaps without health significance. However, if this deception is continuous and several foods are involved, the overall nutritional status of a family or even an entire community could be affected.

Another type of economic fraud is the selling of food supplements for exorbitant prices and with pressure selling techniques. These supplements may contain the ingredients and the amounts of nutrients listed on the label, but the selling price may be far beyond the economic value. Supplements are not a substitute for "three meals a day." In many instances the cost of the supplement will be more than that of food needed for an adequate diet. Some supplements sell for as much as 75 cents per day ($20.00 per month), and even at today's prices an adequate diet can be purchased for this price. If one were willing to eat the fresh ingredients from which the supplements are made or foods similar to these, one could live for several days on 75 cents.

Selling techniques for this type of fraud are of various types. The most common is one of using a rapid-fire bombardment of technical and pseudo-technical terms which are neither understood by the potential consumer nor, oftentimes, by the person selling. Certain words are emphasized in such a manner that the possible buyer feels himself slowly starving to death.

A second technique employs mass psychology. Testimonial parties are given and pushers of the supplement bring friends and everyone tells how much better he feels since taking the "health food." No physicians are involved, and no one ever knows whether or not the previous conditions were real or imagined, or whether any real physical improvement occurred.

Some of the harmful effects to the supplement user are the false security that is implied, the delayed medication if an actual organic abnormality exists, and the fact that in many cases there is not sufficient money left after paying for the supplement to provide an adequate diet. The purchase of food supplements is of course the consumer's choice but it is unfortunate that he be given a feeling of security that does not exist.

Various diet-supplement and diet-crutch cults may be followed with the same devotion that some people give to religious or political beliefs.

Some legal actions have been initiated against the producers of such products and their methods of selling have been questioned. However, the best consumer protection is "won't power." Frauds are promoted by the people who buy the materials as much as by the sellers. Many fatal illnesses might be avoided if a physician rather than a salesman is consulted.

Frauds other than economic may be perpetrated and perpetuated by well-meaning but overzealous writers who report research findings without the scientific background necessary to interpret the true meanings or implications of the research. Such writing may precipitate mass food fads. Before any diet ritual or fad is adopted, the safety and sanity of the procedure should be thoroughly checked. There may be conditions that can develop into something worse than the one you think you will correct.

An example of such a possibly harmful diet is the low-protein diet of oil, glucose, and evaporated milk that was unfortunately publicized as a medically approved reducing diet in the spring of 1956. Possibilities of liver damage and vitamin deficiencies were unknown or overlooked as thousands of "fatties" rushed to embrace the new fad.

Not all food fads are frauds; some are beneficial, others are simply fashions, others may lead to inadequate or harmful diets. Many of the common foods go through fad periods. The soft-frozen custard drive-ins that are on many street corners have replaced the root-beer stands of thirty years ago, and pizza palaces are taking over part of the hamburger stand trade. These and many other fads are common, and each generation has its particular food fashions. However, restricting of the diet by omitting certain foods or by always selecting the same food from any one of the food groups could lead to an inadequate diet. Therefore, when a diet that does not indicate choices or alternates or that omits certain foods entirely is suddenly publicized or flaunted, it should not be accepted.

Because there is little if any legal protection against diet fads and traffickers of food supplements, the following fact should be noted: the American Dietetic Association investigates the background and training and evaluates the ability of its members and only qualified dietitians (although not certified by law) may join. Therefore, it is a wise precaution to check the affiliation of anyone whom you wish to consult as a nutritionist. In other words, make the same careful check of your dietitian as you do of your family physician. Your physician is a member of the American Medical Association, your dentist of the American Dental Association, your attorney of the American Bar Association, and even your psychiatrist of the American Psychiatric Association. Then why take advice on your diet from someone who is not a qualified dietitian and a member of the American Dietetic Association? It is unfortunate that nutritionists and sellers of health foods are not required to pass tests to establish competency in nutrition. All that is required is a selling license.

Quality Standards of Food Grading

Food may be prepared and sold under conditions that meet all of the standards necessary for health protection, and yet these foods may not have high palatability or good eating qualities. Thus *quality control* is necessary to the commercial production of food. These quality controls form the basis for the grading of products offered for sale and may be for purely aesthetic purposes, and in many instances undue emphasis is placed upon them. The criteria for evaluating quality are palatability, general appearance, degree of maturity, and actual size. In addition to these, such intangible influences as public preferences, prejudices, and other psychological factors may be considered when standards are established. Definitions of quality, standards, and grades have been established by the United States Department of Agriculture for many products. Not all products are government graded; however, government definitions of quality are the standards used for the basis of all commercial grading.

The quality grading of individual food items is discussed in the chapters dealing with each particular food. However, grade has little to do with health or nutritional aspects, only with acceptance. Grades do affect price; high quality usually commands a higher price than low quality.

Labeling of Foods

Labeling of all food that enters into interstate commerce is supervised and controlled by the Federal Food and Drug Administration. Many states have labeling laws, similar to the federal laws, that apply to food produced, processed, and sold within the state.

The label is expected to contain accurate statements concerning the product, and certain information is required. The label must include statements concerning the following:

(1) Major ingredients—not necessarily in the order of their quantity.

(2) Artificial coloring or chemical preservatives—this ruling on color does not apply to butter, cheese, or ice cream.

(3) Slack fill or low quality—reasonable standards of quality and fill are required, and if either falls below the accepted standards, it must be so stated on the label.

(4) Dietary properties of foods represented as having certain dietary uses (Fig. 110).

(5) Weight of the package contents.

(6) Address of the producer or distributor.

Certain other revealing information must be given for specific products. Canned peaches must be labeled as to the kind of syrup, the form

Fig. 110. Measuring sodium in a "low sodium" food. In Federal Food and Drug Administration laboratories, the chemist ashes the food sample, dissolves the ash, places the solution in a spectrophometer, and sprays it into a hot gas flame. (Courtesy of Food and Drug Administration, Washington, D. C.)

in which packed, and, if they are below standard in quality, they must be marked "substandard." Foods labeled as enriched or fortified must contain the amount of vitamins and minerals specified in the standard. Also, if food is enriched or fortified this must be stated on the label.

Other statements may be given; however, any statement made, either required or voluntary, should not be false or misleading. Much of the extra information is designed to help the consumer make decisions. This is known as *informative labeling*. Such information might include grade labeling, piece size, numbers of servings, and so forth.

Whenever a discussion of labeling occurs, the question always arises as to the purpose of a label. Is it designed to appraise the buyer of the facts concerning a product or is it designed to encourage him to buy the product? The intent of the labeling laws is to inform and protect the consumer. Therefore, a label that complies with the intent of the law should not be cluttered with so much extraneous material that facts vital to the consumer are lost in the maze.

Weights and Measures

The size and value of *weights and measures* are fixed by Congress, and the *United States Bureau of Standards* maintains these standards. Weights and measures are important considerations when buying any commodity. Whenever it is possible or practical, weights rather than measure or count should be used. If foods are not sold by weight, then standard measures are better than count. Many items are sold using a combination of count and weight or measure and weight. Eggs, for example, are sold by the dozen in the majority of states; however, a dozen eggs must meet a minimum weight standard. Also fruit is sold by the lug, bushel, or barrel; here again minimum weight is specified for each type of fruit in each volume.

Fixing of specifications for the relationship between weights and measures of various commodities is the duty of each state. It is important for the consumer to know the regulations within his particular state. Some states have excellent laws, whereas others have little if any supervision.

Shape and fill of food containers become very important if weights are not known. The federal food law provides that the container shall not be "so made or filled as to be misleading." False bottoms in package boxes or berry boxes with a middle divider for a bottom are no longer permitted for use in interstate shipping. In those states where such boxes are allowed, the actual volume should be carefully checked. When the weight is stated on the package, the container should not be overlarge for its contents, that is, 2 ounces of material should not be packaged in a container that could hold 4 ounces, even though the 2-ounce weight is printed plainly on the package.

A state may have standards for fill of containers but it is still advisable to check the weight information on the label. One ounce may not make a discernible difference in the size of the package but it may make a considerable difference in the food value one receives. For example, one box containing 12 ounces of a powdered food may look much like another box containing 11 ounces and they both may sell for the same price. However, the first box will contain 9 per cent more food than the second.

AVAILABILITY AND DISSEMINATION OF AUTHENTIC INFORMATION

If consumers are to make wise choices, they must be informed. There are many reliable sources of information, and most of it is free for the asking. However, the type of information needed may not always be at hand, and in many cases it is difficult to separate truth from propaganda. One needs to first make the effort necessary to get the information. Then it must be read and understood. This requirement may account for the lack of a wide distribution of consumer information, because recent surveys show that although we are one of the most literate nations in the world, only 25 per cent of the people read books after they leave school. Perhaps if consumer education could be given in some predigested visual form, more people would profit by it. It is as vital, and it could be as interesting, to know which cut of meat gives the most nutritive value for each dollar spent as it is to know who won the World Series.

United States Department of Agriculture Bulletins on the practical aspects of the recent research and development of food technology are available. Many of these bulletins are written in layman's terms and all are unbiased and free from advertising. Lists of available publications on various subjects may be secured from the Superintendent of Documents in Washington, D. C. or from one's own state Department of Agriculture. The experiment station of each state conducts research pertinent to the conditions of that state. Therefore, information available through this source should be of great value to the residents of the state concerned.

The *Agricultural Extension Service* will also have valuable information, which one may get simply by calling or writing the local farm or home advisor. It is not necessary to live in a rural community to take advantage of this service. Classes and workshops may be available only for rural or small urban communities, but literature and radio and television programs are for all. The farm reporter from the local Agricultural Extension office usually issues daily price and market reports. He will note the fresh fruits and vegetables and other farm products in plentiful supply, and in many cases will give suggestions for use of the products.

Colleges and Universities that have departments of Home Economics may have extension classes in which any one who is a high school graduate may enroll. Courses in foods, nutrition, and money management may be given or, if such classes are not available, instructors in foods and nutrition are usually willing to give information or indicate reliable sources. In addition to these services, instructors are available for forums, lectures, etc. One should inquire through the college administration concerning these services. There may be a speakers bureau, and the speakers may be available with or without a fee.

College instructors may also write bulletins or take part in radio and television programs. Entire foods and nutrition courses can be given by means of radio or television. Before any Home Economics program is followed too closely, one should make sure that it has the backing and sanction of a college because not all so-called "home economics" programs are produced by recognized authoritative groups.

Many colleges are having *back to school week* for the alumni or even for people in the local community. These are really workshops or *refresher courses*. They may include all phases of home living, or only one phase, such as food and nutrition, may be emphasized. Such programs are designed to give and evaluate the recent advances in various phases of the subjects discussed.

Adult schools may have classes in foods and nutrition or consumer buying. These classes may offer instruction in cooking skills and meal planning, or they may be advanced classes in nutrition or marketing. In the majority of public schools, the only requirement for enrolling in such classes is that the student be at least 18 years of age. The courses may be carried for high-school or junior-college credit, or they may be taken only for information or recreation. Such classes are very stimulating. The students may be people with little or no formal education, or they may be professional people with advanced college degrees.

Forums for adult schools and junior colleges are often given on nutrition or consumer buying. They are usually a series of evening lectures, each followed by a question and answer period. The topics discussed will vary from year to year or even from lecture to lecture.

Workshops on foods and nutrition may also be available, and these may include demonstrations and laboratory work. Since they are given primarily for homemakers, they will include food preparation, meal planning, feeding of all ages, and other topics of interest to the group.

If publications are written or programs are sponsored under the name of one of the agencies listed in Table 39, they may be considered as reliable. However, if the sponsoring organization is not listed here, there are several criteria that can be used to test the authenticity of any information. This test may take a little time but will usually pay off in the final analysis.

(1) Any author or speaker on foods and nutrition may be evaluated by answering the following questions: Is he listed in the *American Men of Science* or if he is not, is he recommended by someone who is? Is he ethical? Is he conservative? Is he free from commercial bias? If the answers to all of these questions are in the affirmative, then in all probability the information that he will give concerning the subject in which he is a recognized authority will be reliable insofar as he is able to ascertain. Always remember that some of the best informed people in one subject may not be authorities in another. Be wary of a person who never hesitates to give an opinion and who seems incapable of saying, "I don't know." Few people know the answers to all questions even in their own fields of specialization.

(2) The truth of statements made in everyday conversations can be evaluated by a very simple test. When you suspect someone of fabricating material, guide the conversation to a subject with which you are familiar. He will usually continue in the same forceful vein, but here you know the facts and can recognize his fabrication. The best spies and confidence-men can make the most reliable sounding statements out of purely imaginative materials. But one may say, "How can they know the terms that are so peculiar to a specific subject?" That is very easy; since they give the information to people who do not know the facts or the language, any words used are relatively unimportant.

(3) Vague references should be suspected. The term "they" used to refer to fact sources should be avoided or questioned. "They say" is a method of starting all bits of gossip as well as any startling information on diet or nutrition. All "theys" should be identified and the original information checked.

(4) Foods and nutrition research should be conducted in impartial laboratories. Few people who produce and sell materials are able to give impartial information concerning these products. In no way

Table 39. A LIST OF SOME OF THE ORGANIZATIONS THAT PARTICIPATE IN THE PROMOTION OF FOODS AND NUTRITION EDUCATION

Federal

Department of Agriculture
Agricultural Research Service
Institute of Home Economics
Human Nutrition Research Division
Regulatory Programs
Meat Inspection Division
Experiment Stations
Federal Extension Service
Agricultural Marketing Service
Market News
Standardization, Inspection, Grading, and Classing
Rural Electrification Administration

Department of Health, Education and Welfare
Public Health Service
Office of Education
Social Security Administration
Childrens Bureau
Food and Drug Administration

Department of Interior
Fish and Wildlife Service

Department of Labor
Bureau of Labor Statistics

Government Affiliated Agencies

National Academy of Science
National Research Council
The American National Red Cross
Food and Agriculture Organization of the United Nations

Unofficial Agencies

Professional Organizations (incomplete)
American Association of Cereal Chemists
American Chemical Society
American Dietetic Association
American Home Economics Association
American Medical Association
American Public Health Association
Institute of Food Technologists
Institute of Nutrition

Nonprofessional Organizations (incomplete)
American Meat Institute
American Rice Institute
Cereal Institute
Evaporated Milk Association
National Association of Margarine Manufacturers
National Better Business Bureau
National Bakers Association
National Canners Association
National Dairy Council
National Livestock and Meat Board
National Wheat Flour Institute
Poultry and Egg National Board
Western Growers Association
Citrus Growers Incorporated

449

should the information derived from research affect the income of the person doing the research. Such impartial laboratories may be supported by the various governmental agencies, experiment stations, colleges and universities, and research foundations. Research foundations should be apart and entirely separated financially from the supporting industries.

All of the above tests are simple to conduct, are available to lay persons, and may be used on various types of information.

SUMMARY

There exist many agencies that protect the consumer against misinformation and frauds as well as food-borne diseases, short weights and measure, and low standards of quality. They include federal agencies, semi-official agencies, and unofficial agencies. The functions of these organizations are many and include health, economic, and aesthetic protection.

Authentic information concerning foods and nutrition may be secured through publications and news releases from the various agencies. Experiment station bulletins on the practical aspects of recent research and development in food technology are free to residents within their states. The Agricultural Extension Service may also have available valuable information, which may be secured from the local farm or home advisor. Colleges and universities that have departments of home economics may have extension classes in which anyone who is a high school graduate may enroll. Adult schools may have classes in foods and nutrition or consumer buying.

A list of some of the organizations that participate in the promotion of foods and nutrition education is given.

Reading List

1. American Dietetic Association, 1957, *Food Facts Talk Back*, American Dietetic Association, Chicago.

2. American Medical Association, Council on Foods and Nutrition, 1939, *Accepted Foods*, American Medical Association, Chicago.

3. Bogert, L. J., 1960, *Nutrition and Physical Fitness*, W. B. Saunders Co., Philadelphia.

4. Huenemann, H. L., 1956, "Combating food misinformation and quackery," *J. Amer. Diet. Assoc.*, **32**:623.

5. Ives, M., 1957, "Safety evaluation of food packaging materials," *J. Amer. Diet. Assoc.*, **33**:347.

6. Leverton, R. M., 1957, "Distorting facts into fads," *J. Amer. Diet. Assoc.*, **33**:793.

7. McCollum, E. V., 1957, *History of Nutrition*, Houghton Mifflin Co., New York.

8. Mickelson, O., 1957, "Is toxicology enough for a food protection program," *J. Amer. Diet. Assoc.*, **33**:341.

9. Smith, B. Jr., 1956, "Chemical additives in food," *J. Amer. Diet. Assoc.*, **32**:703.

10. U. S. Government Organization Manual 1959–60, "U. S. Dept. of Agriculture," Federal Register Division, General Services Administration, Washington.

11. U. S. National Archives, 1955, with supplement. Code of Federal Register Title 21, Food and Drugs, Federal Register Division, National Archives and Records Service, Washington.

12. State of California 1955, *Health and Safety Code*, Printing Division, Documents Section, Sacramento.

Fig. 111. Athletes require a great amount of energy foods when taking part in competitive sports. (Courtesy of Whittier College, Whittier, California.)

CHAPTER

13 . . THE FUNCTION
OF THE NUTRIENTS
IN THE BODY

IMAGINATIVE PERSONS THROUGHOUT ALL TIME HAVE PERHAPS ASKED WHY one must eat food and why does one always seem to feel better if he eats certain combinations? The answer to these and other questions is developing with the science of nutrition. Human bodies function smoothly only when certain substances reach the tissues in a steady regulated flow. The individual substances, that is, the energy-producing materials, the tissue-building materials, and the catalysts for the use of these substances are derived from what we choose to call foods and are referred to as nutrients.

The foods must be subjected to processes first of *digestion* and then *absorption* before they can take part in the body functions. The fate and functioning of the food nutrients in the body after absorption are referred to as *metabolism.* Each of these processes—digestion, absorption, and metabolism—should be recognized as just as important a step in the whole plan as either of the other processes.

CLASSES AND GENERAL FUNCTIONS OF NUTRIENTS

The forty or more nutrients are divided into six general classes— proteins, carbohydrates, fats, vitamins, minerals, and water. Each class serves one or more functions in the body. No one of the required nutrients functions alone, and each is dependent upon one or more of the others for performing its particular work. It is, therefore, practically impossible to discuss one nutrient without discussing one or more other nutrients.

ENERGY METABOLISM AND FUNCTIONS OF PROTEINS, CARBOHYDRATE, AND FAT

After the nutrients have been absorbed they are distributed throughout the body to perform specific functions. Scientists have used the term "metabolism" to denote the changes that the absorbed nutrients undergo from the time they leave the intestinal tract until they have reached the end products of the nutrition process. Metabolism is of two types: the building of tissues, fluids, enzymes, and hormones (*anabolism*), and the reverse or the tearing down of these substances (*catabolism*).

In any attempt to describe the metabolic process, one confronts the question: which comes first, the breaking down or the building up? Actually both processes go on simultaneously and continuously from the moment life comes into an organism until a short while after death.

Sources of energy must be provided for all of the body's work; building and maintenance materials must be supplied for all of the body parts; and the substances that regulate the rate and efficiency with which these functions are carried out must also be provided. There are many mysteries concerning these processes that have not been solved, and it should be recognized that this book could not begin to describe in detail all of the known facts or the theories pertaining to the unknown. The following discussion is only a brief supplementation of the subject matter presented in Chapter 1 designed to enable the student to understand why a well-balanced and varied diet is needed.

Energy Metabolism

Every motion and every process that the human body performs requires energy (Fig. 111). When the body is as completely relaxed as possible during deep sleep, the heart is beating, breathing continues, the body temperature must be maintained, and all metabolic processes are in progress. Energy is required at all times. The energy that the body uses appears in many forms. However, scientists have found it convenient to measure it in the same unit as heat, the *Calorie*. The Calorie used in nutrition is the *grand Calorie* and is defined as the amount of heat necessary to raise the temperature of one kilogram (1000 grams) of water one degree centigrade.

The concept of energy expenditure by the body is difficult to understand. This situation has been aggravated by the lay concept that "each Calorie eaten is laid away someplace as fat." It may be helpful to remember that a normal adult sitting in a lecture-room (paying strict attention to the lecture or discussion) for one hour usually uses about 100 Calories; during sleep this same individual would use about 65 Calories per hour; typing rapidly, about 140 Calories per hour; and dancing one of the faster steps, about 335 Calories per hour. In a 24-hour period an active person will expend a relatively large amount of energy, and all of the energy needs must be supplied by carbohydrates, fats, and proteins. Food energy supplied to the body in excess of need is stored as fat and if not enough energy is provided by the food, the body fat and then the muscle tissue is used for this purpose. If one is to keep a constant body weight the energy intake must equal the energy output. Therefore, no food is fattening unless too much is eaten.

The total daily expenditure of energy varies from individual to individual and depends upon two general factors, involuntary activities and voluntary activities. The *involuntary activities* constitute those processes over which one has no control. The energy required for these activities is considered to be the amount of energy expended by a person when he is awake, lying still, and who has not eaten for a 12-hour period. This is generally referred to as the "*basal metabolism.*" This basal need for energy is greater than normal when:

(1) The rate of involuntary activities is fast, as determined by the body and environmental regulators.

(2) The number of cellular activities is great, as in growth processes.

(3) The number of active cells (nonfat) is large.

Voluntary activity needs depend upon the type of activity and the force and tension with which this activity is accomplished. A short, active ball player might use more energy than a tall, relatively inactive college professor. Children who consume more food than their parents do and yet remain "skinny" do so not only because they are growing very rapidly but also because they are usually very active.

The average person does not expend as much energy today as a similar person would have spent fifty years ago because of the increase in the number of labor-saving devices and the development of a good transportation system. Either the diet or the exercise should be adjusted to meet this change. Those people who find it difficult to decrease the energy value of their diets could perhaps find a hobby that requires exercise or find a parking lot several blocks from work.

Food must provide heat energy that maintains normal body temperature, and keeping warm may account for a large part of the energy need. When we are well clothed and housed keeping warm is accomplished as a by-product of exercise. This might be referred to as a physical regulation, and under most normal conditions this is all that is needed; however, when the muscles are flabby as in old age, food must be oxidized for the special purpose of heating the body. This latter method could be called a chemical regulation.

Production of heat from the nutrients requires oxygen and regulatory substances such as vitamins, minerals, enzymes, and hormones. The end products of energy metabolism are carbon dioxide and water. Energy released by oxidation of different foodstuffs varies somewhat within each type of food, but for all practical purposes the average figures that follow are useful in the calculation of food values:

(1) 1 gram of carbohydrate produces 4 Calories.
(2) 1 gram of protein produces 4 Calories.
(3) 1 gram of fat produces 9 Calories.

A few other substances such as organic acids and alcohols are oxidized by the body, but they are normally present in such small amounts that they are not considered.

Amounts of energy needed to accomplish certain types of work have been determined by the use of instruments known as *calorimeters*. A detailed description of this instrument and its method of use is given by Sherman and Lanford (see Reading List).

The Table of Recommended Dietary Allowances (see Chapter 1) shows the energy (Calorie) intake for individuals at various ages and under various conditions. These should be considered only as guides and the sources of the Calories should be given some consideration. The Recommended Allowances also give the protein allowance in grams; this figure multiplied by four will give the approximate number of Calories recommended to be derived from protein. As a "rule of thumb" the remainder of the Calories can be equally divided between the carbohydrates and fats; if an unbalance occurs the carbohydrates should furnish the larger amount. This means that the weight of the carbohydrate would be approximately two or more times that of the fat. It is very difficult for anyone to look at a food and know the make-up of its energy-providing substances. Therefore, it might be well to study the food-value tables throughout the book and become familiar with the amount and distribution of energy provided by one standard serving[1] of the various common foods.

Metabolism of Proteins

Proteins are complex chemical compounds, made up of many types of amino acids, or "building blocks." They have many uses in the body and provide energy as a secondary function.

Scientists have learned, first from experiments with rats and later with adult man, that normally only eight specific amino acids must be absorbed intact and that the other kinds needed can be manufactured by the body from these eight. Possibly children do not manufacture two other amino acids (*histidine* and *arginine*) rapidly enough for growth needs, and these also should be present in their foods. These

---

[1] Standard serving as specified by U. S. Department of Agriculture Leaflet 424, 1957.

amino acids that must be pre-formed (a part of the foods) are known as the *essential amino acids*. They have been identified as *lysine, leucine, isoleucine, tryptophane, phenylalanine, threonine, valine,* and *methionine* for the adult, plus *histidine* and *arginine* for children.

Different amounts of each of the eight or ten essential amino acids are required. The amount of each provided by the diet is dependent upon the types and amounts of food eaten.

A protein that as the sole protein of the diet will maintain life and provide for the normal growth of the body is known as a *complete protein*. A protein that will maintain life but will not support growth is referred to as a *partially complete protein*. A protein that will neither maintain life nor promote growth is an *incomplete protein*. The definitions may be misleading as the quantity is as important as the quality, therefore, too little complete protein in the diet may be as limiting as the taking of only one incomplete protein.

A protein that is lacking in one essential amino acid can be eaten with a protein that has a large amount of the missing amino acid, and the latter is said to *supplement* the first. This ability of the proteins of one food to supplement the proteins of another food has economic as well as nutritional importance.

Proteins differ in not only the kinds of amino acids present but also in the number of each and the arrangement of them, thus the possible number of proteins is great.

The numbers and kinds of proteins and their locations in our bodies are factors to be considered. One usually remembers that muscle tissue, blood plasma, skin, hair, and nails contain protein but may over look the fact that the framework of the bone, the enzymes that digest the foods and control the metabolism of the body, some of the hormones controlling the body processes, and even tears contain proteins. The proteins of each specific part of the body have definite compositions. Thus, the body must be furnished with specified amino acids in sufficient amounts for the building of each part of the body.

If some of the amino acids needed for building any part of the body are in short supply in relation to the other amino acids present, the situation can be likened to building a house. If materials are delivered for a large frame for a house but only enough foundation material for a small house, only a small house can be built unless more foundation is purchased. If the small house is built the excess material for the frame will be used for other purposes. In the case of protein building when any one amino acid is in short amount the excess amino acids are used for energy or stored as fat unless supplementary foods supply the missing amino acids. Supplementary foods should be eaten at the same meal as the foods containing the incomplete protein because there is no storage of amino acids.

Proteins differ from other energy supplying nutrients in that they contain nitrogen in addition to carbon, hydrogen, and oxygen. The proteins can be used for energy only after the liver has removed the nitrogen portion from the amino-acid molecules, which leaves a compound not unlike carbohydrate or fat. When this new compound is not needed for energy it can be converted into glucose and then into glycogen (animal starch) or fat. The nitrogen portion can be attached to a fragment of another amino acid or possibly to a carbohydrate fragment, and the new molecule formed is an amino acid. This exchange does take place to some extent. When the nitrogen portion is not used for building new molecules, it is excreted from the body by way of the kidneys. When this portion is excreted some of the carbon is taken with it, and thus proteins become expensive in terms of energy food.

Undue weight should not be given to the differences in the proteins, because all foods that provide proteins, contain several kinds of protein (gelatine is an exception). However, the mixture of proteins found in some foods seems to be more favorable for maintenance and growth than the mixtures found in other foods.

In the foregoing evaluation of protein quality it has been assumed that all other essential nutrients are present in the diet in favorable amounts. However, the presence of certain vitamins, especially niacin, has been found to be a necessary factor in protein adequacy.

Total amount of protein needed each day by adults under ordinary conditions is dependent on the amount of protein in their bodies, the amount of protein used for energy, and the quality of proteins eaten, but not on the amount of work performed. A lean man weighing 200 pounds will have more protein-containing tissue than a fat man of the same weight and will require more protein than the fat man. This same lean man will need more protein than a man weighing only 125 pounds but doing enough work to require the amount of Calories used by the lean heavier man.

It is assumed that unless unusual demands such as burns, infection, pregnancy, and anemia tax the protein supply, that 1 gram per kilogram (2.2 pounds) of body weight each day will maintain an adult; and 1½ grams per kilogram will allow for growth as well as maintenance of a child. Again it should be stressed that these estimates are based on the assumption that the Calorie needs are met and only excess proteins are used for fuel.

At least one-third of the protein of the diet should be derived from animal sources. One serving of meat (4 ounces) is suggested for this purpose, but there are many alternates, for example, one pint of milk; two ounces of cheese; or 1 egg, plus 1 ounce of cheese or 1 cupful of milk.

The functions of proteins in the body are said to be those of building, maintaining (including repairing), and regulating (hormones and enzymes), but, as has been shown, these processes involve manufacturing a large number of complex and specific protein molecules from relatively few simple molecules, the amino acids.

The individual person has two responsibilities in the task of keeping all of the parts of the body supplied with protein:

(1) To eat a variety of protein foods so that the amino acids necessary for building the various proteins of the body will be present.

(2) To have adequate Calories from either carbohydrate or fat to meet the daily energy needs. Unless the adequate energy is supplied, the body will remove the nitrogen portion from the protein and use the remainder for energy rather than for building body tissues.

Metabolism of Carbohydrate

Sugars, starches, glycogen, and cellulose are called carbohydrates. This name was given them because they contain carbon, hydrogen, and oxygen, and the hydrogen and oxygen are in the same proportion as is found in water (*hydrate*). The simplest of the carbohydrates are known as *monosaccharides*. This indicates that they are composed of one (*mono*) sugar (*saccharide*). Next in complexity are the *disaccharides* (two sugars), and the most complex are the *polysaccharides* (many sugars).

Glucose, fructose, and galactose are the monosaccharides important in nutrition. Glucose is widespread in nature and is the principal form to which all complex carbohydrates are reduced during digestion. Sucrose (cane and beet sugar), lactose (milk sugar), and maltose (malt sugar) are the three disaccharides that have nutritional significance. They are all reduced to monosaccharides, or simple sugars, during digestion. Lactose is thought by some physicians and bacteriologists to be of special value in maintaining the bacterial growth in the intestinal tract. The discussion of vitamins will point up the need for a favorable growth of friendly bacteria in the intestines.

The polysaccharides that are of importance in nutrition are starch, glycogen, and cellulose. The starch and glycogen contain many glucose molecules and can be converted to glucose during digestion. Cellulose, a woody or fibrous material, is only softened by both cooking and digestion and cannot be absorbed. It acts as bulk and as such is essential to nutrition.

Regardless of the original source of carbohydrate, all forms are digested to and absorbed as simple sugar, and therefore have the same function in the body. The simple sugars (monosaccharides), absorbed into the blood stream, are transported to the liver, then distributed to the body tissues where they are used primarily for energy. Nutritionists agree that complete oxidation for the release of energy from carbohydrates cannot occur unless thiamine and phosphorus are present in the tissues.

A limited amount of glucose may be utilized in the formation of certain amino acids, however, this change cannot take place unless the nitrogen portion that has been removed from other amino acids is present in the liver.

Some simple sugars not immediately needed for energy are reformed into a complex carbohydrate, glycogen, which is stored principally in the liver. Concentration of glycogen in the liver may become very great and account for as much as 10 per cent of its weight. Glycogen can easily be converted back to glucose to replace sugar that has been removed from the blood by the tissues of the body.

Carbohydrates that are not immediately oxidized or converted to glycogen are changed to fat and stored as such. The total amount of glycogen in the muscles of any individual seldom reaches more than ¼ pound whereas the amount of fat may be several pounds.

Metabolism of Fat

Fats are composed of carbon, hydrogen, and oxygen but in proportions quite different from that found in carbohydrates. All true fat molecules yield one glycerol and three molecules of fatty acids when they are digested, thus they are termed triglycerides. Each fat molecule contains one, two, or three kinds of fatty acids. As no special significance is given to the majority of the fatty acids they will not be listed here, and only those that are essential for certain specialized functions in nutrition will be discussed. The compositions of these fatty acids are specific, thus the foods must contain the special fatty acids necessary for these functions. These particular fatty acids are termed *essential fatty acids* because the body does not have the mechanism necessary for forming them from other fatty acids. *Arachidonic* and possibly *linolenic* and *linoleic* are the essential fatty acids. The quantity needed is very small and they seem to be distributed very widely in the foods. Therefore, they probably are not lacking in diets containing a variety of fats.

Apart from the vital role that fats play in metabolism, they are important in the diet as carriers (solvents) for certain necessary nutrients, especially the fat-soluble vitamins.

Fat not used for energy or specialized tissues is stored as reserve fuel in inactive fat-storing tissues. These tissues are referred to as *adipose*. Whether or not the fat stored is derived directly from food fats or from carbohydrates does not seem to matter, thus, it would seem that fats and carbohydrates are interchangeable for this purpose.

Some deposits of fat in the body are highly desirable, not only for the storage of energy materials, but also to pad viscera against jars, regulate body temperature, and even for enhancing one's appearance.

Fatty deposits were once generally believed to be inert, but some fat from these stores is constantly being used, and fat from the daily food intake replaces it. If the body weight is being held constant the amount deposited equals the amount removed.

If excess fat is to be removed it must be remembered that wherever the fat comes from, the food or the body, 1 gram yields approximately 9 Calories. Thus to lose 10 pounds of body fat, the total food intake for the entire reducing period must be lowered about 40,000 Calories below the real need. Ten pounds of fat would not be accumulated in one day or even one week, therefore, one should not assume that it can be lost hurriedly. It would be most satisfactory if one could lose it as slowly as it was accumulated.

FUNCTIONS OF VITAMINS IN THE BODY

The vitamins are defined as organic catalysts that are derived from a source outside the body, usually food. Like enzymes and hormones, which are also organic catalysts but are secreted by the body, vitamins regulate the rate of an action, and in only one or two special instances do they enter into any action. Like all catalysts they are needed in very minute amounts, but in spite of this, as their name implies, they are vital to our existence.

The first of the vitamins was discovered in 1912. The history of the work leading to this discovery and the development of the large volume of knowledge that has accrued to date concerning this first and other vitamins reads like something out of a fairy tale. For those students who are especially interested in this work it is suggested that they read References 5, 6, 7, 10, and 12 at the end of this chapter.

The functions of the various vitamins have been found to be inter-related with each other and with other nutrients. Many vitamins have been found to work as parts of certain enzymes, or they may act as catalysts to start the action of an enzyme. Under this latter condition they are known as *coenzymes*. It is beyond the scope of this book to deal with all of the intricacies involved, and the following discussion is confined to the over-all effects vitamins produce and the physiological evidences of their absence or suboptimal intakes, that is, deficiency symptoms.

Measurements of the vitamins are quoted in either weights or as International Units (*I.U.*). In order that the student may be able to visualize the small amounts used, these weights and measures will be discussed in considerable detail. The weights used are usually milli-grams or micrograms, and since the average person thinks originally in pounds and ounces a comparison between the two weight systems is necessary.

1 ounce is equivalent to 28.35 grams.
1 gram is equivalent to 1000 milligrams, therefore,
1 milligram is equivalent to 1/28,350 ounce.
1 milligram is equivalent to 1000 micrograms, therefore,
1 microgram is equivalent to 1/28,350,000 ounce.
1 milligram, or 1/28,350 ounce, may be expressed as 0.000035 ounce.
1 microgram, or 1/28,350,000 ounce, may be expressed as 0.000000035 ounce.

If one needed 75 milligrams of a vitamin it could be thought of as 0.002525 ounce or 75/28,350 ounce, and in a similar manner if one needed 2000 micrograms it could be thought of as 2 milligrams or as 0.000070 ounce or 2/28,350 ounce. Visualizing these very small amounts enables one to understand why the vitamins of the foods can-not be seen.

The International Unit is more abstract than the weight system and is used only for vitamin A and vitamin D values of foods. It was developed as a means of relating a rate of growth made by an experi-mental animal (rat) to the amount of a vitamin the animal had con-sumed. This method of measuring was needed for all vitamins before their chemical compositions were known. Today it is used only for those vitamins that may occur in food in forms that do not have vitamin activity (*precursor*) but that the body can change to vitamins. Using vitamin A as an example, the International Unit is defined as the value that is equal to 0.6 microgram of pure beta carotene. This was originally determined by feeding test rats daily a portion of food that would produce on an average the same gain in weight as occurred in a group of similar rats fed daily 0.6 microgram of pure beta carotene. Today the comparison is made by chemical means.

Vitamins naturally divide into two general classes, those that will dissolve in fat or substances that will dissolve fat (*fat-soluble*), and those that will dissolve in water (*water-soluble*). The fat-soluble vitamins are A, D, K, and E, and the water-soluble include ascorbic acid (vitamin C) and the entire B-complex (thiamine, riboflavin, niacin, B_{12}, etc.).

The vitamins were originally assigned letters, but today when many have been chemically identified many have been given names. The beginning student is advised to learn the names whenever they have been assigned rather than use the letter.

Vitamin A

Vitamin A is a colorless, tasteless, fat-soluble substance found only in animal fats. Substances that can be changed to Vitamin A (precursors of vitamin A, or pro-vitamin A) occur in plant tissues. These substances are the natural orange-yellow coloring matter that is seen clearly in carrots and is also associated with the green plant pigment. Pigments imparting this color to vegetables and fruits make up the group of substances collectively known as carotenoids (see Chapter 8). When vitamin A occurs naturally in foods it is referred to as preformed as opposed to that which the body derives from carotene.

Vitamin A affects many life processes including growth, reproduction, lactation, sight, skin, and even length of life. The effect of vitamin A on growth is perhaps the most striking because in experimental animals it is possible to demonstrate that growth occurs in direct proportion to the amount of vitamin A consumed. This relationship is maintained until the amount of the vitamin needed for maximum growth is reached.

An optimum level of vitamin A during growth not only produces a larger body but also better muscular development and tone, longer and stronger bones, and better teeth than are developed when the vitamin intake is limited. Any type of growth requires vitamin A, therefore, quantities should be increased over normal intake during pregnancy and the period of milk production (*lactation*). The amount of vitamin A in the diet not only affects quantity of milk secreted but also the vitamin A content of the milk.

Vitamin A is directly involved in chemical changes in the eye upon which sight is dependent. This is evidenced by night-blindness (difficulty in adjusting the eye to dim lights) when too little vitamin A has been consumed.

Vitamin A has been shown to play a vital role in maintaining healthy epithelial tissue; that is, the outer layer of the skin and linings of the respiratory, alimentary, and urinary tracts, and other similar tissues. Since microorganisms enter through weakened or less healthy tissues, it is said that vitamin A assists in preventing infections. Vitamin A does not prevent the growth of bacteria but only prevents breaks in the skin where the bacteria can lodge and grow. With insufficient vitamin A the skin may become abnormally dry so that it feels leathery or even horny to the touch, and it may slough off in scales.

In animal experiments using a diet that had been proven adequate for growth and reproduction, the vitamin A content of the diet was increased. As a result the first generation as well as successive generations lived longer than animals on a low vitamin A intake. The useful life was increased even more than the span of life, that is, the animals aged slowly.

Although optimum quantities of vitamin A have proven to be beneficial, excessive quantities should be avoided unless prescribed by a physician. Overdoses of vitamin A may be as dangerous as underdoses. The symptoms of overdoses are fissures of the lips, loss of hair, dry skin, and jaundice. These symptoms occur 6 to 15 months after the beginning of excessive doses. The symptoms disappear within 3 days after the vitamin is discontinued.

When more vitamin A is consumed than the body has immediate use for, it is stored. The principal place of storage is the liver, thus livers of all animals are one of man's best sources of the pre-formed nutrient. One serving (100 grams, raw) of beef or lamb liver will normally provide 40,000 I.U. of vitamin A. Calf and pork livers are less potent but are still extraordinarily good sources (30,000 I.U. per 100 grams). Only a few people make use of fish liver, but fish liver oils such as cod liver oil are used universally. Although primarily thought of as sources of vitamin D, these oils are very rich in vitamin A.

Kidney, egg yolk, butter, and milk products containing butterfat are also sources of pre-formed vitamin A, but the amount present varies according to the amount of vitamin A and carotene present in the feed of the animals.

The intensity of the natural yellow color in fruits and vegetables is an indication of the concentration of carotenoid pigment and therefore of potential vitamin A values. Carotenoids are invariably found with chlorophyll, the green pigment. Tomatoes have considerable carotene, but the red pigment camouflages the yellow pigment.

Vitamin D

Vitamin D is closely related to a class of chemical compounds known as *sterols*, some of which are transformed into vitamin D when they are exposed to *ultraviolet* light. This exposure is known as *irradiation*, and one sterol is known as *7,dehydro-cholesterol*. When vitamin D occurs naturally in a food it is said to be pre-formed.

One of our principal sources of ultraviolet rays is the sun, and when the body is exposed to the direct rays of the sun or to artificially produced ultraviolet light the 7,dehydro-cholesterol that lies just below the skin may be changed to vitamin D. Clouds, fog, and untreated glass may hold back these rays even though the rays that cause tanning or burning are admitted. Food containing 7,dehydro-cholesterol that is exposed to the ultraviolet light may also have vitamin D potency increased.

Vitamin D increases absorption of calcium and phosphorus from the intestine and is one of the substances essential for the proper formation and maintenance of the bones and teeth. Although a detailed description of bone growth is beyond the scope of this book, the function of vitamin D in metabolism includes bone formation.

In young growing people the main shaft or body of the long bone (See Fig. 112) is separated by the growing cartilagenous region from a smaller bone known as the head. The bone grows by forming new cartilage cells. As the new cartilage is formed the old cartilage cells

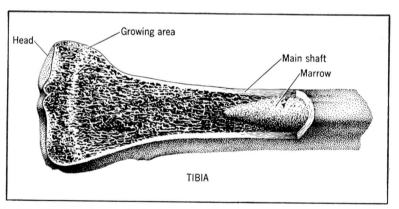

Fig. 112. The long bones of the body are filled with a lacey network of growing tissue.

degenerate, and mineral salts (mainly calcium phosphates) are deposited in the spaces between the cells. This process is known as *calcification*. Before the calcification process can proceed a cavity is formed in the center of the cartilage area and blood vessels invade it. It is by way of the blood vessels that the minerals are brought to the bone. At the time the blood vessels are formed, bone-forming cells develop and are deposited in the place of the degenerated cartilage cells. The exact process by which this is done is not known, but it is known that the bones cannot calcify unless adequate vitamin D, calcium, and phosphorus are present.

In the majority of cases poor calcification is not the fault of the bone, rather the blood does not contain enough calcium and phosphorus. Calcium and phosphorus cannot enter the blood stream in the absence of vitamin D. *Rickets*, a disease that is the result of poor calcification, can be said to be associated with a lack of vitamin D (Fig. 113).

When rickets occurs, the cartilage cells and the bone forming cells continue to develop, but, because they do not calcify, they are soft and tend to form large, soft, spongy ends to the bone. When weight or pressure is put on such bones they will bend. Two of the classical symptoms of the condition are "bowed legs" and "knock knees." Un-

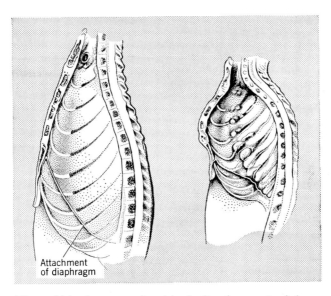

Attachment
of diaphragm

Fig. 113. The rachitic thorax on the right is shrunken, and misshapen as compared to a normal thorax.

fortunately these spongy growths do not disappear, thus when the bones do calcify they will have knobs at the ends, which tend to make the joints appear gnarled. Not only the legs and hands are affected but also the pelvic and chest region may become malformed.

Rickets, although not a fatal disease, may have other tragic results such as small stature, permanent deformity and crowded vital organs (see Fig. 113), and inability to give birth to children without Caesarian section.

When the bones are not forming normally as in the case of low vitamin D intake, growth of the entire skeleton is slowed. It has been shown that vitamin D in excess of the amount needed to prevent rickets may improve growth. A minimum amount of vitamin D is necessary for proper skeletal development, but an increase above the minimum neither increases calcium utilization nor seems to cause ill effect, unless dosages are excessive. Such doses will cause poor appetite, nausea, diarrhea, and headache. The symptoms disappear as soon as vitamin D doses are stopped.

The body is able to build up a reasonably large store of vitamin D from the excess taken, and this can be used in times of lowered intake. The principal organ of storage is the liver. Livers, therefore, are good food sources of vitamin D.

Vitamin K

Another fat-soluble nutrient is named vitamin K to indicate "koagulation-vitamin." As could be assumed from the name it assists with the clotting or coagulation of the blood. It is widespread in nature—cereals, animal tissues, and leafy vegetables. Also, intestinal microorganisms synthesize it. Little attention is given to vitamin K in meal planning since there is little likelihood of not obtaining enough if the recommended amounts of other nutrients are obtained from food sources.

Vitamin E

The need for vitamin E, a fat-soluble vitamin, in human nutrition has not been proved conclusively. It has been found to be essential for normal reproduction in rats. It is abundant in the general food supply, and if all other nutrients are present in adequate quantity vitamin E will, in all probability, be present.

Ascorbic Acid

The history of ascorbic acid and the events leading to its discovery have affected the histories of all nations (see Reference 6). When ascorbic acid is absent from the diet a condition known as *scurvy* develops. All through medical history references are found to substances that would either cure or prevent this disease. These remedies seem very crude today when it is known that fruits and vegetables are all that is needed.

Ascorbic acid (vitamin C) contributes to the building of our bodies by helping to form the substance that literally glues our cells together. This substance is called the *intercellular cementing* substance. This cementing substance is necessary for the formation of the walls of all the blood vessels, and any other continuous group of cells. An imaginative person can see all sorts of tragedies occurring within the body if the cementing substance is missing.

In general it might be said that all of the following conditions may occur to some degree when the intercellular cementing substance is low in amount or absent:

(1) Hemorrhages (blood escaping from the blood vessels) anywhere in the body. This not only causes pain, but also could lead to anemia.

(2) Anemia resulting from a failure of the bone marrow to produce normal blood cells.

(3) Structural changes in teeth and gums.

(4) Defective bone growth and calcification caused by improper development of the bone-forming tissues.

(5) Impaired heart muscles, which may result in an enlarged heart.

(6) Injury to the sex organs, which may prevent reproduction.

(7) Changes in all skeletal muscles.

Suboptimal levels of vitamin C in the diet may result in listlessness, minor complaints of vague pains, failure to perform mental work satisfactorily, low resistance to infectious diseases, and poor healing of wounds. These vague symptoms are difficult to recognize, and they may be more prevalent than is generally realized.

Vitamin C is not stored in the body, therefore it must be included regularly in the diet. The only significant dietary sources of vitamin C are fruits, vegetables, and liver. This vitamin is easily oxidized, and care should be taken to prevent oxidation both during storage and preparation.

The Vitamin B-Complex

A group of water-soluble vitamins classed as the B-complex is made up of many separate vitamins. These vitamins have little in common chemically except their ability to dissolve in water; they do, however, work together in performing many body functions. None of the members of this group is stored in the body. Thus the daily diet must contain adequate supplies. Originally the B-complex was extracted from a food source as one substance and it was thought that this one substance was responsible for all the effects that were observed when the extract was fed to experimental animals. Later it was demonstrated that at least two separate vitamins existed in the water extract, and they were assigned numbers. Thus one was termed vitamin B_1, and the other was known as B_2. Soon after this division was established discoveries were made which indicated that B_2 was made up of at least two separate substances. At approximately this time the numbering system became too burdensome because other vitamins were being identified and numbers were duplicated. Chemical compositions were also being identified. Therefore, names were given to some of these vitamins. "Thiamine" is the name given to the original B_1. In the following discussion names will be used in so far as they have been adopted.

Thiamine was discovered as an outgrowth of the study of a disease called *beri-beri*, which was common in the Orient. Thiamine or foods containing thiamine was found to both cure and prevent this disease.

Thiaminehydrochloride is a white crystalline substance, and usually has a bitter taste and a pungent odor. This vitamin gives the odor and flavor to most of the multi-vitamin preparations found on the market.

Thiamine has many uses in the body, but the longest-known uses are for growth, development, and for maintenance of the health of the nerves. Because of its unusual relationship to the nerves it is sometimes called the *anti-neuritic* vitamin.

Thiamine is also closely related to appetite, and a lack of this vitamin in the diet will cause a very abrupt drop in the appetite. When thiamine is increased the appetite promptly returns. Thiamine will promote appetite only when the loss of appetite is due to a lack of thiamine, that is, there are other causes for a low appetite.

The vigor of the contractions of the muscles of the stomach may be reduced when the amount of thiamine in the diet is reduced. This lowered activity occurs even before the loss of appetite. Later sluggishness of the muscles will extend to the intestinal tract and result in constipation.

Thiamine is necessary for reproduction and lactation, but just how this responsibility is shared with other nutrients also known to be necessary for these functions is not clear. Here again the dependence of one nutrient on another and the necessity of having all of these nutrients simultaneously must be stressed.

All of the body activities associated with thiamine are closely related, and perhaps all may be attributed to the fact that thiamine is necessary for the release of energy from carbohydrate. In this function, thiamine works as an enzyme activator or co-enzyme, however, it does not work alone, and it is believed that phosphorus, manganese, protein, and perhaps other vitamins are also necessary.

Suboptimal levels of thiamine may result in listlessness, easy fatigue, poor appetite, and nervous irritability. These symptoms may not be pronounced but at any degree of severity will interfere with normal activity. The loss of appetite will decrease the intake of other nutrients. The end result could be multiple deficiencies.

Riboflavin is essential for growth and for health at all ages. A diet poor in riboflavin over a long period of time will lead to digestive disturbances, general weakness, poor muscle tone, mental depression, poor condition of the skin and eyes, and low vitality. If the low intake is continued over a period of years the life may be shortened and the useful years of life may be drastically curtailed—physical signs of old age develop early. Riboflavin deficiency causes deterioration of certain parts of the eye that may be evidenced by sensitivity to light, dimness of vision, or "eyestrain." The mental depression may be evidenced by a poor sense of humor, a shortened attention span, or poor memory.

Again it should be stressed that riboflavin, like all other nutrients, does not work alone in any of these functions. It seems to be especially interrelated with thiamine, niacin, other B-complex vitamins, and minerals, especially iron.

Niacin is a substance that has been known to chemists for many years, but it has only recently been considered as an important part of the diet. Niacin first came into prominence as a cure for *pellagra*, a disease that was very common in the Southern states and other corn-eating areas of the world.

Pellagra is no longer common in the United States, but the sub-clinical symptoms—weakness, lassitude, poor appetite, and indigestion —still occur when diets are low in niacin. Headaches, sleeplessness, and poor memory also accompany low niacin intake.

Tryptophane, one of the essential amino acids, is a precursor of niacin. Thus the niacin content of a diet is related to the tryptophane content, and diets containing the recommended amount of animal protein are seldom deficient in niacin. Diets high in corn, which have long been associated with niacin deficiencies, are not limited in niacin but in tryptophane content.

Other B-complex vitamins that have been shown to be necessary in human nutrition are pantothenic acid, vitamin B_6, folic acid, vitamin B_{12}, and possibly biotin, choline, and inositol. No specific recommendations for the amounts needed of these members of the B-complex groups of vitamins have been spelled out in the recommendations of the Food and Nutrition board of the National Research Council. To date there has been no report of deficiencies of these substances when the recommended amounts of thiamine, riboflavin, and niacin have been obtained from diets containing a variety of foods.

Pantothenic acid is an essential part of one of the enzyme systems of the body and is a catalyst in the formation of co-enzyme A. The only physical symptom that has been associated with a low intake of this vitamin is "burning feet." The vitamin is widely distributed in nature and has been found in all forms of living things. Thus if one has an otherwise adequate diet, pantothenic acid will probably not be missing. It is believed that the bacteria normally living in the intestinal tract can produce a considerable amount of this vitamin.

Vitamin B_6 also functions as a co-enzyme. This is probably not a single vitamin. One of the few specific uses ascribed to it has been a relieving of nausea that occurs in early pregnancy.

Folic acid or folacin is involved in the formation of *hemoglobin*, the pigment of the red blood cell. Although it may have other uses none have definitely been proved.

Vitamin B_{12} (*cobalamin*), the cobalt-containing vitamin, is limited in its distribution and is believed to occur only in foods from animal sources such as meat, milk, and eggs. When vitamin B_{12} occurs in vegetables it is believed that it is derived from the bacteria of the soil and not directly from the vegetable.

Vitamin B_{12} is a factor in *pernicious anemia,* a disease in which the red blood cells are not properly formed. Vitamin B_{12} cannot pass through the intestinal wall unless a specific substance is present in the digestive tract. This substance is very obscure and is termed the *intrinsic factor.* This factor is now thought by some research workers to be an enzyme produced by the glands of the stomach, present in abundance in normal gastric secretions. Perhaps the absence of the intrinsic factor is the cause of pernicious anemia, because vitamin B_{12}

must be absorbed in order to be available for metabolic purposes. As emphasized previously, all nutrients must be absorbed into the blood stream before they become available for body activities.

FUNCTION OF MINERAL ELEMENTS IN THE BODY

Nutrients containing carbon, hydrogen, oxygen, and nitrogen have been discussed. However, other elements are also essential for growth and maintenance, and they are referred to as the *inorganic elements*. The inorganic elements needed for metabolic processes are collectively referred to as the *minerals*. They may also be called the *ash* content of the foods or the body as they are not combustible. These elements do not necessarily occur apart from carbon-containing (*organic material*) compounds, nor do they work alone. They may be an intricate part of organic compounds. For example, sulfur is one of the elements found in methionine, an amino acid. If they are not bound to an organic compound, they are usually bound to another mineral and are known as *salts*. In the process of metabolism they may be freed from their organic or mineral substances and act entirely independently of these constituents.

The minerals generally considered to be of importance in nutrition are listed below in the order of the amount found in the body:

(1) Calcium	(9) Manganese
(2) Phosphorus	(10) Copper
(3) Potassium	(11) Iodine
(4) Sulfur	(12) Cobalt
(5) Chlorine	(13) Fluorine
(6) Sodium	(14) Zinc
(7) Magnesium	(15) Molybdenum
(8) Iron	

It cannot be said with certainty whether all of these are essential, however, as they are always found in the body it is believed that they are. Much new information concerning all minerals is being collected at the present time by the use of so-called *tracer elements*. These are chemically marked elements used in research to watch the path of the individual elements through the body. It is expected that with the increased use of such techniques knowledge concerning the fate of all elements will be greatly clarified.

The minerals are absorbed from the intestinal tract into the blood stream and the amount of each that is absorbed depends upon several general factors:

(1) The presence of other nutrients.
(2) The need for the materials.
(3) The health of the individual.
(4) The form in which the mineral occurs.
(5) The concentration of the mineral.

Certain of the elements are considered together because they usually act together or in a similar manner. Calcium is usually associated with phosphorus, and iron with copper.

Calcium and Phosphorus

Calcium and phosphorus are absorbed from the intestinal tract with the aid of vitamin D. Both of these minerals are known to be needed in quantity for the formation and maintenance of bones and teeth. The absence of either calcium, phosphorus, or vitamin D results in insufficient mineral deposits for skeletal or tooth formation. The need for calcium and phosphorus is not confined solely to these tissues even though 99 per cent of the body calcium and 90 per cent of the body phosphorus are found in the bones and teeth.

Calcium is needed for coagulation of blood, maintenance of the right degree of firmness in the soft tissues, normal action of the heart muscle, normal general muscle contraction, and normal growth. Phosphorus is needed for every cell of the body. In addition to bone formation it participates in a great many of the activities that must be carried out in the body. The simple sugar that is to be oxidized and used for body energy must go through a number of different steps, several of which involve phosphorus. Phosphorus is also involved in the metabolism of protein.

Anything as substantial as a skeleton would appear to be fixed for life once it has reached its predestined size. However, the long bones are not solid, as they appear, but are filled with a lacework of bony material, blood vessels, and a fatty material. If the calcium needed for soft tissues is not provided in the diet, the lacy interior of the bones is utilized (see Fig. 112). In extreme cases of low-diet calcium, the bone may eventually be tapped, but bone is reluctant about releasing materials without replacements. Some replacement of minerals in the bony tissues is constantly being made, and the blood stream will contain calcium and phosphorus enroute to the bone, as well as the catabolized minerals.

Milk is one of the richest sources of calcium and phosphorus. As was pointed out in Chapter 1, one pint of milk per day in the American diet seems to be needed if an adequate supply of calcium is to be assured. Populations in countries where the milk supply is low may not show calcium deficiencies. This may be at least partially accounted for by these possibilities:

(1) These people may have other sources of calcium not usually contained in the diets of people in the United States such as bones of small fish, lime-treated corn products for tortillas, long cooking of bones in making meat stock; calcium extracted by the addition of acid to the water in which bones are cooked, or large intakes of certain leafy vegetables such as turnip and mustard greens.

(2) These people may have a total diet which might favor absorption.

(3) The bodies of these people may adjust and make more efficient use of the nutrients habitually consumed in minimum amounts than do those people who always have a large supply.

(4) Climatic conditions and the entire tempo of living might conceivably influence total body need for these minerals.

(5) Drinking water and other beverages may contain calcium.

Iron and Copper

Although they do not form a chemical union, iron and copper function together in many instances. Iron is needed in very small amounts, but its functions are vital since it is an integral part of the following substances:

(1) Color substance (*chromatin*) of every cell *nucleus.*

(2) Pigment of the red blood cells (*hemoglobin*).

(3) *Hemoglobin* of the muscle (*myoglobin*).

(4) Certain enzymes of the body (*cytochrome, cytochrome oxidase,* and *catalases*). Ninety per cent of the energy released in the tissue is said to be controlled by these enzymes.

The greater part of the body iron is found in the red blood cells (55 to 60 per cent). Thus any study of iron is closely related to a study of *anemia*, a disease in which there is a notable lack of hemoglobin. Appreciable quantities of iron are necessary for the formation of hemoglobin. A small quantity of copper also appears to be necessary in this process but only as a catalyst, and it does not appear in the finished product. Cobalt, riboflavin, folic acid, vitamin B_{12}, and possibly other substances seem to stimulate the production of red blood cells, which are formed continuously in red bone marrow, thus it could be said that they are necessary for the utilization of iron.

Hemoglobin consists of a particular type of protein combined with an iron-containing pigment, *heme*. Hemoglobin is encased with other substances in microscopic, biconcave disks, the red blood cells (*erythrocytes*). The hemoglobin picks up oxygen as the blood is circulated through the lungs and carries it to the stationary cells throughout the body. As soon as the oxygen is released to the cells, the red blood cells are ready to return to the lungs, but the number of trips they can make each day is limited. If there is an insufficient amount of hemoglobin in each cell, most of the erythrocytes go the rounds with a limited supply of oxygen. This results in limited oxygen for the production of heat and energy. This means decreased work output and forced curtailment of activities because one tires very quickly. In other words, the bodily need for oxygen cannot be filled if the quantity of hemoglobin is low.

Deficiency in any of the materials needed for the complete functioning of the red blood cells impairs their oxygen-carrying capacity. These deficiencies resulting in anemia may be caused by:

(1) An insufficient number of erythrocytes, or low blood count—bleeding or internal destruction of erythrocytes, as well as insufficient production of cells.

(2) A normal number of erythrocytes with the cells not containing their full quota of hemoglobin—insufficient iron, copper, and protein.

(3) Malformed erythrocytes resulting from a lack of protein or the vitamins necessary for the formation of the fibrous, spongy network (*stroma*) of the cell—this deficiency is known as pernicious anemia.

Although deficiencies of iron and copper result in anemia, the disease can be caused by other dietary deficiencies, infections, or loss of blood. Notable among the other dietary deficiencies is lack of protein.

The body is very frugal with its supply of hemoglobin iron. When the erythrocyte has served its term, the iron is salvaged and stored in the liver and spleen, and the rest of the cell is discarded. In spite of this saving quality, iron is continually lost and thus must be replaced by way of the food supply.

Iodine

Iodine functions in the body as an essential part of *thyroxin*, the hormone secreted by the thyroid gland. This gland is one of the many *endocrine* glands, each of which secretes one or more hormones. The *hormones* are organic catalysts secreted into the blood stream and then carried throughout the body where they exert their specific controls.

Thyroxin controls the rate of energy metabolism. In this capacity iodine affects the basal metabolic rate of the body and therefore its energy requirement. When iodine is in short supply the thyroid gland, in an effort to produce a sufficient amount of thyroxin, may enlarge, and this condition is known as *simple goiter*. When the iodine supply is very low even the enlarged gland cannot produce enough thyroxin, and the energy metabolism will be slowed down. The person becomes sluggish and very sensitive to cold, the muscles become flabby, and the mental processes are slowed down. When the iodine deficiency occurs in children the growth of their long bones may be stunted and mental processes permanently slowed. In these extreme cases thyroxin must be given; iodine alone will not be completely corrective.

Under certain abnormal conditions the gland may produce excessive quantities of thyroxin. In such cases the person will become nervous and irritable and have a very high rate of energy metabolism. In extreme cases of overactivity the gland enlarges, the eyes protrude, and the condition is known as *exophthalmic goiter*. Because gland enlargement can be either a deficiency or an excess, medical diagnosis of enlargements of the thyroid gland should be sought before dietary corrective measures are instituted.

Fluorine

A minute amount of fluorine in the diet is considered desirable to decrease the incidence of tooth decay (*dental caries*). Whether fluorine is essential to any other process of the body is unknown. The effectiveness of fluorine in dental health during the period of tooth formation has been stressed for children, and adults may also be benefitted.

An oversupply of fluorine during the tooth-forming period may cause a condition known as *mottled enamel*. Mottled enamel develops during calcification of the teeth and may be prevalent in areas where the drinking water has a natural high fluoride content. The amount of fluorine is very critical, and therefore great care should be exercised in its use. The amount of fluoride considered desirable is one part of fluoride for each one million parts of water. This minute amount does not affect the flavor of the water.

One of the ways to increase the fluoride content of the diet is to add a fluoride salt to the drinking water. Many cities have instituted a practice of fluoridation of the entire water supply. Since, in many cities, this practice must be approved by the city population it becomes a matter for a widespread education program.

Approximately a decade and one-half ago investigators at the National Institutes of Health, along with other workers over the United States, demonstrated by use of statistical evidence that in communities where the drinking water naturally contained fluoride that natives had as much as 60 per cent less tooth decay than natives of communities whose water did not contain fluorine. If the people resided in the community where the fluoride occurred until their teeth were completely formed, they retained much of the immunity to decay even when they drank fluoride-free water later.

Studies have also been made after fluorides have been added to the water supply and the results were as good as when the fluorides occurred naturally. If sturdy teeth can be secured by such a simple method it would seem unwise to deprive children of good teeth throughout a lifetime by preventing the fluoridation of a water supply. Fluoridation will not eliminate all caries, but it will help a great deal. This, coupled with a good diet, should do much to make the teeth of future generations last a lifetime.

People should be warned against promiscuous use of tablets, mouth washes, and dentifrices containing fluorides. Excessive use of these could conceivably raise the fluoride content of the diet to the point where mottled enamel occurs.

Trace Elements

Cobalt, molybdenum, manganese, and zinc in addition to copper, iodine, and fluorine, are known to be essential in minute amounts. These seven elements are known as *essential trace elements* because just a "trace" of each suffices for the necessary physiological action. *Cobalt* is an integral part of vitamin B_{12}, *manganese* is necessary in the functions of thiamine and niacin, and both *molybdenum* and *zinc* have been shown to be activators of enzymes.

Trace elements are widespread in nature. When a mixed diet is eaten, chances of deficiencies are remote.

There are forty or more nutrients known to be needed to build and maintain healthy bodies and to provide energy for activities. Physiological function, and chemical-physical properties of the nutrients in the science of nutrition are discussed. The nutrients are categorized

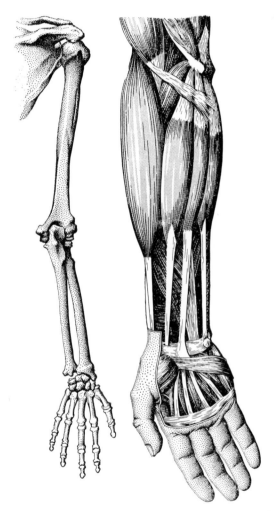

Fig. 114. A wide variety of foods is necessary to supply the nutrients necessary to form the various parts of the body and to support its activities.

THE FUNCTION OF THE NUTRIENTS IN THE BODY · *479*

into six classes, namely, proteins, carbohydrates, fats, minerals, vitamins, and water. The interdependence among single nutrients and classes of nutrients is stressed along with the sensibleness of providing a constant supply of replacements to the body by moderate food intakes at regular intervals (Fig. 114).

Reading List

1. Bogert, L. J., 1954, *Nutrition and Physical Fitness,* W. B. Saunders Co., Philadelphia.
2. Council on Foods and Nutrition, American Medical Association, 1959, "Vitamin preparation as dietary supplements and as therapeutic agents," *J. Amer. Med. Assoc.,* **169**:41.
3. DeCoursey, R. M., 1955, *The Human Organism,* McGraw-Hill Book Co., New York, Chapter 15.
4. Food and Nutrition Board, National Research Council, Recommended Dietary Allowances, Rev. 1958, Publication No. 589 of the National Research Council, National Academy of Sciences, Washington, D. C.
5. King, C. G., 1959, "Advances in Nutrition," *J. Amer. Diet. Assoc.,* **35**:109.
6. Krehl, W. A., 1953, Biography of James Lind," *J. Nutrition,* **50**:3.
7. Jansen, B. C. P., 1950, "Biography of C. Eijkman," *J. Nutrition,* **42**:3.
8. Leverton, R. M., 1954, *Food Becomes You,* University of Nebraska Press, Lincoln.
9. Leverton, R. M., 1957, "Distorting facts into fads," *J. Amer. Diet. Assoc.,* **33**:793.
10. McCollum, E. V., 1957, *History of Nutrition,* Houghton Mifflin Co., Boston.
11. Phillips, P. H., 1956, "Recent progress in dietary research and dental caries," *J. Amer. Diet. Assoc.,* **32**:110.
12. Sebrell, W. H., 1955, "Biography of Joseph Goldberger," *J. Nutrition,* **55**:3.
13. Sherman, H. C., and C. S. Lanford, 1957, *Essentials of Nutrition,* The Macmillan Co., New York.
14. Watt, B. K., and A. L. Merrill, 1950, *Composition of Foods—Raw, Processed, Prepared,* United States Department of Agriculture, Agr. Handbook No. 8.

APPENDIX **A** . . . MASTER MIXES

THAT CAN BE

COMPOUNDED FROM

PREMEASURED

INGREDIENTS

I. QUICK-BREADS MIX

Ingredients	Market Unit* No.	Market Unit* Size	Weight, oz.	Approximate Measure
Flour, all purpose	1	5-lb. sack	80	20 C.
Sugar, powdered	1	1-lb. box	16	3½ C.
Baking powder (sulfate-phosphate)		. . .	4	½ C.
Salt		. . .	1½	3 Tb.
Milk solids, instant	2	1-qt envelopes	8	3 C.
Fat, hydrogenated	1	1-lb. can	16	2 C.
Totals			125½ oz.	29 C.

* If purchased in the market units listed, no measuring will be necessary.

Method of combining mix: Empty dry ingredients into a large dishpan or heavy paper sack and mix thoroughly (sift any ingredients that have small lumps). Cut or lightly rub the fat into the dry ingredients until the crumb resembles corn meal. Store in an air-tight container.

Muffins

Measure 2 C. mix into bowl. Add 1 beaten egg and ¾ C. water. Mix only enough to wet the dry ingredients (15–20 strokes). Fill oiled muffin pans ⅔ full; let stand 15–20 minutes; bake at 425° F approximately 20 minutes. Makes 12 (2-inch) muffins.

Muffin Variations

1. *Apple cinnamon*—add ¾ C. (1 large apple) chopped apple and 1 tsp. cinnamon to mix before proceeding as for plain muffins.
2. *Sesame seed*—add ¼ C. toasted sesame seeds to mix before proceeding as for plain muffins.
3. *Banana*—reduce water to ½ C. and mix with ½ C. mashed ripe banana.
4. *Bacon*—add ¼ C. crisp bacon bits to mix before proceeding as for plain muffins.

Fritters

One C. mix, 1 beaten egg, ½ C. water, ½ C. chopped fruit or vegetable (drained crushed pineapple, chopped sour cherries, chopped apple, chopped peach, corn, etc.). Mix as for muffins. Heat fat to 365° F. Dip a metal cooking spoon into the hot fat then scoop up about 1 Tb. batter and lower it into the hot fat. The hot fat on the spoon should allow the fritter to slide easily into the fat. Repeat until the surface of the fat is covered with fritters; cook each fritter at least 3 minutes. Remove from fat and drain on absorbent paper. Shake in bag with sugar to coat surface (corn fritters are usually served with syrup).

Shortcake

Measure 2 C. mix into bowl. Add ½ C. water; stir only until dry ingredients are wet. Turn onto floured cloth; pat to ¾ inch thickness; cut into desired shapes; and place on lightly oiled cooky sheet. Let stand 15 minutes; bake at 425° F 12–15 minutes or until light brown.

Waffles

Two eggs, separated, 1½ C. mix, 1 C. water. Mix as for muffins except that egg whites are stiffly beaten and folded into the batter.

II. CAKE MIX

Method of combining mix: Empty the dry ingredients into a large dishpan or heavy paper bag and mix thoroughly (sift any ingredients that have lumps). Cut or rub the fat into the dry ingredients until no discernible lumps remain—ingredients must be intimately mixed. Divide the total volume into eight 10-ounce portions (approximately 2 C.) and store in plastic bags or glass jars (tightly covered) until ready for use.

This mix is somewhat sweeter and richer than commercial cake mixes and does not require as much water as commercial mixes of

| Ingredients | Market Unit* | | Weight, oz. | Approximate Measure |
	No.	Size		
Flour, cake	1	2-lb. box	32	9 C.
Sugar, extra-fine	1	2-lb. box	32	4½ C.
Baking powder (sulfate-phosphate)		. . .	3	⅓ C.
Salt		. . .	1	2 Tb.
Milk solids, instant nonfat	1	1-qt. envelope	4	1½ C.
Fat, hydrogenated	1	1-lb. can	16	2 C.
Totals			88 oz.	17⅓ C.

* If purchased in the market units listed, no measuring will be necessary.

equivalent weight. Products made from the mix are velvety and have a slightly lower volume than products from commercial mixes.

Cakes

Two C. mix, 1 egg, and ⅓ C. water. Add half the water and the egg to the mix and beat 150 strokes (1 minute); add the remainder of the water and ½ tsp. flavoring and beat 150 strokes (1 minute). Put batter into baking pans and allow to stand 15–20 minutes at room temperature. Bake at 375° F; layers require 25–30 minutes, cupcakes require 15 minutes.

This amount of batter yields 12 (2-inch) cupcakes or one 9-inch layer.

Cake Variations

1. *Orange*—add 1 tsp. grated orange rind and use orange juice in place of water.
2. *Spice*—add 1 tsp. cinnamon, ¼ tsp. cloves, ¼ tsp. nutmeg.
3. *Applesauce*—add ½ C. chopped nuts, ½ C. raisins, 1 tsp. cinnamon, ¼ tsp. cloves, and use ½ C. thick *unsweetened* applesauce for liquid instead of water.
4. *Poppyseed*—add ½ C. poppyseeds to plain cake after beating is finished.
5. *Chocolate*—melt 1 square (1 oz.) bitter chocolate; cool; add to mixture with egg.
6. *Black-walnut*—use ¼ tsp. black-walnut flavoring and add ⅓ C. chopped black walnuts.
7. *Caramel*—substitute 2 Tb. caramel syrup for 2 Tb. water.

III. PASTRY MIX

Ingredients	Market Unit* No.	Market Unit* Size	Weight, oz.	Approximate Measure
Flour, all purpose	1	5-lb. sack	80	20 C.
Salt		. . .	1½	3 Tb.
Fat, hydrogenated	1	3-lb. can	48	6 C.
Totals			129½ oz.	26 C.

* If purchased in the market units listed, no measuring will be necessary.

Method of combining mix: Empty flour into a large dishpan, heavy paper sack, or onto a large square of heavy brown paper; add salt and mix thoroughly (sift any ingredients that have lumps). Cut or lightly rub the fat into the flour until the fat particles are the size of small peas. Store in an air-tight container.

Pastry

Place 1 C. (gently packed) or approximately 5 oz. (135 gm.) mix into mixing bowl; sprinkle with 2–2½ Tb. water or milk; gather into a ball and proceed as directed for pastry (see p. 264).

This amount of pastry yields one 9-inch crust.

APPENDIX B . . GLOSSARY OF TERMS*

Acid. Any substance containing a replaceable hydrogen ion which reacts with an alkali to form water and a salt. Has a tart taste.

A la Carte (Fr.). Any foods prepared to order.

A la King. Any food, especially meat, served with a thick rich white sauce. It may be seasoned with chopped bell peppers, pimentoes, and/or nuts.

Alkali. Any caustic substance that can neutralize an acid and has a pH higher than 7.0.

Alkaloid. One of the large group of organic alkaline substances usually having a bitter taste.

Amyl. Starch or pertaining to starch.

Antioxidant. A substance that prevents a chemical union with oxygen; usually the antioxidant itself has an affinity for oxygen and combines with it.

Antipasto (It.). An assortment of appetizers.

Appetite. Any desire, but especially for food; however, not necessarily hunger.

Aspic. A jellied dish made with meat stock and/or vegetable juice.

Astringent. Any substance that causes surface tissues of the body to contract.

Atmospheric pressure. The pressure exerted on the earth's surface by the atmosphere. This is 14.7 lbs. per sq. in. at sea level.

Au gratin (Fr.). Food sprinkled with cheese and then browned.

Au jus (Fr.). Served with its natural juice or gravy.

Au lait (Fr.). With milk.

Au naturel (Fr.). Plain or simple; natural.

Avitaminosis. A condition of the body caused by deficiency of a single vitamin. Avitaminoses—deficiency of more than one vitamin.

Bake. To cook with dry heat; when applied to meat it usually is referred to as roasting.

Baste. To ladle liquid over meat, fowl, or other food while roasting or baking to prevent drying of the surface.

Béchamel Sauce (Fr.). One of the basic white sauces.

Benzoate of Soda. A food preservative used in the processing of many foods. The Federal Food and Drug Administration permits its use to a maximum of 0.2 per cent providing it is listed on the label with the ingredients.

Biological test. A test involving experiments on organisms.

Bisque (Fr.). A thick cream soup or stew usually made from shellfish. Also used to denote a rich frozen dessert that contains macaroons and/or nuts.

Blanch. To dip first into very hot water and then into very cold water. This procedure may be used to destroy enzymes and to loosen skins. Also refers to bleaching as of celery or lettuce.

Boil. To cook in water that is at the boiling temperature.

---

* Definitions apply only to usage in foods and nutrition.

Boiling point. The temperature at which the vapor pressure of the liquid is equal to the atmospheric pressure; at sea level pure water reaches boiling at 212° F or 100° C for standard conditions.

Borsch. A Russian soup containing beets.

Brew. To steep.

Brine. A strong salt (saline) solution.

British thermal unit (Btu). A unit of heat; the amount of heat necessary to raise the temperature of one pound of water one degree Fahrenheit (from 59° F to 60° F).

Café (Fr.). Coffee. Common use indicates a public place where coffee is served.

Café au Lait (Fr.). Coffee with hot milk, usually half milk and half coffee.

Café Noir (Fr.). Black coffee.

Calorie. A unit of heat; the large (Grand) or kilocalorie is the amount of heat needed to raise one kilogram of water from 15° C to 16° C. This is the Calorie used in nutrition. The small calorie is the amount of heat needed to raise one gram of water one degree centigrade.

Canape (Fr.). A very small sandwich used mainly for hors d'oeuvres.

Carbohydrate. A class of compounds composed of carbon, hydrogen, and oxygen. The term originates from the fact that carbon is present and the hydrogen and oxygen are present in the same ratio in these compounds as it is in water. Sugars such as glucose and sucrose, gums, pectin, starches, and cellulose are typical carbohydrates.

Carême, A. Chef to King George IV; many dishes are named for him.

Casein. One of the proteins of milk.

Catalyst. A substance which changes the speed of a reaction but is not affected by the reaction.

Cellulose. A carbohydrate that is the principal supporting framework of plants; not broken down in digestion.

Clabber. To form a smooth curd as in milk or cheese.

Coagulate. To convert into a soft solid mass, by chemical action or heat; to curdle, clot, congeal.

Colloidal Solution. A dispersion of substances of colloidal size. Colloids are aggregates of molecules invisible even in an ordinary microscope.

Cream. To soften fat or blend it with another ingredient.

Cream Sauce. A white sauce made with cream.

Crème (Fr.). Cream or creamy in texture.

Crêpes (Fr.). Pancakes, usually very thin.

Culture. Cultivation of microorganisms.

Curdle. To form into curd; to coagulate, clot, or congeal and then break apart.

Cure. A process or method of preserving; the substance added to cause the preservation is often called a cure.

Dehydrate. To extract water by a special process or evaporation. Dehydrated fruits and vegetables have insufficient moisture for growth of molds or yeasts.

Demi-tasse (Fr.). A small cup or half cup; may be used to refer to strong black coffee.

Dextrin. A complex carbohydrate resulting when starch is altered by the action of acids, diastase (an enzyme), or heat, and it loses its gelatinous character. Dextrinized: to be changed to dextrin.

Diffusion. Process of becoming widely spread by Brownian movements (natural forces).

Disperse. To scatter or spread out.

Diuretic. A substance that causes an excessive excretion of urine.

Dredge. To sprinkle with or dip into a dry powder such as flour.

Emetic. A substance having the power to cause vomiting.

Emulsion. A mixture of two or more liquids not mutually soluble. If the two liquids are thoroughly shaken together, one will divide into globules that will be completely surrounded by the other. The liquid that divides is known as the dispersed phase and the other as the continuous phase.

Emulsification. The process of producing an emulsion.

En Brochette (Fr.). Term used to signify cubes or slices of meat cooked on a skewer.

Enchilada. A Mexican dish consisting of a rolled stuffed tortilla.

Entree (Fr.). A conventional term for side dishes now used to indicate the main dish of the meal.

Enzymes. Organic catalysts produced by the tissues of animals or plants at the site of action. They are organic compounds frequently protein in nature, and they act as catalysts. Since they may be protein, they are changed by heat; however, all enzymes require optimum conditions of temperature, pH, etc. The action of enzymes is in general specific, *e.g.*, the enzymes that act upon carbohydrate are unable to act upon other foods.

Fat. An organic compound made up of carbon, hydrogen, and oxygen in a specific molecular structure termed triglycerides. In common usage the term fat signifies a mixture of triglycerides that are solid at ordinary room temperature whereas oils are liquid at the same temperature. The term fat is also used to refer to the lipid (fatty) part of animals. Fats do not form tissues, but fatty deposits are laid down in protein tissues.

Fat-soluble. Denoting that a substance will dissolve or go into solution in fat or oil.

Fermentation. A process in which a carbohydrate is oxidized to alcohol and acids with or without the evolution of gas.

Firing. A process of applying heat to dry a substance rapidly as in processing tea.

Foodstuffs. Substances that can be consumed, absorbed, and utilized by the body and that furnish nutrients.

Food supplement. A food added to other foods in order that the nutritional value of the latter will be improved.

Gateau (Fr.). Cake. Gateau de Nace is a richly decorated cake provided by the bride's parents for the guests at a wedding, a custom which originated for the Roman form of marriage.

Gelatine. An incomplete protein hydrolyzed from collagen in animal tissue and extracted by hot water. Collagen occurs in connective tissues, cartilage, and all skeletal tissue. Also used to refer to the commercial products. Gelatine is very hydrophilic and one tablespoonful of the granulated product will gel two cups of liquid.

Glacé. Glazed, frozen, or iced; candied fruits or nuts.

Gram. A unit of weight in the metric system. There are 28.35 grams in one ounce.

Gumbo. A mixture containing okra.

Heat-labile. Destroyed or changed by heat.

Hemoglobin. A chromo-protein of red color; the coloring substance of the red blood corpuscles.

Heterogeneous. Consisting of or composed of dissimilar ingredients.

Hollandaise (Fr.). Dutch style. A tart butter-egg sauce served with fish or vegetables. It is usually made with butter, egg yolks, lemon juice, and seasoning.

Homogeneous. Thoroughly and completely mixed; samples are composed of similar ingredients.

Hormone. An organic catalyst originating in the body and secreted into the blood stream and then transported to the site of action; differentiated from an enzyme, which is secreted at the point of use.

Hors d'oeuvres. Savory tidbits served with cocktails or as appetizers at the beginning of a meal.

Hydrolysis. A chemical reaction in which a compound is decomposed with the absorption of water and the formation of new compounds. The water is divided and added to the new compounds. $AB + H_2O \rightarrow HA + BOH$.

Hydrophilic. Water-loving.

Hygroscopic. Taking water from the atmosphere easily; sugar is hygroscopic.

Immiscible. A quality of a substance that remains separate from a second substance with which one attempts to mix it—as oil from water.

Infusion. An extract made by steeping a substance in water as in tea making.

Inorganic Compound. One that does not contain carbon.

International Unit (I.U.). A unit of measure for vitamins A and D. An International Unit of vitamin A is equivalent to 0.6 microgram of beta carotene. An International Unit of vitamin D is the activity of 0.025 microgram of an international standard reference material which is a crystalline preparation of vitamin D_3.

Irradiate. To expose to ultraviolet or other light rays.

Jardinière (Fr.). Mixed vegetables stewed in their own juices, gardener's style.

Julienne. Vegetable cut into match-like strips, so called because Jean Julien, a French chef, was the first to use them.

Junket. A sweetened and flavored milk dessert, coagulated by a commercial enzyme preparation, rennet.

Jus (Fr.). Natural juice or gravy (not thickened).

Kabobs. An Indian dish, usually made with lamb, mutton, or fowl; the meat is cut into chunks or slices, marinated or seasoned, and cooked on skewers.

Kippered. Refers to a method of preparing fish and indicates that it is split, salted, dried, and smoked.

Lactation. The secretion of milk from the mammary glands.

Labile. Unstable or subject to change.

Lyonnaise (Fr.). Lyons style, that is, flavored with shredded onions. (Usually used with cold boiled potatoes that are fried with butter and onions).

Macedoine (Fr.). A mixture of evenly cut fruits or vegetables.

Marinate. To soak in a French dressing or other liquid containing acid. The liquid is termed a marinade.

Marzipan (Fr.). A paste formed by crushing sweet almonds with sugar. Also refers to the confections made from the paste and shaped into miniature foods such as bananas, steaks, strawberries, etc. and colored.

Melt. A variety meat that is the spleen; a soft puffy gland similar in appearance to the liver.

Menthe (Fr.). Mint.

Microgram. A unit of weight in the metric system which is 1/1000 of a milligram, or 1/1,000,000 of a gram or 1/28,350,000 of an ounce.

Mignon (Fr.). Small and delicate; filet mignon is a slice of the tenderloin of beef.

Milligram. A unit of weight in the metric system; 1/1000 of a gram.

Minerals. Inorganic substances that remain after food is burned. Term is used synonymously with ash.

Miscible. Capable of being mixed.

Mousse (Fr.). A frozen mixture made from sweetened flavored, whipped cream. It may contain gelatine or other stabilizing substances. It is frozen without stirring. Also used to denote certain hot dishes with smooth texture.

Napolitaine (Fr.). Naples style. Many or several colored.

Noix (Fr.). Walnut, used also to indicate other nuts.

Nuclei. The "seed" of a substance as in crystal structure.

Nutrients. Substances that supply the body with its necessary elements.

Nutriments. That which nourishes.

Obesity. An abnormal condition in which there is an excessive deposit of fat on the body.

Organic. Type of compounds that contain carbon.

Osmosis. The passage of a solvent through a semi-permeable membrane separating solutions of different concentrations. The solvent seeks to equalize the concentration of solutions on both sides.

Oxidation. The process by which a substance forms a chemical union with oxygen.

Parboil. To boil or simmer until partially cooked. This is usually a part of a preliminary preparation, and the final cooking may be done by another method.

Parch. To brown with dry heat. Whole grains may be parched.

Pare. To remove the surface layer by cutting.

Pasteurize. A process of heating milk or other substances to a moderate temperature for a definite time. Pathogenic bacteria are killed, and development of other bacteria is delayed.

Paté (Fr.). Paste. Paté de Foie-gras is goose-liver paste.

Peel. To remove the surface layer by stripping.

pH. A symbol which indicates degree of acidity. pH 7.0 is neutral; pH 0.0 to 7.0 is acidic; and pH 7.0 to pH 14.0 is alkaline.

Physiological. Of, pertaining to, or caused by disorganization of functions or metabolism.

Pigment. A coloring matter or substance.

Pilaf or Pilau. Rice stewed with meat stock.

Piquante (Fr.). Pleasantly pungent.

Pre-formed vitamin. A vitamin that is formed or produced outside of the body and therefore not converted by the body from a precursor or pro-vitamin.

Protein. A complex chemical compound consisting of a combination of amino acids. The basic elements are carbon, hydrogen, oxygen, and nitrogen.

Pro-vitamin. Substances from which the body can synthesize vitamins.

Purée (Fr.). A strained, sieved, or blended fruit or vegetable pulp, usually made from a cooked product and may or may not contain the cooking liquid.

Ragoût. A thick highly seasoned soup or stew with vegetables.

Ramekin. A porcelain, earthenware, or other mold in which individual portions of food mixtures are baked and served.

Rancid. Decomposition caused by oxidation, enzyme action, hydrolysis or other chemical change, which produces a rank taste in food high in fat content.

Render. To extract fat from the connective tissue by means of heat.

Rennet. Dairymen's name for extract of calf's stomach that contains rennin.

Roe. Fish eggs.

Saline. Containing salt or pertaining to salt.

Salisbury Steak. Chopped beef mixed with bread crumbs, egg, and milk, seasoned and fried or broiled.

Sally Lunn. A sweet yeast cake first made by a person named Sally Lunn.

Samovar. Urn of copper or other metal in which water is kept boiling.

Sear. To brown the surface of meat quickly by the application of intense heat (500° F). This method is seldom used today and is not recommended.

Smörgåsbord. The Swedish name for hors d'oeuvres.

Steep. To extract flavor, color, and other soluble substances by allowing a product to stand in liquid just below the boiling point.

Suspension. Substances of relatively large size that remain distributed through a liquid or gas without settling.

Table d'hote (Fr.). Meal consisting of several courses served at a fixed price.

Tartar Sauce. A tart sauce with a mayonnaise base to which are added chopped gherkins, capers, and parsley.

Tasse (Fr.). Cup.

Theine. An alkaloid in tea, now identified as caffeine.

Toast. To brown by means of direct or reflected heat.

Tortilla. A thin round cake made of fine cornmeal and baked on a grill without fat; a Mexican bread.

Translucent. Transmitting light but diffusing it so that the objects beyond cannot be seen.

Transparent. Transmitting light and permitting objects beyond to be seen.

Truss. To fasten the wings and legs of birds to the body by means of skewers and string.

Tutti-frutti (It.). Fruits or vegetables cut into small pieces for salad.

Vacuum. A space devoid of air or other gas.

Vacuum pack. Term applied to foods packed in a container from which gas has been removed.

Viscera. The internal organs of any animal.

Vitamin. A chemical substance which occurs naturally in plant and animal tissue which is required for normal growth, normal functioning of the cells of the body, and maintenance of life. In the absence of each vitamin specific abnormalities in the tissues or metabolism occur.

Volatile. Easily vaporized.

Water-soluble. Easily dissolved or soluble in water.

Weiner Schnitzel. An Austrian term for a thin slice of meat, usually egged, crumbed, and fried and served with anchovies and capers.

Welsh Rarebit or Rabbit. Melted cheese on toast.

Whey. A watery by-product from manufacture of cheese. Most of the milk proteins and fat have been removed but the milk sugar and some of the mineral constituents and vitamins remain in the liquid.

Wurst. German name for all types of sausage.

Zymase. An enzyme that ferments sugar into alcohol (present in yeast).

Zwieback. The German term for twice-baked bread.

APPENDIX C . . . COMMON ABBREVIATIONS

C.	cup	min.	minute
Cal.	Calorie	ml.	milliliter
cc	cubic centimeter	no.	number
ft.	foot or feet	°C	degree Centigrade
gal.	gallon	°F	degree Fahrenheit
gm.	gram	oz.	ounce
in.	inch	pt.	pint
kg.	kilogram	qt.	quart
l.	liter	s.	small
lb.	pound	T.	tablespoon or tablespoonful
lg.	large	t.	teaspoon or teaspoonful
meas.	measure	Tb.	tablespoon or tablespoonful
med.	medium	tsp.	teaspoon or teaspoonful
mg.	milligram	wt.	weight
microgm.	microgram		

COMMON EQUIVALENTS AND MEASURES

3 tsp.	–	1 Tb.	16 oz.	–	1 lb.
16 Tb.	–	1 C.	16 oz.	–	1 pt.
8 Tb.	–	½ C.	8 oz.	–	1 C.
4 Tb.	–	¼ C.	1 tsp.	–	5 ml.
1 C.	–	½ pt.	1 l.	–	1000 ml.
2 C.	–	1 pt.	1 gm.	–	0.035 oz.
2 pt.	–	1 qt.	1 kg.	–	1000 gm.
4 qt.	–	1 gal.	1 kg.	–	2.2 lb.
2 Tb.	–	1 fluid oz.	1 oz.	–	28.35 gm.
			1 lb.	–	454 gm.

Measuring Dry Ingredients (volume)

Equipment for measuring dry ingredients should hold only the amount specified, and all measurements should be level. The instrument used for leveling should be flat with a straight edge.

Measuring Liquid Ingredients (volume)

Measuring cups designed for measuring volumes of liquids have space above the mark that indicates the maximum quantity to be measured in the container. The cup is made of glass and fractions of cups are marked on the glass. The marks should circle the cup so that one can sight across the cup for accurate measure.

Measuring Fats

Plastic fats may be measured by the water displacement method if the water that clings to the fat will not affect the finished product; fat for cakes or cookies may be measured by this method but not fat for pastry. Pour enough cold water into a glass measuring cup designed for liquids to make one cupful when the desired amount of fat is added. Add only enough fat to the water to raise the water level to the mark for 1 cup. The fat should be entirely under water. Drain the fat thoroughly, because any remaining water will increase the liquid content of the product.

If the water displacement method is not used, fats are measured like dry ingredients.

Packaged plastic fats already subdivided need not be measured in special equipment—butter and margarine. One-fourth pound is equivalent to ½ C. The fourth-pound sticks may be cut in half to make two ¼-C. portions. The packages may be marked for tablespoonfuls.

Oils or melted fats are to be measured as other liquids.

Weighing is a more accurate means of establishing quantity than are volume measures. Therefore, whenever possible weights should be used. Many of the household items are used in amounts too small to be weighted accurately by using pounds or ounces as the unit. However, kilograms and grams make very satisfactory household weight units. Gram balances may be purchased at relatively low cost. The following table may be used as a guide for translating volume measurement to gram weights.

COMMON WEIGHT-MEASURE EQUIVALENTS

Food	Volume	Weight, in gms.	Volume equivalents in 1 pound
Eggs	1 medium	48	9 eggs (approximately)
Egg whites	1 medium	30	15 whites (approximately)
Egg yolks	1 medium	18	25 yolks (approximately)
Fat	1 C.	200	2¼ C.
Flour, all purpose	1 C.	110	4 C.
Flour, cake	1 C.	100	4½ C.
Flour, whole wheat	1 C.	120	3¾ C.
Milk, whole, nonfat, and buttermilk	1 C.	244	2 C.
Milk, nonfat solids	1 C.	114	4 C.
Sugar, brown and white	1 C.	200	2¼ C.

E . ADJUSTMENTS

FOR COOKING

AT VARIOUS ALTITUDES

APPROXIMATE BOILING TEMPERATURES OF WATER AT VARIOUS ALTITUDES*

| | Boiling Point, | |
Altitude, in feet	°F	°C
Sea level	212.0	100.0
2000	208.4	98.4
5000	203.0	95.0
7500	198.4	92.4
10,000	194.0	90.0
15,000	185.0	85.0

Note that the lower the temperatures at which vegetables and starch pastes are cooked, the longer the cooking time will be. Eggs to be cooked-in-the-shell may be *boiled* at 7500 feet altitude or more, rather than simmered.

CAKE-MAKING AT ALTITUDES ABOVE SEA LEVEL

Cakes are usually made with flours that have a low gluten content, and the formulas are balanced for production at sea-level conditions. At high altitudes the leavening agent and sugar are reduced slightly and liquids are increased. Also, at high altitudes it may be necessary to reduce the fat slightly—1 to 2 Tb. Eggs may be increased at high altitudes. This is rather important for sponge and angel food cakes.

* Values from Handbook of Food Preparation, Am. Home Economics Assn

One or all of these adjustments may be required; however, each recipe must be balanced individually. Repeated experiments with each recipe will be necessary in order to establish successful proportions.

The formulas for baked products other than cakes need not be adjusted because the slight difference in texture will not be apparent. Cakes, which are very delicate, may appear coarse or fall if adjustments are not made.

CAKE RECIPE ADJUSTMENT GUIDE FOR HIGH ALTITUDES*

Adjustment	3000 Ft.	5000 Ft.	7000 Ft.
Baking powder: reduce for each tsp. in formula	⅛ tsp.	⅛ to ¼ tsp.	¼ to ½ tsp.
Sugar: reduce for each cup in formula	no change	no change	1 to 2 Tb.
Liquid: increase for each cup in formula	1 to 2 Tb.	2 to 3 Tb.	3 to 4 Tb.

* Values from Handbook of Food Preparation, Am. Home Economics Assn.

Ascorbic acid (vitamin C), 469
antioxidant, 37, 38
body functions, 8, 469
deficiency, effects of, 469
in food preparation, 3, 38
food sources, 17, 59, 158, 159 295, 300,
309, 469
inactivation by radiation, 311
oxidation, 36–38, 295, 469
pasteurization effect on, 161
Recommended Daily Allowance, 10
storage, in the body, 469
Ash, content of foods, 473

Bacon, 76, 77
Canadian, 79
Bacteria, effect of heat on, 47
effect of salt on, 43
in eggs, 117
in food residues, 23
in fruits and vegetables, 330, 331
in milk, 163, 166
role in digestion, 23
for salt-rising bread, 43, 271
Baked products, 193
bread, 206–208
buying and prices, 206
in diet plan, 16
federal definitions, 206
nutritive values, 228
quality, characteristics, 227
factors affecting, 218–221
staling, 222
Baking, batters and doughs, 220, 221
fruits and vegetables, 321, 322, 323
pastries, 267, 270
utensils, effect on products, 220
Baking powder, definition, 215
effect on baked product, 218
measurement, 34
phosphate, 216
reaction in baking, 216
residue from, 216
sulfate, 216
sulfate-phosphate, 216
tartrate, 216
Baking soda, 215
in food preparation, 40
measurement, 34

Balance, scales, 34
Barley, 193, 211
flour, 202
Basal metabolism, 456
Basic custard method of mixing, 130–
132
Basic Seven, 12, 13, 21
Batters, cover, 276–278
Batters and doughs, 213
baking of, 220, 221
factors affecting quality, 218–221
function of ingredients in, 214–218
fundamental ingredients in, 213
mixing of, 213–241
nutritive value of, 228
proportion of ingredients for, 226,
227
Beans, dried, 103
see also Legumes
Beating, 33
Beef, corned, 79
cuts, 70–73
dried, 79
purchasing of, 60
Beriberi, 4, 470
Beverages, 372
carbonated, 39, 372
contribution to nutrition, 364
chocolate and cocoa, 177
coffee, 364
tea, 367
Bile, in digestion, 23, 25
Biscuits, baking of, 232, 233
characteristics, 227
mixing, 223, 232
nutritive values, 228
proportions of ingredients, 226, 227
staling, 222
variations, 233
Blood, red cells, 476
and water balance, 6
Body regulation, food need for, 7
Boiling, changes of temperature, 40, 41
definition, 40
effect of rate, 40
factors affecting boiling point, 41
Bone, growth and formation, 466–469
Botulism, 330
Bowls, mixing, 219
shape and size, 32

Calcium, in relation to vitamin D, 466, 474
  relative cost of, 168
Calorie, 7, 18, 455, 457
  Recommended Daily Allowances, 10, 457
Calorimeters, 457
Candling of eggs, 120
Candied fruits and vegetables, 324
Canners, pressure, 40
Canning of meats, 80
  of milk, aseptic, 161
Capon, 82
Caramel, 132, 352, 358, 359
Carbohydrates, absorption of, 461
  in cereals, 16, 195
  changes in heating, 46
  digestion of, 22
  doneness test for, 46, 48
  enzymes for digesting, 22, 23
  in fruits and vegetables, 297
  functions of, in body, 7, 8, 460, 461
  glycogen, 461
  hydrolysis of, 22
  metabolism of, 460, 461
  in milk, 156, 157
  storage of, in the body, 8, 460
  sources of, 460
  source of body fat, 252, 460
  source of energy, 7, 336, 460
Carbon dioxide, in batters, 215
  in beverages, 39
  as end product of oxidation, 5
  formation, 215
  sources, 215
Carbonated beverages, *see* Beverages
Carotene, 14
  in eggs, 114
  in fruits and vegetables, 17, 291
  relation to vitamin A, 114, 463, 464
Carotenoids, 316, 464
Casseroles, 325, 326
Catabolism, 454
Catalyst, definition, 8
  organic, 462
  in oxidation, 38
Catsup, 381, 382
Cauliflower, ascorbic acid in, 37
Centerpieces, 422
Cells, relation to water, 6

Cellulose, in digestion, 22, 23
  in fruits and vegetables, 297
  softening of, in cooking, 46
Cereal Institute, 440
Cereals and cereal products, 193
  amount per capita available, 56
  amount in one serving, 16
  bran, 195
  breakfast, 193, 198
  carbohydrates in, 195
  care, 198, 199
  cooking, 209
  cracked, 198
  definition, 193
  in desserts, 212
  enrichment, 16, 196, 198
  factors in cost, 199
  fat in, 195
  flaked, 198
  flavor, 195
  granular, 198
  labeling, 198
  lysine in, 194
  manufacture, 198, 199
  minerals in, 197
  nutritive value, 16, 193, 204
  packaging, 199
  partially cooked, 199, 210
  production, 198
  proteins in, 193, 194
  purchasing, 198
  ready-to-eat, 198, 199
  raw, 199
  recommended daily intake, 16
  refining of, 194–197
  restoration of, 196
  uses for, 210–213
  vitamins in, 195, 196
  whole-grain, 198
Certified milk, 160
Cheese, 169
  aging or ripening, 157, 170, 182
  appetizers, 182
  classification, 171, 172
  definition, 163
  desserts, 182
  domestic, 170
  fat in, 163
  formation, 163
  foods, 171

Fats in the diet, thiamine-sparing action, 249
triglycerides, 250, 461
Fats in food preparation, 263, 264
aeration, 38
antioxidants in, 38, 256
as antifoaming agent, 263
basic proportions for foods high in, 277
buying and care, 253, 262
care of used, 273
classification, 253
cooking medium, 45, 264–271
differences among, 253
in emulsions, 264
in food preservation, 264
in heat transfer, 264
hydrogenation, 256
hydrolysis, 262
lubricant, 263
measuring, 36
oxidation, 36, 38, 262, 265
oils, 252
in pastries, 265
palatability value, 247, 252, 263
plastic, 253, 255, 256
processing, 256
properties, 253
rancidity, 38, 262
role in batters and doughs, 218
shortening, 262–263
smoking temperatures, 271, 272
soft, 256
spoilage, 262
storage, 262, 263
superglycerination of, 256
as a tenderizer, 263
Fat-soluble vitamins, 464–468
Fat sources, 18
bacon, 260
butter, 253
cereals, 195
chocolate and cocoa, 370
chicken, 260
content in selected foods, 251
cream, 164
eggs, 115, 116
fruits and vegetables, 297
"hidden," 248, 249, 250
ice cream, 172

Fat sources, margarines, 254
meats, 260
milk, 156
oils, 257
pastries, 264, 265
plant, 256
pork, 256, 260
soy-lecithin spread, 254
suet, 260
Fatty acids, essential, 8, 247, 250, 461
from digestion, 22
Federal Extension Service, 437
Federal Security Agency, 436
Federal Trade Commission, 438
Fish, 135
antibiotics in preservation, 84
cooking temperatures, 98, 99
crustaceans, 84
freshness criteria, 84
keeping qualities, 84
mollusks, 84
nutritive value, 56, 57, 58, 59, 107
planned-overs, 102, 103
preparation, 87, 92, 96, 98, 99
preservation, 84–85
purchasing, 82
storage, 86
varieties, 82
Fish and Wildlife Service, 438
Flavones, 211, 315
Flavor, changes during cooking, 46, 47, 317
in fruits and vegetables, 317
in meats, 90
volatile constituents, 317
Flavorings, 373, 375
Flour, 200
aging, 201
all-purpose, 201
amount in one serving, 16
barley, 202
in batters and doughs, 214
bleached, 200
buckwheat, 202
cake, 17, 139, 201
corn, 202
cottonseed, 202
cracked-wheat, 201
durum-wheat, 202
entire-wheat, 201

Flour, factors in cost, 201
factors affecting quality, 200
family, 201
gluten in, 200
Graham, 201
grades of, 200
hard-wheat, 200
lima-bean, 202
measuring of, 34
nutritive value of, 205
oat, 202
pastry, 17, 201
packaged mixes, 201
peanut, 202
phosphated, 201
potato, 202
rice, 202
role in baked products, 214
rye, 202
self-rising, 201
semolina, 202
soft-wheat, 200
soybean, 202
sweet-potato, 202
as a thickening agent, 349
wheat, 200
white, 200
whole-wheat, 201
Flour mixtures, 213
see also batters and doughs
Fluorine, as a nutrient, 473, 477, 478
role in dental caries, 477
in drinking water, 478
Foams, 33, 44, 129, 134–141, 181, 182, 264
Folacin, 472
Folic acid, 23, 59, 472, 476
Fondant, see Confections
Fondues, 135
Food, budgets for, 395, 396
buying, general, 387, 397
composition tables, 11
energy source, 455
guides for selection, 11
labeling, 443
long range planning, 395
nutrition, body need for, 6
price comparisons, 397
processed, 79, 80, 171, 301
see also Nutrition, value tables

Food preparation, acids in, 47
agitation, 31
air in, 36–38
alkalis in, 47
browning, 31
doneness tests, 47
dry heat, 44
heat, 43, 45
measuring, 33
moist heat, 45
osmosis, 42
oxidation during, 36, 37, 38
standards, 31
water, 39
weighing, 34
see also specific foods
Food and Agriculture Organization, 11, 439
Food and Drug Administration, 166, 206, 215, 245, 260, 436
Food and Drug laws, 433
Food and Nutrition Board, 10, 439
Food grading, quality standards, 443
Food guides, 11–18
see also daily food guide
Food habits, 9, 414
Food inspection, laws governing, 435
Food poisoning, 147, 208, 331
Food Standards Committee, 437
Fortification, of cereals, 196
of margarines, 254
of milk, 158
Forums for Consumer Education, 447
Fraud in foods, 435, 440–443
Freezing point of water, 41, 180
French dressing, 261, 262, 277, 278
French Rissoles, 280
Fritters, 277, 278, 326, 482
Frostings, 41, 355
Frozen foods, eggs, 123
desserts, 41, 177–181
fish, 85
fruits and vegetables, 305, 306, 307, 326, 327
meat, 80
milk, 158
retention of ascorbic acid in storage, 37
temperature, relationship to chemical changes, 37

Fructose, 342, 343, 460
Fruit, amount in one serving, 18
browning of, 38
as desserts, 134, 326
dried, 309
nutritive value, 337
sugar content, 338
Fruits and vegetables, acidifying,
314
amount in one serving, 18
as protective food, 289
buying, 301, 305
canned, 307
carbohydrates in, 297
cellulose in, 297
contamination, 331
cooking, 314–324
changes during, 313–320
reasons for, 311, 312
steam method, 322–324
crisping, 314
fats in, 297
flavors in, 313, 317
frozen, 305, 306, 307
grading, 302, 303, 304
health aspects, 330
imports, 287
juices, 311
dried, 311
marketing, 304
maturity, 317, 319
nutrient content, factors affecting,
290, 291, 294, 295, 296, 297
nutrient losses in processing, 301, 312,
313, 314
nutritive value, 287, 298, 299, 300
pigments, 314, 315, 316
planned-overs, 326
preparation, 311–327
processed, 297
proteins in, 297
protopectins in, 297
quality, 302–304
radiated, 311
role in food plans, 17, 290
in salads, 327
salted, 310
sanitation, 330, 331
spray residues on, 331
storage of, 295

Fruits and vegetables, texture and tenderness, factors affecting, 317, 319,
320
variety in, 287, 288, 289
Fruit soup, 325
Fruit whips, 134
Frying (deep-fat), 45, 271–278
absorption of fat in, 271
acrolein formation in, 271
care of used fat in, 273, 274
cooking times for, 278
cover batters for, 276, 277, 278
definition, 45
fruits and vegetables, 321
pastry, 267
retention of nutritive value during,
281
safety precautions, 275
selection of fat, 271
smoking points of fats, 271–272
techniques, 274, 275, 276
temperatures, 95, 274, 278
Fudge, 352, 354, 359

Gall bladder, role in digestion, 23
Gastric juice, 25
Garnishes, 30, 141, 329
Gels, 129
General stores, 393
Glass, as a medium of heat transfer, 44
Glazes, with egg, 130
Glucose, in cereals, 195
dextrose, 342
in food preparation, 336, 342, 343
hydrolysis, 22
metabolism, 460, 461
Glycerine, effect on boiling point, 42
Gluten, in alimentary pastes, 202
in breadmaking, 236
effect of liquid on, 200, 214
formation, 200, 214
framework of baked goods, 214
in hard wheat, 200
properties of, 200
in soft wheat, 200
Glycerol, 22, 250
Glycogen, 6, 460, 461
Goiter, 477
Government controls for foods, 434,
435